THE APE
AND THE CHILD

Ready for bed (ages 16 and 18½ months).

THE APE
AND THE CHILD

A STUDY
OF ENVIRONMENTAL INFLUENCE
UPON EARLY BEHAVIOR

by

W. N. KELLOGG

Associate Professor of Psychology,
Indiana University

and

L. A. KELLOGG

WHITTLESEY HOUSE

MCGRAW-HILL BOOK COMPANY, INC.

NEW YORK AND LONDON

1933

Published by

WHITTLESEY HOUSE

A Division of the
McGRAW-HILL BOOK COMPANY, INC.

*Printed in the United States of America by
The Maple Press Company, York, Pa.*

151.3

DIRECTIONS FOR BINDER

Author _Kellogg_

Title _The ape and the child._

Date _____

Binders Name _Barnard_

BINDING

Give Binders Sample No

Full Buckram _____

½ Morocco _____

Bind to Sample

As to {
Color _____
Lettering _____
Material _____
}

COLOR

Light Brown	✓ Red	Law Sheep
Dark Brown	Maroon	Dark Green
Black	Olive	Light Blue
Dark Blue	Light Green	Yellow
		Drab

SIZE IN INCHES

" 7" 8" 9" 10" 12" 14" 16"

33

BIND ALL COVERS IN
BIND TOP COVERS IN
Follow exactly arrangement of lines, punctuation,
lettering, as on back of this slip and return this slip in the
bound volume.

206-Library Bureau Cat. no. 1112

Preface

IT was in 1927 that the general plan for the investigation reported in these pages was first evolved. The idea was then entirely new to us, although a subsequent review of the scientific literature and discussion of the proposed research with colleagues and associates showed that studies of a similar type had previously been thought of but apparently never completed. For some time after our initial interest in the problem we made no definite progress towards carrying it out. Indeed the enthusiasm of one of us met with so much resistance from the other that it appeared likely we could never come to an agreement upon whether or not we should even attempt such an undertaking.

At length, through the stimulation and encouragement of Professor J. Robert Kantor of Indiana University, we made tentative inquiries about the physical possibilities of a venture of this sort. Then at once the extreme difficulty of procuring an anthropoid ape sufficiently young to make the research feasible became apparent. In the effort to solve this difficulty we were led to consider attaching ourselves to the expedition of a well-known explorer which was about to visit Sumatra, the home of the orang-utan. When this proved impossible because of the financial requirements, the question of purchasing a subject from the wild-animal importers was investigated. Finally we tried to borrow or buy a suitable specimen from one or another of the large zoological societies, but again without success. Had we at that time any knowledge of the personal deprivations to be demanded by the undertaking, it is doubtful if we would have persisted further in the endeavor to bring it about.

PREFACE

The performance of the research work itself was largely dependent in the present instance—as is oftne the case in scientific study—upon the cooperation and sponsorship of many individuals and institutions. The financial needs of the project were met by a fellowship grant from the Social Science Research Council of New York City. Our obligations to this organization are manifest. We are indebted in no lesser measure to Professor Robert M. Yerkes of Yale University for the loan of a baby chimpanzee from Yale's Anthropoid Experiment Station at Orange Park, Florida, for permission to use the facilities of the Station, for comments and suggestions as the work progressed, and for assistance in securing the necessary fellowship grant. Our further obligations to Dr. and Mrs. Otto L. Tinklepaugh of Yale University for constant aid and encouragement during the progress of the study are so deep-rooted that we cannot hope to repay them by this meager acknowledgment.

Without the additional aid of Professor Robert S. Woodworth and Professor Albert T. Poffenberger of Columbia University, and of President William Lowe Bryan and Professor William F. Book of Indiana University, all of whom lent their influence in obtaining the backing of the Social Science Research Council, the financing of the undertaking would have remained uncertain. Thanks are likewise extended to Dr. Carlyle F. Jacobsen and to his wife, Dr. Marion M. Jacobsen of Yale, for assistance in preparing written records and in administering the Gesell tests; to Dr. Joseph G. Yoshioka of Yale for direction with the anthropometric measurements and for help in other ways; to Mrs. Helen S. Morford of Yale for assistance with stenographic and recording details; and particularly to Mr. William C. Atwater, superintendent of the Experiment Station, for willing and continuous cooperation throughout the entire period of the research.

x

Professor J. Robert Kantor and Professor Roland C. Davis, our friends and colleagues at Indiana University, are others to whom we owe a debt of gratitude; to the former for his enthusiasm about the possibilities of the undertaking as well as for his reading of the manuscript; to the latter for careful reading and rereading of our questionable efforts at composition and for valuable criticism and corrections during the work upon the final copy.

We are grateful also to the editor of the *American Journal of Psychology* for permission to reprint a portion of the material in Chapter I, which originally appeared as a note in that periodical; and to the editor of the *Psychological Review* for permission to adapt some of the discussion in the same chapter from an article published under the title of "Humanizing the ape" in 1931.

It has been our aim in the preparation of the book to simplify the treatment so as to make the account suitable and interesting for the lay reader. We have hoped to accomplish this result without the sacrifice of scientific accuracy or the elimination of any essential details. But it has often been necessary in such an endeavor to omit specific reference to published articles where credit would properly have been given in a more technical discussion. There can be little doubt, moreover, that in certain instances the actual source of the material we have used, or perchance misused, is lost even to ourselves. For such errors and omissions we apologize and acknowledge as well as we are able in this blanket fashion a debt to many unnamed authors.

W. N. KELLOGG.
L. A. KELLOGG.

BLOOMINGTON, INDIANA,
May, 1933.

Contents

CONTENTS

THE APE AND THE CHILD

Chapter I

AN EXPERIMENT OUTLINED

LET US SUPPOSE that by some queer accident a human infant, the child of civilized parents, were abandoned in the woods or jungle where it had as companions only wild animals. Suppose, further, that by some miraculous combination of circumstances it did not die, but survived babyhood and early childhood, and grew up in these surroundings. What would be the nature of the resulting individual who had matured under such unusual conditions, without clothing, without human language, and without association with others of its kind? That this is not so fanciful a conception as to lie altogether outside the realm of possibility is attested by the fact that about a dozen instances of "wild" foundlings of this sort are known to history. To be sure the reports about them are in many cases so garbled and distorted that the true facts are hard to sift out. In some, however, the accuracy of the accounts is well established.

One of the earliest of these children to attract scientific notice was "the wild boy of Aveyron" who was found roaming a French forest by a group of sportsmen in the year 1799. He had apparently been living on roots, berries, and such other provender as might be found in the woods. When discovered he was naked, scarred, and unkempt, and sought to resist capture by hurriedly climbing into a tree. Although he appeared to be fully 11 or 12 years old, he was quite unable to talk and was without knowledge of the most rudimentary habits of personal cleanliness. He was taken to Paris and subjected to a long period of methodical and painstaking education by a young French doctor named Itard. Despite the fact that considerable progress was made toward fitting him for the complexities of civilized life, the training on the whole was regarded as unsuccessful.

A later example, the case of Kasper Hauser, although hardly an instance of a "wild" person, is nevertheless similar in many respects. This boy, who has been regarded as a royal pretender or as an heir to some princely German house, was apparently put out of the way by political schemers during the early part of the nineteenth century. He was kept in solitary confinement until he was 17 years old in a dark cell so small that he could not stand upright. During this period he was fed chiefly on bread and water and was seen by no one but his keeper. When released from the cell in 1828 he could walk only with the greatest difficulty; he scarcely knew how to use his hands and fingers; he could not understand what was said to him; and he was able himself to speak only one sentence. Intensive educational training was in his case also only partially successful. This, in the opinion of some authorities, was because the prolonged isolation had wrought such a serious effect upon him.

Probably the most recent instance of a similar nature is that of the "wolf children" of India. These children, two young girls, are reported to have been found as late as 1921 in a sparsely settled region of eastern India, living in a cave inhabited by wolves. A brief account written some years after their capture, presumably by one who actually took them, is as follows:

Eight years ago I was on a tour of my villages. One evening one of my people said, "There are ghosts in the woods. We are much afraid." So I watched the next night. Just before sundown three old wolves came up out of a hole. Then two cubs and at last a queer human-like animal. The man with me wanted to shoot. But I forbade him. No one would go near the den so I got men from seven miles distant who knew

4

not of the ghosts. They dug out the den. Two wolves ran off, the third was killed with an arrow. She being the mother refused to run away. Down in the bottom of the den cuddled up with furry cubs were two queer little girls devoid of clothing. Against their desires we gathered them up and brought them home. Whether they were illegitimate and thrown away or torn from their mother's cottage door by the wolves, we do not know. For the first four or five years they ran about on their hands and knees. After being compelled to, they could stand but not run. The younger never learned to talk, could only grunt and growl. The older one lived to be a little over six years of age with the mentality of a two and one-half year old child. She learned to talk and developed a vocabulary of about one hundred words. They never asked questions. Their jaws were large and square supposedly from gnawing bones. Both have been dead for some time.*

Supplementary material from another report says that the two upon capture ate and drank like dogs, making little or no use of their hands in these activities, and that later efforts to dissuade them from pouncing upon and devouring small birds and mammals were never successful. Unfortunately neither of the "wolf children" was examined by scientists before it died, and information concerning the details of their behavior is extremely scanty.

The customary way of explaining the fact that a human being of this sort does not respond well to the efforts of those who would civilize and educate it, is to say that it is feeble-minded, that it is mentally deficient, or that it is congenitally lacking in the ability to learn and adapt to its new surroundings. Even had such children lived under civilized conditions, they would still have failed to duplicate the accomplishments of normal individuals. The opportunities enjoyed by the average child would have left them little better in their

* Reprinted from the *American Journal of Psychology*, 1931, 43: 508–509, by permission.

ability to react than they were when they were found. This reasoning carries with it the assumption that because these children were not up to the average for their ages when their reeducation was discontinued, there must have been something wrong with them before they were placed in the jungle or prison surroundings. That they were unable to adapt completely to civilizing influences is taken as proof of an original deficiency. In fact, going one step further, it is often argued that the "wild" children were probably abandoned in the first place because they displayed idiotic or imbecilic tendencies at a very young age. Their unusual environment in this sense is a sort of result rather than the cause of their condition. The cause is ultimately a matter of hereditary deficiency—a basic lack in the genes of the parent cells.

But there is a second way of accounting for the behavior of the "wild" children, according to the theory of external or environmental influences. It would be quite possible according to the latter view to take the child of criminal delinquents, provided he was normal at birth, and by giving him the proper training, to make him a great religious or moral leader. Conversely it would be possible to take the child of gifted and upright parents and by placing him in a suitable environment, to produce a criminal of the lowest order. Heredity, in this view, assumes a secondary role and education or training becomes the important item.

Instead of supposing that the "wild" children were inherently feeble-minded, as is usually done, the proponent of the environmental doctrine would hold that originally such children were probably normal. He would point, no doubt, to the fact that a child who is deficient in any respect whatever would have a smaller chance of survival in a jungle environment than one with normal abilities. On the strength of this supposition, it might be maintained that the "wild" children had made natural and adequate adjustments to their

6

environment. They could even be said to have developed responses which were peculiarly suited to their immediate needs. Those placed with animals may actually have learned, in a literal sense of the word, to be wild themselves, in the same way that a Caucasian child reared among Chinese grows into the Chinese customs and language, or a baby that has been kidnaped by gypsies knows in later years only the gypsy manner of living.

Although such reasoning may account for the fact that these nameless foundlings when suddenly transplanted to a highly organized society had no civilized or cultured reactions, it does not explain as well as the hereditary view why they failed to respond satisfactorily to their training. A necessary corollary to the environmental doctrine, which will take care of this factor, is that the early years of life are the important ones in determining the particular direction of development. Or, put another way, the influence of outside stimuli in establishing new behavior becomes increasingly less effective as the organism matures and passes to middle age. Educators for some time have considered the period before adolescence as particularly impressionable. "As the twig is bent, the tree's inclined" seems to be the rule which is operative in development. Once the early reactions are firmly established, once the particular kind of behavior, be it honest or dishonest, is fixed, it becomes an integral part of the individual. He can thereafter rarely modify his habits of living to any appreciable extent. It is as though the environment, a titanic sculptor, had permanently chiseled the features of a piece of statuary. When the model nears completion its parts can be altered to only a relatively small degree. Some authors have been so impressed by arguments of this sort that they have called the underlying principle "the inexorable law of habit." Of the influence of this law, William James wrote more than forty years ago:

It dooms us all to fight out the battle of life upon the lines of our nurture or our early choice, and to make the best of a pursuit that disagrees, because there is no other for which we are fitted, and it is too late to begin again.

Although James selected the years between 20 and 30 as the period in which the plaster finally set, the recent tendency has been to regard childhood and even infancy of greater significance in the acquisition of ways of behaving which may remain a permanent influence. Examples from everyday experience in substantiation of such views are not hard to find. Unless the study of a foreign language is taken up at an early age, it is quite likely that the student will never be able to speak that language without an accent, even though he may devote the remainder of his life to its mastery. Similarly, foreigners who immigrate to this country almost never become thoroughly Americanized until the second generation. Habits of neatness and cleanliness formed during youth are seldom changed throughout the lifetime of the individual. Those complex kinds of behavior which we customarily call "character traits" begin to display themselves during childhood, we say. But this is only another way of saying that as we behave in childhood so do we behave in later life.

It now becomes clear that the environmental explanation of the failure of the "wild" children to respond adequately to their education is that their training was begun too late. By the time it started, the subjects had advanced to too mature an age to uproot the fundamental habits so basically entrenched by earlier experience. The children need not originally have been feeble-minded, but instead so profoundly impressed with the experiences of earlier years that later efforts to teach them the reactions of the average educated child would not bear full fruit. They had passed the age where the learning of civilized commonplaces was easy and natural, and had already consumed the most formative years in learning other things. The

8

wild animal cannot be thoroughly tamed unless its taming starts soon after it is born, which, paradoxically, is before it has actually become wild.

Of course if it be objected that the placing of so much emphasis upon the inflexibility of early habits is not justified, this line of reasoning breaks down. In that event the proponent of the doctrine must fall back upon a secondary defense. He may then argue that none of the "wild" or captive children, in all probability, was trained properly or diligently enough to exhaust without question all the potentialities of such training. Perhaps the persons intrusted with the education of these unfortunates gave up in discouragement before the task was really completed. Who can say in these particular instances (in spite of the statements of educators who sometimes worked for years upon their charges) what the results of further effort would have been? Although not all the cases can be subjected to criticism of this sort, the limited facts about many of them leave it nevertheless as a possibility to be reckoned with.

Here, then, are two complete but entirely distinct methods of accounting for the same phenomena—the one according to the influence of inborn factors, and the other as a matter of environment. There remains the possibility of a middle-of-the-road interpretation which would adopt some features from each of the extreme views. The supporter of either doctrine as a means of accounting for the condition of the "wild" children would no doubt admit that opposing influences played an important part in the development of these children even though they might not in his eyes play the principal part. Probably most persons interested in this topic today would subscribe to some sort of a compromise conception as safer and more likely to agree with the facts.

To say, however, that individuals grow because of the combined influences of heredity and environment is

9

quite another thing from saying that one individual may *differ* from a second individual because he has a different heredity or because he has a different environment. Persons of different heredity, reared in like environments, grow differently. But persons of similar heredity, reared in different environments, may also grow differently. If differences in the development of two individuals appear when one of the factors which enter into their development is "held constant," the differences must then have been produced by the variable factor. Concerning the "wild" children, these statements become as follows: That they are different from normal civilized children can be attributed, assuming they possessed a normal heredity (that is, a heredity sufficiently like that of civilized children to permit civilized development), to environment. Or assuming they were feeble-minded (abnormal heredity), their deficiency in development can be attributed either (1) to the heredity itself, or (2) to the combination of the abnormal heredity and the abnormal environment. The unanswerable question is: Were they or were they not mentally deficient before they were placed in the jungle surroundings?

Even though we know that heredity and environment are both factors in development, it is still possible that the particular influence of one or the other may affect the resulting organism in certain special ways. The enthusiastic proponent of eugenics who would advance the human race by a careful selection of parents is obviously partisan to one of these influences. On the opposite side is the theory of euthenics, which would improve mankind by changing the environmental conditions. Philosophy has long debated questions of this sort; and the scientific investigator in whose hands they ultimately rest has attacked them from many angles. Still, the need for additional factual evidence in this as in many other fields of knowledge can hardly be disputed.

Without doubt, one of the most significant tests which could be applied to a problem of this nature would be to put to rigid experimental proof the stories of the "wild" children themselves. To accomplish this end it would be necessary to place a normal human infant in uncivilized surroundings and to observe and record its development *as it grew up* in this environment. Such an experiment should throw important light upon the precise influence of outside stimulation in the development of the young baby. Yet obviously, in spite of all the scientific zeal which could be brought to bear upon an undertaking of this kind, it would be both legally dangerous and morally outrageous to carry out.

Although it would be impossible, therefore, to duplicate the conditions under which these foundlings are reported to have been discovered, it would be both possible and practical, it occurred to us, to reverse these conditions. Instead of placing a child in a typical animal environment, why not place an animal in a typical human environment? Why not give one of the higher primates exactly the environmental advantages which a young child enjoys and then study the development of the resulting organism? This plan is in fact similar to that suggested by Professor Lightner Witmer, who wrote in 1909:

I venture to predict that within a few years chimpanzees will be taken early in life and subjected for purposes of scientific investigation to a course of procedure more closely resembling that which is accorded the human child.

If such an experiment were to produce valid results, it would admit of no halfway measures. To carry it out in any comprehensive manner one would have to obtain an infant anthropoid ape, as young as possible, and rear it in every respect as a child is reared—even to the most minute detail. According to our plan, the animal subject was to be fed upon a bottle, clothed, bathed, fondled, and given careful human treatment in every phase of its daily existence. It would be placed in a perambulator and wheeled. It would be induced at the proper time to walk upright as the human child is assisted in this process. It would learn to eat with a spoon as soon as it was able to eat at all by itself. Throughout its upbringing its mistakes would be gently and persistently corrected as are the mistakes of a child. It would be made a thoroughly humanized member of the family of the experimenters, who would serve respectively in the capacities of adopted "father" and "mother." Many of the highly developed customs of our society might thus become integral parts of its behavior equipment in much the same manner that they are built into the human baby. As far as its immediate surroundings were concerned, the animal would never be given the opportunity to learn any other ways of acting except the human ways.

One important consideration upon which we would insist was that the *psychological* as well as the *physical* features of the environment be entirely of a human character. That is, the reactions of all those who came in contact with the subject, and the resulting stimulation which these reactions afforded the subject, should be without exception just such as a normal child might receive. Instances of anthropoid apes which have lived in human households are of course by no means unknown. But in all the cases of which we have any knowledge the "human" treatment accorded the animals was definitely limited by the attitude of the owner and by the degree of his willingness to be put to boundless labor. It is not unreasonable to suppose, if an organism of this kind is kept in a cage for a part of each day or night, if it is led about by means of a collar and a chain, or if it is fed from a plate upon the floor, that these things must surely develop responses which are different from those of a human. A child itself, if similarly treated, would most certainly acquire some genuinely *un*childlike reactions. Again, if the organism is talked to and called like a dog or a cat, if it is consistently petted or scratched behind the ears as these animals are often treated, or if in other ways it is given *pet stimuli* instead of *child stimuli*, the resulting behavior may be expected to show the effects of such stimulation.

In this connection it was our earnest purpose to make the training of the ape what might be called *incidental* as opposed to *systematic* or controlled training. What it got from its surroundings it was to pick up by itself just as a growing child acquires new modes of behavior. We wished to avoid deliberately teaching the animal, trial by trial, a series of tricks or stunts which it might go through upon signal or command. The things that it learned were to be its own reactions to the stimuli about it. They were furthermore to be specifically responses to the household situation and not trained-in or meaningless rituals elicited by a sign from a keeper. The spoon-eating training, to take a concrete example, was to be taken up only in a gradual and irregular manner at mealtime, as the subject's muscular coordination fitted it for this sort of manipulation. We would make no attempt to set it down at specified intervals and labor mechanically through a stated number of trials, rewarding or punishing the animal as it might succeed or fail. Such a proposed procedure, it will be readily seen, is loose and uncontrolled in that it precludes the obtaining of quantitative data on the number of trials necessary to learn, the number of errors made, or the elapsed time per trial. It has the advantage, nevertheless, of being the same sort of training to which the human infant is customarily subjected in the normal course of its upbringing.

The question of companions and playmates, a necessary part of any child's surroundings, we supposed could be taken care of by having selected children, borrowed possibly from a nursery school or from neighbors, who might spend an hour or two daily in the little ape's company. It would be essential that these be the offspring of understanding parents, and that they also treat the animal as an equal and not as an inferior or as a pet. The experimental technique *par excellence* would indeed be achieved, we thought, if it should prove possible to adopt the baby ape into a family with one child of approximately the ape's age. The human infant, in the same environment, might then serve as a "control" subject against which the reactions of the subhuman could be compared step by step. Genetic case studies of the two individuals would be possible, supplemented by such tests as it seemed feasible to make throughout their development. The normal reactions of the human infant to the new situations confronting it would perforce be either faster or slower, or more or less adequate, than those of the ape in the same situations, so that differences and similarities could be directly observed. A detailed comparison under almost ideal experimental conditions was thus suggested, providing these plans could be satisfactorily worked out.

At the conclusion of such an endeavor we should be in a position, it seemed to us, to make definite inferences regarding the two organisms. If the chimpanzee had failed to develop as did the child but remained instead on a subhuman level, then we could say that hereditary factors or "animal instincts" were dominant and that training did not seriously affect the resulting organism. Or, put in another way, if demonstrable differences in behavior existed at any given stage of the experiment and if the surroundings and treatment up to that point had remained the same for each subject, the conclusion could be drawn that the differences were due to native influences. Development along divergent lines within the same environment would show the importance of heredity. It could be maintained, should such results be secured, that the ape, given full opportunities to acquire a complete repertory of human reactions, had progressed only part of the way.

But if, on the other hand, the chimpanzee in the human situation acquired many characteristically childlike responses, such results would show the importance of the "human" stimuli upon its growth. The extent to which the subjects learned to react in the same ways despite their different heredities would therefore demonstrate the effect of the common environment. Of course, in addition to showing environmental influence, the presence of identical responses in the ape and the child would also show that the heredities of the two, although different, were at the same time *similar enough* to permit like reactions to the same stimulation. Yet without the special influence of the civilized environment to serve as an activating cause in bringing out these likenesses, they would surely never come to light.

Now no one, we hope, will be fool enough to suppose from reading a proposal of this sort that either of the writers has so far lost his senses as to presume that you can make a human being out of an animal. There are obviously many natural differences between man and the apes which no amount of environmental equalizing can overcome. The anthropoid, for example, is considerably stronger than the human, and would as a result be capable of greater feats of climbing and acrobatics. Again, the ape has a smaller brain volume. Upon the assumption of a correlation between neurological development and behavioral capacity, the animal would thus be expected to be inferior to the human in tasks of great complexity. Relative differences in arm and leg length, and in hand shape, need hardly be pointed out as predetermining at the start possible differences in agility and manual dexterity, while the more rapid rate at which the infant ape begins to move about and stand is also to be remarked. It has been maintained in fact that an ape of one year is about equivalent in physiology and maturation to a child of at least twice that age. These and other considerations would readily enough eliminate the possibility of any glowing presuppositions. We had felt, nevertheless, that in formulating these plans, we should consider all possibilities, and so be prepared for any contingency. We should, moreover, align ourselves with no particular theory, but rather be in search of facts wherever they might lead.

Having outlined the project, we may now pass to a brief statement of its consummation. On June 26, 1931, a young female chimpanzee in the colony of the Anthropoid Experiment Station of Yale University at Orange Park, Florida, was forcibly separated from her mother, in whose cage she had previously been living. This little animal, named Gua, had been born in captivity in the Abreu Colony in Cuba on November 15, 1930. She was turned over to the writers following the separation and was soon thereafter taken to their home, where her humanizing was begun. Her age at that time was 7½ months, or almost exactly 2½ months less than that of the writers' only child, Donald, who had been born August 31, 1930. From the point of view of experimental technique, the close correspondence between the ages of the boy and the ape proved indeed to be a fortunate coincidence.

These two individuals lived together as companions, playmates, and members of the same household until March 28, 1932. Their surroundings and treatment were as nearly alike as it was possible to make them. At that time, 9 months after the initiation of the research, Gua had attained the age of 16½ months, while Donald was 19 months old. The experiment was then discontinued and the ape was returned by a gradual habituating process to the more restricted life of the Experiment Station. During the nine months a continuous series of tests, comparisons, observations, and experiments were made upon the two subjects. These covered nearly every phase of their structure and behavior for which we had or could construct measuring facilities. Many of the tests unfortunately were of a crude and inaccurate nature; others were more precise.

It should be noted at this point that the chimpanzee is probably fitted for an experiment of this sort as well as or better than any other animal. Speaking of the development of chimpanzees, Köhler has said:

> . . . in particular it has been shown that the chemistry of their bodies, in so far as it may be perceived in the quality of the blood, and the structure of their most highly-developed organ, the brain, are more closely related to the chemistry of the human body and human brain-structure than to the chemical nature of the lower apes [the monkeys] and *their* brain development.

The chimpanzee, therefore, as one of the great apes, is to be sharply distinguished from the lesser monkeys and baboons. Without a doubt he is one of the closest living relatives of man, whom he approaches in many physical characteristics. Adult members of the species attain a weight of from 120 to 160 pounds; they possess not the slightest vestige of a tail, and their general bodily dimensions (aside from the longer arms and shorter legs) compare favorably with those of a mature human; the average length of life, although this is not certainly known, is estimated to be only a little less than that of human beings, while the long period of dependent infancy and the age of puberty approximate as well the corresponding periods in man. On the strength of such superficial comparisons, there was a high degree of probability that the chimpanzee could adapt pretty well to the human environment.

One regrettable factor which we thought might predispose against favorable results was the age of Gua at the time of her transfer. The ideal situation would have been to obtain an animal for this work as soon as it was born, or very shortly afterward. But there are practical considerations in every concrete case which can seriously affect the best of theories. As a result our desires had to be modified to fit the circumstances. In view of the final outcome of the experiment, we now feel it is quite likely that what Gua had learned at the tender age of her removal from the cage was of less serious consequence in influencing her "human" life than might at first have been supposed.

The story of the nine-months development of the ape and the child in the same or in similar situations, of their maturation, habits, and achievements makes up the material of the pages which follow. It is not the intention of the writers to present this material in diary or biographical form, but rather to discuss completely a single topic before going on to the next succeeding topic. It will also be our aim to proceed as well as we are able, from what may be called the simpler activities to increasingly more complex ones. The behavior of the two will thus be considered in the general topical order of eating and sleeping, muscular coordination and walking, the senses, play, social behavior, emotional behavior, learning, memory and recognition, intelligence, and language. After reviewing in this manner the principal results, we shall conclude with the attempt to draw a few inferences which will, we hope, throw some small light upon certain of the problems already raised.

It should be noted specifically in connection with the subsequent discussion that the ages of the subjects are invariably given in complete half months, as 8½, 10, 13½, or 15½ months. Yet, quite obviously, the incidents and developments recorded did not necessarily occur at fortnightly intervals. As used in this record each age figure *may* include the two-week period up to the next larger figure. An act occurring "at the age of 14½ months," for example, may have appeared when the subject was exactly the age named; again, it may have been noted when he was one day less than 15 months old. The device of stating the ages of the subjects in arbitrary half-monthly steps was adopted as a convenience in composition which it was believed would not seriously affect the accuracy of the report.

Before entering directly into a review of the behavior at large of the two subjects, it will be our immediate object in the next section to consider first a few necessary and preliminary details. We shall first compare them with respect to body weight and size, strength, reflexes, and fundamental structural differences, since many of these are directly related to the activities to be examined in the later chapters.

Chapter II

SOME BASIC SIMILARITIES AND DIFFERENCES

IN GENERAL appearance, Gua may be said to differ but little from many other chimpanzees. The most obvious exception to this statement is the fact that, at the time of her transfer to the human household, she is much younger and hence smaller than most captive specimens. The skin upon her face is of a smooth tan color and her dark brown eyes are set under overhanging brows which have a somewhat lumpy or uneven contour. The ears are large but close to the head and are colored like the face. She has a wide mouth and extremely mobile lips, while her external nose is so flat that it consists of little save the nasal openings. Growing backward from the eyebrows over the top of the head is a smooth covering of black hair which falls naturally into a neat pompadour. The rest of the head and the neck are covered with longer hair, also black, which protrudes downward in a little tuft on each side of the face just behind the cheeks to give the somewhat grotesque appearance of sideburns or jowl whiskers. The palmar surface of the hands and soles of the feet are of the same light tan as the face and ears.

Although the hair of her coat is a deep black, shading into a silver gray in the abdominal region and on the inner side of the legs and arms where it becomes more sparse, the major part of her skin beneath this hair is even whiter than the skin of a Nordic white. The exceptions to this, aside from those already mentioned, include areas on the back of the head and on the inside of the arms and legs which tend to be slightly darker; while the skin on the outer surface of the arms and legs and on the backs of the hands and the tops of the feet (excepting the fingers and toes) is of a genuine blackish hue.

Anthropometric or bodily measurements show her upright standing height at the start to be 57.5 centi-

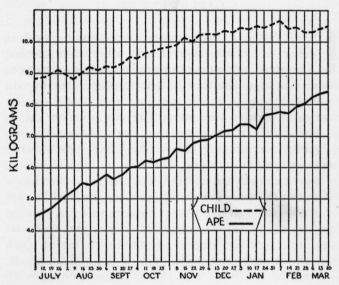

FIG. 1.—Growth in weight of each of the subjects throughout the period of the research.

meters (22.6 inches). This is somewhat less than the standing height of the child, which is 67.4 centimeters (26.6 inches). At the end of the experiment the height measurements are for Gua 73.0 centimeters (28.7 inches) and for Donald 80.1 centimeters (31.5 inches). The little ape in the nine-months interval has therefore grown in stature some 17 per cent, while the human subject within the same time has grown only about 10 per cent. The weights of the two show a similar difference in the rate of physical development. Thus Gua's original weight of 4.46 kilograms (9.8 pounds) increases by 89 per cent in 38 weeks. Donald's weight, which at the start is 8.86 kilograms (19.5 pounds), or nearly twice as much as Gua's, increases only 19 per cent throughout the same period.

The average of 31 body measurements on each subject gives a composite increase in size of about 19 per cent for Gua and 11 per cent for Donald. These figures along with the weights offer good evidence of the relative rates of maturation. It is worthy of note, however, that in many particulars their physical dimensions ultimately become very similar. In general the circumferential measurements, such as the distance around the legs, arms, neck, chest, and abdomen, are much the same at the end of our observations. Gua's increase in seven such measurements amounts to as much as 21 per cent of their original size, while Donald's percentage of increase within the same time is only about one-third as great. The head circumference of the ape measured in a horizontal plane immediately above the ears is approximately two-thirds that of the child, although it increases slightly more during the nine months than his does. The ears of the two are about the same in length but Gua's are wider. The faces are of nearly the same length, but in this case it is Donald's which is the wider. Principal differences in the arm and leg lengths appear in the measurements of the forearm and knee-to-foot distances. Gua's forearm is longer than Donald's, although the upper arms of the two are about the same. Gua's knee-to-foot measurement, on the other hand, is markedly shorter than Donald's although the thigh measurements differ but slightly.

An idea of the astonishing proportions of the chimpanzee hand can be gained by comparing the length of the hand measured from the wrist to the tips of the fingers, to the length of the forearm, measured from the wrist to the elbow. In the human these lengths are roughly in the ratio of three to five, while in a chimpan-

Gua clings tightly to the experimenter even though she has been separated from her mother for only 48 hours.

(Facing p. 22)

In the middle pictures the subjects are standing. In the lower pictures they are lying down and are photographed from above. The squares in the backgrounds are 10 centimeters to the side.

zee of Gua's age they are more nearly in the ratio of one
to one. The absolute length of the forearm of the
particular chimpanzee which we have under observation is, in fact, nearly 20 per cent greater than the corresponding length of the child's forearm, and the
length of her hand is approximately 50 per cent greater
than his. Gua's forearm and hand are relatively so
long that at the age of 8 months she can reach with
ease with her left arm across the top of her head and
touch her right shoulder, and *vice versa;* while Donald's
head and neck, like that of the typical human baby,
are relatively so much larger, and his arm so much
shorter, that he can reach at the age of 10½ months
only about to the middle of the top of his head. It is
the unusual forearm and hand length of the ape which
therefore account for her longer arm reach. Related
also to the arm length is the greater development of
the shoulder muscles, which permits of easy climbing,
swinging, and lifting. Differences in this respect are
important in the bodily dexterity and muscular coordination of the two subjects.

In some instances it is possible, we find, to move the
chimpanzee joints through wider angles than the corresponding human joints. An example in point is the
action of Gua's hips, which can be bent upward and
backward toward the spinal column so that the knees
are against the back in the thoracic or chest region.
Her feet can then be touched sole to sole, *behind the
back,* somewhere between and a little below the shoulders. When this maneuver has been completed her
position except for the shorter legs is similar to that of a
contortionist who puts his feet behind his head. The
arms can also be twisted in the armpits enabling the
ape to make a double rotation without difficulty in such
play movements as skinning the cat. In the same way
the chimpanzee wrist can be bent towards the forearm
so far that the palm of the hand will lie flat against the
inner surface of the arm. But the hand cannot be

bent backward, away from the volar surface of the arm, as far as the human hand. Instead, it stops abruptly when the palm forms approximately a continuous straight line with the bones of the forearm.

The fingers of the animal seem to be similarly jointed. Although their arc of movement is not necessarily greater than that of the corresponding human fingers, they cannot, like the wrist, be moved "backward" at all, but they must stop their extension when they are almost in a straight continuous line with the palm of the hand. Yet in spite of this limitation in one direction, they can all be moved farther in the opposite direction, that is, farther towards the palm of the hand, than the corresponding human members can be so manipulated. It is possible, as a result, to lay Gua's fingers throughout their entire length flat upon the palm of the hand to which they are attached.

The greater amplitude of inward or volar flexing, as well as the extreme length of the hand is likely to give it at times more the aspect of an ungainly hook than of a fine prehensile organ. An interesting paradox in this connection is the fact that the chimpanzee's toes resemble in casual appearance the fingers and thumb of the human hand more closely than do chimpanzee hands resemble human hands. In general dimensions, the ape's feet are greater in both length and breadth than Donald's.

With respect to the hardening or ossification of the bones, Gua is shown from X-ray photographs to be roughly comparable to a child of more than twice her age. Despite the advantage in calendar months possessed by Donald, therefore, the ape is skeletally his superior. There seem, nevertheless, to be but few important differences in the thickness or diameter of the body bones. Exceptions to this are the fact that the cranium of the animal is noticeably heavier and the finger bones stouter, enabling her from an anatomical standpoint to place greater stresses upon them. The differences between the skulls can be audibly detected by tapping them with the bowl of a spoon or with some similar object. The sound made by Donald's head during the early months is somewhat in the nature of a dull thud, while that obtained from Gua's is harsher, like the crack of a mallet upon a wooden croquet or bowling ball. The fontanels of the human are closed, like those of most children, by about the eighteenth month; but the head of the ape is thoroughly hardened when first it can be examined at the age of $7\frac{1}{2}$ months.

An additional proof of her advancement is the fact that she possesses 16 of her ultimate total of 20 milk teeth when she is separated from her mother. The only teeth which have not yet arrived are the canines, and all of these put in an appearance by the time she has reached the age of 10 months. Yet when Donald is 10 months old he has only two teeth, the lower central incisors. And even at the conclusion of the experiment he possesses no more than 13, since the four second molars and three of the canines are still absent. The difference in the rate of dentition is thus again clear evidence of the difference in the rate of maturation. Concerning the order in which the teeth erupt, it should be noted that the chimpanzee obtains its canine teeth last, while in the human the canines come next to last and the second (or "two-year") molars complete the set. The milk teeth of the chimpanzee, as judged by those of Gua, are larger or coarser, but noticeably less sharp, so that, despite powerful jaws, her teething bite is by no means as painful as the teething bite of the human infant. Both subjects habitually grit the teeth, producing a clearly audible grinding sound.

That the general skin condition of the little animal is not greatly different from that of her human associates is shown by many observations. The ape probably possesses fewer sweat glands than the child, since these are apparently to be found only on the smooth body surfaces, including the palms of the hands, soles of the feet, and face. We are rather astonished, however, to discover that encasing Gua's feet in non-ventilated leather shoes for twelve hours or more a day produces the same unpleasant effect as a result of perspiration which is familiar to many civilized humans. The shoes also show a tendency to rub away, through continued friction, some of the hairs about her ankles, much as human clothing leaves similar traces on portions of the body of the wearer. The chapping of her hands, which in cold weather becomes so severe that cuts or cracks appear upon the knuckles, is further evidence of Gua's susceptibility to manlike ills. The skin so affected feels dry and scaly. And finally she is even addicted to such characteristic human blights as pimples and corns! We find three of the former at different times upon her face and neck, and small corns are sometimes produced over the toe joints from the pressure of her shoes. The pimples, which are very small, emit upon pressure a puslike material whiter than, although similar to, that which is generated in human pores.

As far as skin temperatures are concerned it soon becomes obvious that when Gua is cold her extremities, comprising the hands, feet, ears, and even the nose, are the first parts of the body to chill. The phenomenon of the cold nose is, to be sure, common enough in snouted animals such as dogs and cats, but we had hardly expected to find it in the chimpanzee, where the nasal projection is almost entirely lacking. It is no doubt to be accounted for on mechanical grounds by the breathing of cold air inwards through the nostrils, and the evaporation of moisture from their inner surfaces.

Weekly physiological measurements, including systolic and diastolic blood pressures, rectal temperatures, and pulse and respiration rates present further opportunities for comparison between the subjects. The blood-pressure readings are obtained by the auscultatory method with a standard Tycos sphygmomanometer. The only variation from the usual procedure is to fold the air cuff once upon itself in order to fit it to the diminutive arms of the organisms tested. No regular physiological measurements are made until the subjects have become thoroughly quiescent and all evidence of emotional or other disturbance has entirely disappeared.

In regard to blood pressures a consistent difference is apparent which continues throughout the entire nine months. The average readings for this period are about 100/60 millimeters of mercury for Donald and 110/80 for Gua. The pressures show a tendency to increase slightly from month to month, although there is no similar trend indicated in any of the other physiological records during the period of our observations. The respiration rate of the ape, like the blood pressure, is also higher than that of Donald, averaging 46 as against his 36. One might infer from such differences that the chimpanzee possesses a generally more rapid rate of metabolism. If an inference of this sort, made on the basis of such meager evidence, is correct, it would account to some extent for the greater activity and strength of the animal.

But there is no further suggestion from the other measurements in support of this supposed condition. Gua's pulse, in fact, is lower than the boy's average figure of 135 by 10 beats to the minute, while her pulse pressure, it will be seen from the figures already given, is also lower. Her normal rectal temperature on the average is likewise a fraction of a degree less than Donald's although this can be explained by the fact that the anal orifice of these animals protrudes within the genital swelling instead of being protected by a thick wall of surrounding flesh as is the case with humans. As a result, the rectal area of the ape is probably subject to greater cooling through contact with the outside air.

Having briefly compared the two in physiological and structural characteristics, we may now proceed to a consideration of some fundamental attributes of their behavior. We should first like to know the greatest speed with which they can respond to a sudden stimulus administered without warning. In the attempt to measure this *speed of involuntary movement* we seat the two together facing a motion-picture camera by means of which their reactions can be recorded. Their ages at the time this test is first undertaken are 10 and 12½ months respectively. When all preparations have been completed, the camera is started, and after a few seconds a revolver is suddenly fired behind them.

An analysis of the film is subsequently undertaken to determine just how much time elapses before the subjects begin to respond to this violent "startle" stimulus. The "reaction time" as determined from the pictures consists of the interval between the first appearance of smoke and recoil from the revolver and the first evidence of movement in the subject. Although the accuracy of such a method is controlled largely by the speed of the camera (which when operated at its normal rate may permit a good-sized error), there can be no doubt at all about the fact that the reaction time of the child is considerably longer than that of the animal.

As a check on these findings the same test is made some months later, when Gua is 16 and Donald 18½ months old. Five other humans whose ages range from 17 months to 8 years and 6 months are on this occasion included in the picture and respond at the same time to the surprise auditory stimulus. Gua is found to react in less than 0.2 second or about as rapidly as the children 6, 7, and 8 years old. The younger participants take longer intervals, the little girl of 17 months remaining still for nearly 0.5 second before movement is initiated.

In addition to having greater speed of movement, the chimpanzee is likewise stronger than the human subject.

Measuring the speed of reaction to a "startle" stimulus. The subjects are seated before a motion-picture camera while a revolver is suddenly fired behind them. Analysis of the film gives the time which elapsed before they began to move (see page 28).

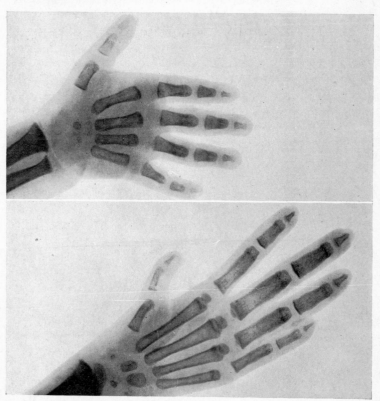

(X-ray photographs by Dr. W. McL. Shaw, Jacksonville, Fla.)

X-ray photographs of the right hand of each subject show their bony development. The child is slightly over 11 months old and the chimpanzee about $8\frac{1}{2}$ months. Note the difference in the growth of the carpal bones of the wrists, the proportionate sizes of the hands, and the relation of finger to thumb lengths. The X-ray of Gua's hand is reproduced through the courtesy of Professor Robert M. Yerkes of Yale University. (Three-fifths natural size.)

(Facing p. 28.)

The ape is considerably stronger than the child.

Above: At the age of 9 months she clings with one hand to the finger of the experimenter as he lifts her from the ground in play.

Below: At 11 months she permits herself to be carried by putting both her arms about the neck of the carrier.

That adult specimens are several times as powerful, weight for weight, as mature men is common knowledge, so that Gua might be expected to possess greater strength than Donald. By the time the ape has reached the age of 8 months her biceps and other arm muscles *when relaxed* feel nearly as hard to the touch as the *tensed* muscles of many men. She can chin herself with one hand, skin the cat with ease, and climb up and down upon the standing human form—entirely without the use of her feet—by holding to one's clothing. There are a few occasions, in fact, when she very nearly proves master of a difficult situation because she possesses almost enough strength to resist successfully the efforts of the experimenter to make her perform some special task. One of these instances occurs when she is 9½ months old. In this particular case she seems to be afraid of the anthropometric instruments, and objects to being placed upright upon the stadiometer with her back to its vertical surface, so that her standing height can be measured. There is nothing vicious about her resistance, for she seems simply to want—with a fury born of fear—to leave the equipment and crawl for protection into the arms of the experimenter. To force her to stand upright we place one hand against her chest and another against her knees and push against these parts till her back is flat against the wall of the room into which the instrument is built. But when the measuring piece is lowered to the top of her head she becomes so terror-stricken that she is almost able to bend her knees in spite of our best efforts. Such is the capacity of this tiny infant weighing at the time in the neighborhood of 5.5 kilograms (12 pounds)! It should be added in Gua's defense that she is never known throughout the nine-months period to employ her strength unless she is afraid. And it is then used only in the attempt to take her from the special object of fear and towards the protection of those who care for her.

29

One can readily see from such behavior that the ape even during the early months is considerably tougher than any human of two years can possibly be. She seems to be disturbed not at all by a tumble from the seat of a chair even though she may land directly upon her head or back. On some occasions she appears deliberately to throw herself in a sort of dive to the floor as if she enjoyed it. Our records when she is 10 months old contain the following appropriate notation:

When I start to leave the room she will scramble after me and hurl herself at my retreating legs in a typical football tackle. Perhaps to characterize her as a tough young football player, "hard as nails," would give a fairly accurate picture. In comparing her with Donald I am often reminded of the analogy to Topsy and Eva.

Or again, at the age of a year:

At present one might describe Gua by saying that she possesses the learning and mental capacity of a year old child, the agility of a 4-year-old, and strength which in some ways probably surpasses that of an 8-year-old.

Because of this striking difference in muscular power we are naturally interested in the general rate of spontaneous activity of the two subjects, although accurate information upon such a topic is hard to obtain. It would be impossible to say just how much more physical exercise is performed during an average day by one of them than by the other. The ape, according to our best observations, seems to be active more continuously than the child, but her activity is not characterized by as many spurts of violent movement, or interspersed with as many periods of relative quiet. As a result she may be said to be less variable in her expenditure of energy than the human. About the only indication that the boy is tired or fatigued is the increased irritability he occasionally manifests before nap- and bed-times. When Gua appears to be similarly fatigued she will lie down upon the floor or crawl into the lap of the attendant observer. It is noticeable that she seems to recover from her exhaustion with astonishing quickness.

From their early morning awakening at 6 or 7 o'clock, depending upon the time of year, until their retirement at 6:30, the routine of the subjects is one which permits few waste moments. It serves in itself as a stimulation to activity. The major part of each day is consumed with measurements or tests, periods of controlled observation or the taking of photographs, and intervals of play, automobile or perambulator rides. Breakfast is at 7:30 or 8 and supper at 6 o'clock. After the noonday nap comes the daily bath and play or a walk till 3 o'clock, when an extra ration of milk is provided. There are numerous incidental rest and play periods which serve as diversion for the principals. On rare occasions the entire day is spent in riding or recreation and frequently for half a day all routine work may be ignored.

From time to time the schedule is changed in order to meet the indispositions of the infants or experimenters, or the exigencies of a new series of tests. The arrangement in effect during the fifth month of the research, which is shown below, may be taken as a fair sample of the daily activities throughout the entire period.

A.M. 7:00   Reveille.
     7:30   Breakfast.
     8:00–8:30 Sit in high chair while adults breakfast.
     9:00–11:30 One or more of the following:
                    Ride in perambulator.
                    Physiological measures.
                    Observation of special behavior.
                    Automobile ride to Experiment Station (for weighing).
                    Photographs.
                    Outdoor or indoor play.
                    Experiments, tests, or measurements.
     12:00   Lunch.

31

P.M. 12:15–1:30 Nap.
    1:30–2:00 Walk or play out-of-doors for Gua.
              (Donald still sleeps.)
    2:00–2:30 Bath.
    3:00   6–8 oz. milk.
    3:30–4:00 One or more of the following:
              Outdoor or indoor play.
              Observation.
              Photographs.
              Experiments, tests, or measurements.
    6:00   Supper.
    6:30   Retire.

In any series of observations which purport to throw light upon the genesis of behavior an examination of the *reflexes* should play an important part. These bits or elements of activity are almost universally classified as predominantly native because of their regularity upon repeated stimulation within the same organism and because of their similarity from one individual to the next. Had we been able to undertake a study of the reflexes of the two subjects beginning at birth, it might have been possible to obtain evidence upon the comparative ages at which certain of them first appear. But such data were quite out of the question in this instance since each subject already possessed most of the reflex behavior of which it would ultimately be capable at the time the research was begun.

In the initial two weeks of observation, sucking, swallowing, sneezing, coughing, hiccoughing, yawning, coordinated eye movements, chewing and biting, and trembling or shivering were all noted in Gua. Her "grasping reflex"—the clenching of the fist—was particularly strong, and marked "withdrawing" and "rejecting" reflexes as a means of getting away from undesirable objects were also present. To emotional stimulation she demonstrated clear-cut reflex behavior of erection of the hairs during fear or anger, increasing blood pressure, pulse and breathing rates, and urination and defecation.

32

All of these, with the few exceptions to be noted, had been present in the child for many months. He had never been known to defecate in emotion, although urination during shocking or upsetting situations was observed in one or two instances. He was also never seen to shiver or tremble nor had his hair been known to "stand on end." But such omissions can be explained by the probability that he had not been subjected to stimuli adequate for producing these responses.

The only weakness or deficiency in any of the reflex movements of the ape involved her postural or balancing adjustments. At the age of $7\frac{1}{2}$ months she would frequently fall backward both from a sitting position and on those occasions when she would attempt to stand erect, as in stretching or reaching upward. That these accidents occurred without exception during the first few weeks of her association with humans is significant. They seemed, furthermore, to take place despite her obvious attempts to save or right herself. One might infer from such behavior (1) that the postural reflexes were not at first entirely developed and that subsequent maturation improved her ability to keep from falling in this manner. In view of her very young age we think this is the most likely interpretation. Or one might conclude (2) that because of her then brief contact with human beings she had not yet *learned* to look upward at such nearly vertical angles as were necessary without losing her orientation to the visual environment. She needed, as a result, to adapt posturally to this new situation, since all her previous intimate association had been with organisms of shorter vertical stature than humans. In opposition to the latter view is the fact that she often fell *forward* upon her hands during the first two weeks and was also uncertain and awkward in walking. It need hardly be mentioned that Donald at 10 months could not stand upright at all and that he frequently lost his balance while sitting.

The following reflexes which were subject to periodic test demonstrate in many cases differences of note between the two babies:

Pupillary Reaction. When a bright light was suddenly flashed into the eyes of either individual, the pupils would contract sharply. It was noticeable that Donald's pupils were larger both after and before contraction than the ape's and that they appeared likewise to contract at a slower rate. The fact that the eyes of the child were apparently larger than those of Gua may be responsible in part for this variance.

Contractile responses of the same general nature could be readily produced by bringing some small object suddenly very close to the eyes of either of the organisms. The pupils would then make accommodating adjustments to the change in distance of the visual stimulus. There was no noticeable alteration in the pupillary reactions of either subject throughout the nine-months experimental period.

Coordination of the Eyes. The shifting of the two orbs as a single organ was examined by moving a flashlight back and forth and up and down in front of the eyes, or by shining its sharply focused beam at different points upon the walls or ceiling of a dimly lighted room. There was no evidence of *strabismus* or cross-eyedness in either individual. Even if the stimulus could be seen with only one eye, the other being shielded from it, the covered eye in every case was in perfect *rapport* with the exposed or seeing one. A noticeable difference in the reactions of the subjects during most applications of this test was Gua's greater inclination to fixate the moving spot of light continuously. The child, on the contrary, seemed to shift his gaze more often to one of the experimenters, to the flashlight itself, or to other objects in the room. Two possible interpretations: (1) He was more distractible. (2) He saw into the situation better by observing all its details.

In following the moving light, the eyes of the ape could be readily seen to proceed in a somewhat more jerky or irregular fashion than the child's. There appeared to be a larger percentage of saccadic or jump movements in her visual pursuit of such a stimulus.

The convergence of the eyes towards a near object was not noticed until Donald had become 17 and Gua 14½ months old. That this convergence, if present, was not observed before these ages must be attributed to the activity and distractibility of the subjects and to the consequent difficulty of making such observations upon them.

Wink Reflex. Both individuals would wink involuntarily if suddenly touched near the eyelid, or if stimulated by a loud sound or by a bright flash of light. The ape's responses in this respect were the faster of the two and were accompanied by a downward movement of the whole eyebrow which was either absent or so minute as to be unnoticeable in the human. When the stimuli were rapidly repeated in series, each subject tended to squint the eyes, and particularly to squint the eye on the side from which the stimulus proceeded more than the eye on the opposite side. Within the final month or two a series of repeated touch, light, or sound stimuli would produce smiling and laughter on the part of the boy and corresponding playful reactions in the ape. During approximately the same period the chimpanzee would inhibit her winking to a series of stimuli after fewer individual applications of the stimulus than were necessary with the child. The ape would likewise wink *after single stimuli* which were so mild they would elicit no observable response in the human subject.

Plantar Reflex. This movement was produced by scratching the sole of the foot with the point of a pencil or other similar object. In the human infant there was usually a bending or flexing of the ankle, while the toes would curl toward the bottom of the foot. Earlier ap-

plications of the test suggested in a few instances responses of the so-called Babinski type, in that the great
toe would sometimes move slightly in a direction opposite to the movement of the other toes. This reaction
was by no means marked nor was it of regular occurrence, and it disappeared entirely after the first month
or two. Near the end of the experimental period the
boy's whole limb would be slowly withdrawn from the
stimulus.

The responses of the ape were similar although more
rapid and extensive. On some occasions they spread
to her whole body, causing her to push the stimulating
object from her with both hands. There was never in
her case any suggestion of the Babinski reaction.

Patellar Reflex. By smartly striking the patellar
tendon just below the kneecap, the knee-jerk reflex
could be obtained in each subject. It was somewhat
difficult to elicit because of the tendency of both infants
to be continually on the move. As a result a considerable preliminary period was usually devoted to getting
the subjects in a properly quiet and relaxed condition.
A further difficulty with Gua was the extreme smallness
of the sensitive area of the patellar tendon. Still, under
satisfactory conditions the foot would kick from 5 to
7.5 centimeters (2 to 3 inches) in the human and from
2.5 to 5 centimeters (1 to 2 inches) in the ape. There
was no observable difference in the latency or response
time of the two subjects.

Abdominal Reflex. To produce this reaction the
rounded end of a bone stylus in general dimensions
about like an unsharpened lead pencil was drawn downward across the chest and abdomen of the subject.
The response of the child was a tightening of the abdominal muscles and a slight upward movement of the
legs as if to cover the stimulated area. Usually laughter
or smiling followed each stimulation. The ape responded
in the same general fashion although with much more
violence. In some instances her knees would be drawn

36

up over the abdomen, her arms moved downward across the legs, and her head thrust forward upon the chest. She would thus literally roll herself into such a ball that restimulation was difficult. "Conditioning" in the chimpanzee was so rapid that after a few trials she would perform the folding reaction as soon as she saw the stylus approaching.

Startle Reflex to a Loud Sound. The situations used to arouse the startle response, in addition to revolver shots, were the dropping or throwing of a tin plate or plates immediately behind the subjects, the slapping of boards upon the floor, and the slamming of doors. Both individuals were more sensitive to such stimuli during the first part of the experimental period than toward the last. The change in this regard may have been caused by maturational factors, or it may again have been the effect of adaptation or adjustment to the test situation. At no time was a clearly observable jump or start as easily elicited in the child as it was in the ape. During the early months, he would respond with a small though pronounced jump which was usually followed, some 3 or 4 seconds after the sound had been made, by crying or wailing. But as the boy grew older he was seldom observed to make true "startle" reactions. Instead he would turn after a brief delay and look slowly towards the source of the sound.

The ape, for her part, could be counted on to jump in almost every instance. At first she would follow this reaction by crying and running to the arms of the experimenter. Later she would orient to the auditory stimulus almost immediately and, if nothing fearful was observed, she would remain where she was.

Ear Reflex in Gua. A high-pitched whistle or a harsh shrill noise would cause the external ear, or *pinna*, of the chimpanzee to move backward through a minute distance so that the rear of the ear lobe was slightly closer to the skull. There was no analogous response in the human infant.

37

Chapter III

HEALTH, EATING, AND SLEEPING

IT IS OFTEN maintained that the chimpanzee is difficult to rear in close contact with humans because of its great susceptibility to human diseases. And yet our experience with Gua seemed to indicate that, as long as she was given the care and attention of an average human baby, she displayed no striking propensities for ill health. She caught cold occasionally, perhaps with somewhat greater ease than Donald. She also suffered now and then from sores or abrasions, which she got from falling, upon her lips, head, and knees. Once she placed her fingers upon the red-hot burner of an electric stove. But from these and other minor ailments she recovered rapidly, and proved altogether to be a very responsive patient.

All precautions which might be taken with a young child were followed without exception, however, in Gua's case. She was given heavier clothing on cold days and was well covered at night; her appetite and bowel movements were closely watched, as was her general activity or tendency to be sluggish or overly sleepy. If her tongue was coated, if her skin appeared to be flushed or pale, or if she felt abnormally hot or cold to the touch, this was immediately investigated. As we have already seen, temperature, respiration, and blood pressure were systematically recorded. In addition a pediatrician was consulted when expert medical advice was needed. As remedies she was never given anything by us except cod liver oil or viosterol, a few drops of argyrol in the nostrils and camphorated oil on the lips for colds, a skin salve occasionally for abra-

38

sive sores, and milk of magnesia, of which she required a large dose, for bowel disturbances.

It was suggested from X-ray photographs that the chimpanzee at the time of removal from her mother might be suffering from rickets. Discolored blemishes in the enamel of her teeth pointed also to the possibility of an early dietary deficiency. But the lack of further enlargement of the damaged areas and a later improvement in the condition of the bones of the body were taken as indications that these troubles, if real, had been satisfactorily arrested.

Only once during the experimental period did she ever become seriously ill, then with an ailment diagnosed as intestinal influenza with gastric hyperacidity. For a day or two she was very weak, and lay in bed in a stuporous condition from which she had to be forcibly aroused to take water and orange juice. It is interesting to note that during this illness her physiological processes, including pulse, respiration rate, and blood pressure, were markedly subnormal, whereas human children when similarly affected, usually have symptoms of fever and increased pulse rate. The remedy—a rigorous control of diet—was so effective in Gua's case that it was possible to resume the regular daily activities after a brief respite.

On the average the ape consumed about as much food as a healthy child of her own size and weight. She usually took as a result a little less of milk and solid substances than the human subject, but the differences in this respect were always slight. She proved to be astonishingly hungry during the first few days she was in our charge, doubtless because she had not eaten well during the prolonged and excited preparations for the separation. When milk was offered her in a cup she would dash towards it with such vehemence that she not infrequently spilt most of it in her very efforts to obtain it. Cups, from which she had drunk only rarely

39

while in a cage, soon became for her objects of great attraction. Often while her food was being prepared she would investigate all the cups in sight, whether full or empty, and reach for milk bottles, drinking glasses, or any similar cylindrical containers as well. She showed no interest in the rubber nipple of a baby's bottle, even though she had been nursing from her mother but a few days before. Since she obviously did not at all understand its function and at the same time drank willingly enough although clumsily from a cup, no special effort was placed on inducing her to take milk from a bottle. As soon as she was transferred to the human environment, she was therefore fed entirely by means of a spoon and a cup in her own high chair.

A striking reaction in this connection was the movement of wiping her mouth upon the back of her hand and on the forearm after eating or drinking. If Gua was standing upright at the time, the hand would be drawn across the mouth in a manner quite like that of humans. If she was seated in her high chair and resting partly upon her arms or elbows, the mouth would be likely to be moved across the back of the hand.

Some evidence of the degree of her hunger, as well as of the whole-hearted rapidity with which she adopted her new associates, may be obtained from the fact that during the first few days, while being carried by the experimenter she made unmistakable biting and mouthing reactions in his chest region. These were taken to be attempts to find something resembling the teat or nipple of the mother from whom she had only recently been taken. In one such instance she seized a button on the experimenter's clothing at which she pulled with obvious intent. Upon another occasion she pulled with her mouth about where the left nipple of the mother should have been, and after a moment of fruitless effort, she shifted her position to the region of the right breast, which she attacked in the same manner.

There was some evidence of thumb sucking also, although this appeared to be more in the nature of play with the hands than a well-directed sucking attempt. It was the *thumb*, however, which was placed in the mouth, and not the fingers or toes. Several scattered observations of this sort were made in the first few days, but after that such behavior was never noticed again.

Within two weeks she had learned not to reach impatiently for her cup while the milk was being prepared, but was more willing to wait until it was offered her. In three weeks she climbed into her high chair and sat there of her own accord whenever the activity of warming the food was under way.

At first she was given seven full feedings a day but these were soon reduced to five and before many weeks to four. Her diet was also slightly modified so that within a few days it became the same as that of Donald. It then consisted of about 20 ounces of milk a day, especially prepared according to the usual infant's formula, a little boiled infant's vegetable (as strained soup, tomatoes, or carrots), a bit of graham cracker, and a few ounces of orange juice. Cod liver oil was subsequently added to the diet, which remained otherwise unchanged except in the modification of the milk formula, till she reached the age of 10 months when the component of solid foods began to be slightly increased. The extent to which this transfer was successfully made, and the close similarity between Gua's fare and that of a human baby, may be seen from the following menu, which gives her complete diet at the time of the ending of the research.

Breakfast (7:30–8:00 A.M.):

1. Warm milk (8 oz.). Canned evaporated unsweetened milk, mixed half-and-half with water.
2. Cooked cereal (2 oz.). Any sort of warm breakfast porridge.
3. Cooked fruit (2 oz.). Apple sauce, prunes, or peaches.
4. Rarely a soft boiled egg—substituted for cereal.
5. Cracker or zweiback.

Mid-morning:

> 2 oz. orange juice (with 1 teaspoon cod liver oil).

Lunch (about 12):

1. Warm milk (8 oz.).
2. One or two warm cooked vegetables (2 to 4 oz.). Vegetable soup, spinach, mashed green beans, boiled cabbage, or mashed carrots. Occasionally 2 oz. of beef broth.
3. Prepared dessert (2 oz.). Junket, Jell-O, custard, tapioca pudding.
4. Occasionally a little raw vegetable. Lettuce leaf, piece of celery or raw cabbage leaf.

Mid-afternoon:

> 2 oz. orange juice (with 1 teaspoon cod liver oil in cold weather or on dark days).

Supper (about 6):

1. Warm milk (8 oz.).
2. Cooked cereal (2 oz.) as above.
3. Cooked fruit (2 oz.) as above.
4. Cookie, cracker, or zweiback.

The only foods in this list which were not eaten by the human subject are the raw vegetables occasionally given Gua for lunch. She had disclosed her liking for these by pilfering samples from the kitchen stores, which were not always as easily available to Donald because of his more limited locomotion. This preference on her part also extended itself to flowers, which she ate, if not forbidden, with great relish, to the leaves of certain plants and bushes, and to the soft green bark of young saplings, which she occasionally scraped off or gnawed with her teeth.

She seemed to be subject to temporary aversions for particular foods which extended at different times to practically everything on her menu, even including the milk. The single exception in this regard consisted of the fruits which were almost always a great favorite with each of the infants. A new food, when first introduced, was usually avoided and concerted efforts were necessary on the part of the experimenters to win its ultimate acceptance. This to a certain extent was the case with Donald as well, except that his aversions were usually less intense and also less persistent than those of the chimpanzee. Gua seemed, moreover, to have a propensity toward the rejection of prepared foods of uneven consistency such as lumpy cereals, or the skins of peas or prunes. Her dislike was expressed in a very obvious manner through the medium of facial expression as well as (at the start) through the ejection of the food. In many cases she would make a typical grimace, with mouth drawn away from the teeth, upper lip raised, and nose wrinkled.

Upon the occasion of her first bath she at once seemed to show a strange liking for the taste of soapsuds, not only by licking them from her lips, but by taking surreptitious bites from her well-lathered arms and hands. Remembering the childhood days when mothers habitually washed the mouths of children as a form of punishment, we sought to discourage the infant ape in this practice by giving her a generous overdose of suds. We therefore offered her the entire cake of soap and when she opened her mouth to receive it, we gave it a good push inward. To our astonishment, she immediately reached for the cake again and finally succeeded in biting off a piece which she chewed at first with apparent zest. But after a little mastication it was rejected and subsequent offers of soap were received with considerably less enthusiasm.

As further evidence on the food preferences of the two it may be noted that both Donald and Gua disliked finely chopped spaghetti when first they tasted it, as they did also rice and toast. They both, on the other hand, accepted custard and soft-boiled egg, although Gua came subsequently to be less attracted to eggs than Donald. The initial tastes of sweets and candies were followed in each subject by obvious supplications for more. Upon being introduced to tapioca pudding

43

the chimpanzee acted in much the same way and ate ravenously for a few spoonfuls. But she stopped and ejected them as soon as a few tapioca balls became wadded together in her mouth. The child, who would have none of this dish when it was originally offered, accepted it later as a favorite. Neither cared for bacon, although Donald developed a liking for it. He ultimately accepted as well toast, rice, baked potato, cereal, and vegetable soup, none of which the ape would take for several months except in disguised form. The rice, in fact, she never accepted at any time.

At the younger ages the "trickery" methods customarily employed with infants seemed to work successfully in getting them to eat unwanted dishes. Thus if we disguised the mashed green beans by straining their pulp into Gua's milk she might eat them. The alternating of spoonfuls of beans or of spinach with spoonfuls of milk was another device which worked well enough during the early months. Strong-arm procedures of forcing food upon her, as for example by holding the lips closed, or of starving her into eating the rejected dishes, or of shutting her off in a room by herself or in her bed when she would not eat, were also attempted once or twice but never with enough success to warrant their continuation. In one such instance, to our great surprise, Gua went without eating for as long as 43 hours because she refused at each presentation some specially prepared infant's soup. Be it said to the credit of the little animal that she ultimately won her fight for independence in this respect and was never thereafter given exactly the same dish. Probably the most effective method, aside from the employing of trickery, involved the *laissez-faire* principle of letting her have her own way with regard to a special food during any one meal. We would then return unobtrusively to the same dish a meal or two later and so with quiet persistence work it into her diet. In this manner the taking of the new food was not made a special issue and no opportunity was afforded for aggravation or emotional excitement over it.

The question of whether the chimpanzee is omnivorous to the extent of occasionally eating small birds, rodents, insects, and birds' eggs seems to be one upon which opinion is divided. The more general view no doubt is that, although individual captive specimens have occasionally been known to be meat eaters, this ape by and large is probably herbivorous. Our own limited observations in this regard suggest that such minor meat-eating proclivities as Gua may originally have possessed had about disappeared by the fifth month of her civilized existence. She was at first observed to pick up insects which came within her reach and immediately to place them in her mouth. They were then apparently chewed for their juices, the crushed shell being later ejected. Small insects she would often seize with her lips directly, in spite of our persistent admonition against this. At one time when she was 11 months old she even caught a chameleon, which was carried to her mouth in a flash. She would probably have devoured or at least bitten it had we not at once interceded.

Strangely enough, insect eating was never observed after this occasion. Although she would now and then pick up and handle small dead insects, no subsequent effort, to the best of our knowledge, was ever made to transport them to her mouth and she usually soon pushed or threw them away of her own accord.

To put to a more careful test the possible tendencies in this direction, we subsequently gave her both live and dead insects towards which she seemed to show nothing more than a curious interest. Occasionally she would even manifest a fear or timidity in pushing the specimen cautiously with her index finger, or if it was thrust suddenly towards her by backing away and crying. If offered a morsel of cooked meat at mealtime she would usually take it, although after chewing it a

45

few times she would "make a face" and eject it. Beef broth she accepted occasionally if we insisted. When she was 15½ months old she spied apparently for the first time in her life some thin slices of goose-liver sausage. These happened to be upon the plate of one of her human friends at the noonday meal. She immediately barked and started to step from her high chair towards the sausage while she stretched her hand in its direction. This food, which was a dark reddish gray surrounded by a white rind, we seriously suspected her of mistaking for sliced fruit. She was nevertheless given a morsel at once but she almost immediately ejected it with a "face." Excepting her early behavior of chewing small insects there was no evidence of a general tendency towards a liking for animal flesh.

The little ape's appetite for water belongs in quite another category, for it had reached an astonishing intensity by the time she came into our charge. During the warm summer months she seemed to possess an almost insatiable thirst. From one point of view this is rather surprising in that the smaller skin area possessing sweat glands in these animals probably limits the exudation of moisture from the pores to but a fraction of that lost by humans. On the other hand it is probable that because of the fewer sweat glands she actually got less relief from heat through the evaporation of perspiration than humans do. Her cooling may consequently have been dependent to a greater extent upon the actual contact of cold water with the inner surfaces of the body. Although Donald consumed hardly any water, getting sufficient quantities from the water content of his milk, Gua if left to herself would drink a cupful in a few gulps.

Within six weeks after she had come to us, water faucets had begun to exert such an attraction upon her that anything resembling a pipe or a garden hose was subject to her immediate investigation. She even braved the terrors of a lawn sprinkler on one occasion to get near enough to the source of the water to obtain some. And she was continually discovering new lawn spigots and outdoor hose connections whose presence had previously been unknown to either of the experimenters. To these she would go with lips extended to catch any stray drops which might hang from them. In some cases, if the spigot was so high as to be out of her reach, she was observed to bite at the pipe below the spigot. At the age of 10 months, when she was better able to climb, she would conquer the heights of the kitchen and bathroom sinks several times a day, and wait patiently for a drop of water as a reward.

A large water main used to fill a swimming pool was once examined by her, even though she had never seen any water as much as drip from it. It was noticeable that she went to this main in the region of a heavy valve operated by a wheel, but paid little attention to the other parts. The similarity in general formation between the wheel and the handles of smaller faucets is obvious enough to us, although the question may be raised, in view of the great differences in size, whether Gua's activities can be safely construed to indicate that she perceived this likeness.

A striking fact in this connection, particularly in view of her more than average interest in faucets and spigots, is that only once during the entire nine-months period did she ever succeed in opening a faucet. Since the act was never thereafter repeated, there is good reason to suppose that her success in this instance was accidental. With the coming of cool weather, her craving for water waned considerably so that at the very age when she should have been better able to master the problem of turning on a faucet, she no longer possessed the same motivation. But it should be noted that the child as well never succeeded in operating a water faucet during the period of our observations—this in spite of the fact that his attention was occasionally directed towards them through his association with

47

Gua, and that he seemed to be more consistently interested in the movable parts than she was.

That her strong appetite for something to drink never entirely left her is attested by the following incident which occurred when she was 14½ months old. One of the experimenters had been writing at a small table while Gua sat in the same room playing beside him. It became necessary for the human to depart momentarily, so he laid his fountain pen upon the table and left Gua by herself. When he returned abruptly a few minutes later, he found the chimpanzee on top of the table complacently seated upon a pile of notes. The point of the fountain pen was in her mouth and its barrel extended horizontally before her. A hasty examination showed that the lips of the ape were covered with ink, and her mouth and tongue were nearly black with its discoloration. The point of the pen had not been bitten or damaged in any way, although the ink reservoir itself was quite empty. The stain upon the mouth, tongue, and throat of the little animal was so intense that it had only partially disappeared some hours later.

About two months after Gua had come into civilized surroundings she was introduced to the clean linen of a human bed together with a full complement of bed and night clothing. Her mattress was placed in an inclosed rectangular crib with screened sides and top resembling in general structure and dimensions a child's "Kiddie-Koop." She had been sleeping in this inclosure almost since the beginning of her human existence, although the mattress and other accessories were not at first provided. The change to a soft sleeping surface she accepted with such evident pleasure that when the new equipment was temporarily removed a few days after its installation, she cried persistently. It was immediately returned for the peace of all concerned, and in

Gua gets a drink from an outdoor faucet (age 10 months).

(*Facing p.* 48.)

Above: The daily bath.

Below: Gua's crib is of the general style and dimensions of a child's "Kiddie Koop." Inside is a smaller compartment with mattress and full equipment of bedding, where she sleeps.

this manner she slept for the remainder of the nine-months period.

During sleep and drowsiness many of the ape's reactions were so characteristically human as to suggest a close bond between herself and higher organisms. If her eyes were heavy she would rub them with the back of her hand and wrist in a movement which differed in no essential aspects from that of a young child. If forced to sit up when sleepy, or if suddenly awakened from sleep and held in an upright position, her head would nod forward upon her chest, be rapidly pulled up again as the stimulation of its own movement aroused her, only to sink slowly downward once more. Behavior of this sort was apparent soon after she had come to us, and was observed repeatedly as time went on.

When thoroughly asleep she was relatively unre-sponsive to sounds although unusual or sudden move-ments of her bed, of the coverings, or of the body of the person on whose lap she might be resting would generally awaken her. She was noticeably "soothed" by such rhythmic swaying motions as are frequently employed to rock the human baby. When very young she would sometimes fall asleep if carried, and she showed the same inclination during her rides in an automobile—especially before she became old enough to stand at the window and view the panorama of passing scenery.

From the ages of 7½ to 9 months she was inclined to sleep longer than Donald, and would almost invariably take a short nap after each feeding. When she first consumed four full meals a day, therefore, she usually had three naps before the final feeding after which she was put to bed for the night. As she grew older, her propensity for sleeping during the day decreased, so that before long she was taking only one daily nap and that after lunch. At the termination of the research she seldom slept more than an hour during her noonday rest, while Donald at the same time was sleeping for two hours or more. She was put to bed at night when the child was, awoke in the morning at about the same time, and proved in the main to be a quiet and well-behaved sleeper. When she became fully adapted to her quarters and surroundings, she seldom made any noise or disturbance at night, even if she awoke, unless she was wet, cold, or in other ways needed attention.

The sleeping postures which the ape assumed, allowing for minor differences in her bodily build, were essentially the same as those of humans. She would literally sprawl herself in almost any attitude, on her back, side, or abdomen, with arms and legs extended or flexed as the case might be. Once at the age of 11 months she was observed in a prostrate position with her head thrown back and her mouth partially open. Although the nostrils were clear, she was breathing audibly through the mouth, and the lax position of the lips, which partially bared the teeth, was so striking that we started upon seeing her thus. She seemed to be able to sleep upon her side with somewhat greater comfort than many persons, probably because the relative narrowness of her shoulders made it possible for her head to rest nearly horizontally without the use of a pillow to support it.

A few further variations of an analogous nature may be mentioned. Once or twice, for example, she was observed lying face downward but with her head bent *backward* so that the face, which was turned neither to the right nor to the left, was resting on the chin. This was usually done when she was stretched lengthwise upon a pillow with the head protruding over its edge. It is perfectly possible of course for the normal human when similarly resting to place his head in the same relative position, no doubt with little more discomfort than Gua would possibly have experienced had she remained thus for very long.

Again she was known on cold nights to lie face downward, with the arms folded under her chest. This posture was likewise observed in the child. Sometimes with her arms folded in this manner, she would pull her knees up under the hips so that she literally crouched in sleep upon her knees and elbows. This also was observed in the human subject.

When lying upon her abdomen with arms and legs extended, it was not uncommon for her to place the

FIG. 2.—Sleeping postures peculiar to the ape. The drawings are made from a point directly above the reclining animal. In the left-hand position the forward leg is drawn upward and inward so that it is almost beneath the knee. The knee-ankle line is therefore nearly vertical. In the right-hand position the knees are drawn upward until the thighs form a continuous straight line.

two thighs perpendicularly to the trunk, in a straight continuous line one with the other. The knees were then bent downward at right angles to the thighs. Such a position of the legs was made possible by the larger range of movement of the thigh joints of the ape.

She often lay prone in the familiar human posture of facing three-quarters to the side, the under arm going behind and downward, and the upper arm held in a forward and upward position (see Fig. 2). Her legs when she assumed this attitude were as a rule spread much as were the arms, with the under leg back and the upper one forward. On some occasions she would raise the knee of the leg on the upper side to such an extent that the knee-ankle line was nearly vertical. Her forward leg up to the knee might in these instances have been said to be virtually "standing" by itself.

A question of evident significance at this point is whether Gua ever displayed anything in the nature of *chimpanzee nest building*. When alone in the forest chimpanzees customarily break off and bend together the smaller branches of trees to make a basketlike nest for the night. Gua had certainly had no experience in this behavior nor had she in all probability ever observed older apes engaged in such activities. Nevertheless, after she had been sleeping upon a soft mattress for a few weeks, she began nightly to disarrange and disturb the bed clothing to so great an extent before she finally fell asleep that serious preventive measures were taken. Such behavior persisted, except for occasional intermissions, until the end of the research. If Gua happened to be very drowsy when she went to bed, there was no disarranging of the bedding. If she was caught in the act and punished she would usually desist for the evening. And if the covering was straightened after she had gone to sleep she no longer upset it. Otherwise the disturbing procedure became a pretty definite preliminary to her sleeping. There was, as far as we could tell, no *purpose* or *object* to this behavior and certainly there was no observable pattern, even of the crudest sort, in which she stirred the bedding.

Two possible explanations, it seems to us, may be advanced to account for the facts. The first is that nest building in chimpanzees is inherent or instinctive and that, when Gua had reached the age and possessed the facilities to give such behavior appropriate expression, it began to assert itself. The persistence of the activity, in spite of the environmental discouragement that was offered, may be regarded as evidence for such a view.

Yet there are some psychologists who would probably consider such an interpretation doubtful. They might think it somewhat like saying that the Eskimo who is visiting friends in New York City would still build an igloo (providing the necessary snow and ice were handy) because he had an instinct to build one.

The second explanation is that the ape was displaying the almost universal tendency of infants for bedtime play. It was, according to this conception, a matter of pulling out covers just to pull them out, of wadding them in balls and of throwing them over one's head to no definite end beyond the end of play itself. It was a question of that pure sort of twilight exercise so common in young children at the time of retiring. The failure to modify her activity in this respect must then be accounted for by saying simply that she would not remain long corrected by the methods we employed.

Chapter IV

DEXTERITY, ARM MOVEMENTS,
AND WALKING

THE TENDENCY of an infant to reach for an object held in front of it with one hand or the other, instead of with both hands or with its mouth, has often been regarded as a measure of its early development. Indeed man's well-known proclivity for the use of one hand more than the other is a fascinating topic in itself and has many practical bearings upon education and the upbringing of children. Perhaps the most important consideration in this respect is the view that stuttering and similar handicaps are inextricably bound up with the problem of using the right or the left hand. Interest in the question of hand or side preference has recently extended to the realm of animal psychology where certain investigators have sought to show that rats, squirrels, and even cows will in some cases habitually react with, or use, one side of their bodies in ways that they do not use the other side.

In view of the importance of this question we are induced at an early date to undertake simple tests for the purpose of recording, if possible, the development of hand preferences in Donald and Gua. To this end the subject is seated in a high chair with arms extended so that one hand rests on each corner of the tray of the chair. A bit of food, a toy, or other small object is then presented directly in front of him and midway between the resting positions of the two hands. The hand used in reaching for the object is considered the "preferred hand" for that trial.

Results of a series of such attempts show that near the start of the nine-months period Gua reaches with her left hand more often than with her right. In contrast to these initial findings, it develops within a few weeks that her preference has shifted to the right hand, where it remains between the ages of 8 and 12 months. One may be inclined to argue that the first tests are invalid because of the subject's immaturity and to infer as a result that her real or ultimate preference is to use the right hand. The difficulty with such a conclusion is the fact that between the ages of 13 and 16 months Gua again reverts to a left-hand preference, thus indicating, one might say, a marked instability in this type of reaction. If we total the number of reaches recorded in the entire period of the research, we obtain these figures.

Total L hand reaches 107
Total R hand reaches 110
Total with both hands 2
—
219

Handedness tests are more difficult with the human subject especially during the early months, because there is no solid food for which he has a strong attraction, and because playthings offered in the required manner lose their interest so rapidly that only a few trials can be made at a sitting. It is possible, therefore, to accumulate for Donald only about two-fifths as many trials as Gua has made. Summarized, his results for the nine months are:

Total L hand reaches 37
Total R hand reaches 36
Total with both hands 13
—
86

For each of the subjects there is so little difference between the total number of reaches made with the right as against those made with the left hand, that for all practical purposes the two can be regarded as equal.

But it should be noted that the child as well as the ape *does* display preferential tendencies *upon different applications of the test*. At the age of 10½ months his score in a total of 20 trials is 20 right and 0 left reaches. At 15½ months he makes in 22 trials, 17 with the left hand, one with the right, and 4 with both hands. Again at 18½ months, although the preference is less marked, he reaches in 24 trials, 11 times with the left and 6 with the right hand. If tests are made at only one sitting, or at any particular stage of development, the records indicate a preference for the use of one hand or the other; but if they are scattered over a long enough interval of time, the evidence for preferential reaching vanishes. Such findings, which are by no means original with these writers, may either suggest that handedness tendencies because of their inconsistency are not inborn, or, if you will, that a simple procedure such as that here employed does not adequately measure true tendencies.

An odd fact which appears in our results is that with the exception of Gua's initial trials both subjects reach with the right hand more than the left during the first part of the nine months. In the same fashion they generally prefer the left hand during the latter part. How can one account for this strange coincidence? There are two possible causes which suggest themselves. In the first place, shortly after the start of the research each subject at meal time is now and then given a spoon, and efforts are made by encouragement and assistance to induce him to eat with it. The spoon is arbitrarily placed in the right hand, which thus, entirely aside from any influence within the organism, is given added practice not furnished the left. The test results throughout the period of early spoon training are clearly in support of a right-hand preference for each subject. There are further incidental observations, particularly upon Gua, which show at this time that she uses her right hand more often in ordinary play.

The common transfer to the left hand is not so easy to account for. Probably the most plausible explanation is the fact that each of the experimenters fell, quite without design, into the habit of carrying the subjects, when this was necessary, in their left arms. They themselves developed an incidental hand or arm preference. This had the effect of placing the subject's right hand either around the neck of the experimenter or upon his shoulder. As a result when objects were approached (during the carrying) for which the subject might reach, his left hand was more free to make the reaching reaction. After the left-arm carrying on the part of the observers had become a fixed habit, each subject, when given a dish of food and a spoon, would occasionally of his own accord transfer the spoon to the left hand. It is certainly possible, on the strength of these known influences, to account for the shifting hand preferences as an outgrowth of external stimulation.

One theory advanced to explain right- or left-hand tendencies is that they are related to the special development of one half or the other of the brain. The cerebrum when examined after death has frequently been shown to be slightly larger and heavier in one hemisphere than the other. It has been argued from such observations that the greater brain development was somehow correlated with the greater use of the hand whose nerve connections originate in that particular hemisphere. According to this theory, moreover, one entire side of the body is likely to be slightly stronger and more adept in its movements than the opposite side, because of its association with or control by the larger brain center. An opportunity to put such a view to the test in the behavior of Gua seemed to present itself by giving her *foot-preference* tests. Since the feet of the chimpanzee are grasping organs like the hands, it seemed to us that they could be tested in the same manner. If it were found as a result of such measures that a left-foot preference correlated with a left-hand preference, and similarly that a right-foot preference correlated with a right-hand preference then evidence for the side preference view would be established. If on the other hand there were no relationships between the reaching tendencies of the feet and those of the corresponding hands, the conception of a dominating brain center which affected one entire half of the body would not be supported. Particularly propitious circumstances for a test of this sort seemed to obtain in Gua's case because of the fact that she wore shoes all day long. As a result little or no opportunity was offered for her to develop independent reaching habits with the feet which might either conflict or coincide with the existing preference of the hands.

In actually making the footedness tests, we seat Gua upon a table with her legs spread apart at an angle of nearly 90 degrees. Her hands are either held or tied behind her or held together over her head. A small piece of orange used as a reward is placed in a position midway between the feet. She thereupon grasps it with the toes of one foot or the other and transfers it to her mouth.

Curiously enough, the net result of the foot-preference tests shows a crude sort of relationship to the handedness tests. This is by no means clear-cut nor does it extend through all the trials, but there are more positive than there are negative indications that reaching with the foot *tends* to parallel reaching with the hands. Gua's choices during the early and middle months are for the most part toward the use of the right foot; and about at the age when she begins to manifest a left-handed tendency, the foot preference changes correspondingly.

To conclude from such findings that the brain theory of sidedness is supported would be going considerably beyond our results. They might be said to argue somewhat against this view since the preferences which we do find are only transient and vacillating, whereas it is not likely that the relative weight or development of the brain hemispheres could so change. Still, the relationship, such as it is, between hand and foot reaching *does* suggest a positive sort of transfer from one portion of the body to another portion on the same side. That the brain centers must be important in such an irradiation or "halo" effect seems also to be a safe enough assumption. Whether the over- or under-development of one side or the other of the cerebrum is the cause or the effect of the sidedness tendencies in more mature organisms is a question upon which our own rough records can throw little light.

In manual dexterity, particularly with regard to the grasping of small objects and the making of fine coordinated finger movements, the ape, it is well-known, is inferior to man. The finest prehensile movements of which Gua is originally capable are made with the lips. In getting a morsel of food from the tray of her high chair, or in picking up such a minute object as a pin, her reactions toward the start are invariably to stoop forward and use the mouth. There are good reasons why this should be the case. (1) The lips of the chimpanzee form an important tactile organ with an apparent capacity to feel and manipulate small objects considerably surpassing that of the corresponding human parts. (2) The length and awkward shape of the hands and fingers preclude their being employed with as much efficiency as human hands and fingers, as for example in making the fine thumb-and-finger pincer movement. (3) In the beginning, when Gua can walk only on all fours, it is much easier for her to carry objects in her mouth than in her hands. This in itself predisposes toward a greater use of the lips. To encourage her in the increasing use of her hands and fingers, toys and tidbits which are held out to her are not released if she tries to take them with the lips. This method seems to be generally effective, and its use is soon followed by a change in behavior in which the hands come to be employed with greater frequency and proficiency.

That Gua's *coarse* or *gross* hand movements are relatively clumsy may be accounted for in part by the backward limitations in the angles of movement of the wrist and finger joints (see Chapter II). The gross

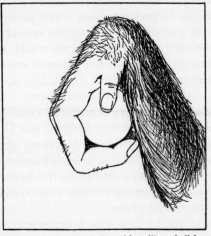

Fig. 3.—The chimpanzee grasps a bulky object like a ball by rolling the hand and fingers around it frequently using the arm itself as part of the grasping mechanism.—The fact that the wrist can be flexed farther towards the volar surface of the arm than is the case with man makes this possible.

grasping response for her involves not only the closing of the fingers but usually the movement of the wrist towards the arm as well. It consists of a sort of rolling up of the object in a manner which sometimes suggests the curling movement made by the end of an elephant's trunk (see Fig. 3). The thumb is seldom used in such reactions. Her inability to bend the wrist and fingers backward, often in addition, makes it difficult for her to release objects from her grasp. Thus in her efforts at building with blocks she can put one block upon another readily enough, but she does not seem able to get her long curved fingers away from the second block without upsetting the whole tower, even though it may consist of no more than two blocks.

To study specific differences between the child and the ape in "fine prehension," as in picking up small or thin objects, a series of *prehension tests* is undertaken at intervals of three months. The individual under observation is seated in his high chair, upon the tray of which are placed at different times four articles in general difficult to pick up. Gua is not permitted to use her mouth for grasping or seizing the test objects. Since they are seen only when the trials are made, they remain new and strange and no instructions or encouragement are ever necessary to induce the subjects to struggle for minutes in the effort to obtain them.

The first is an ordinary letter-size envelope. To our considerable surprise neither Donald nor Gua has any difficulty in grasping it and the reactions of the two are very similar. Each places one or both hands, palm downward, upon the envelope and curls the fingers under its far edge. Their responses remain essentially the same each time the test is given.

The second object is a wire hairpin 7 centimeters in length. The child customarily gets this with a fine pincer movement of the thumb and index finger. He has little trouble in grasping it even upon his first attempt; yet the ape finds the hairpin by no means so easy to obtain. She tries on numerous occasions to seize it with her lips. When prevented from doing this she claws or rakes it to the near ledge of the tray of her high chair. When it is on edge in this position, she brings her fingers together in a gross grasping reaction so as to inclose it in her fist. Her method upon each testing is much the same.

The third article is a ten-cent piece. This is also secured by Donald by means of a fine pincer reactoin, although in some cases he first lifts it on edge by getting the nail of his index finger under the far edge. In one or two instances he has much trouble and works for several seconds before he succeeds. Gua, for her part, finds the coin so difficult to pick up that she does not obtain it at all during her first prehension tests, although she is successful later. In her various attempts to get it she uses some of the methods to be described below.

The fourth article is a flat nail file. It is 15 centimeters long and 1.25 centimeters wide at one end, and it tapers to a sharp point at the other end. Both subjects here encounter by far the greatest difficulty. The procedure by which the human succeeds is again essentially the use of the pincer reaction. Gua fails entirely to get the nail file the first two times the test is given but succeeds finally at the age of 15½ months.

One of the methods which she ultimately employs in securing these and other small or flat objects for which fine prehension is necessary is to extend the arm downward at an angle toward the object to be picked up with the palm in a vertical plane and the fingers clenched. The positions of the hand and arm are not greatly different from those of a boy about to "shoot" a marble. The index finger is next extended, like a hook, beyond the object, which is drawn toward the second finger. The object is then lifted between the second joints of the first and second fingers.

Another method is to place the hand on the surface from which the object is to be secured with the palm on edge and the thumb upward. The fist is then closed about the object, which is pinched between the little finger and the palm.

In grasping a minute article like a pill her procedure is often to put the knuckles of the closed fist down over it and squeeze it between the back of the nail of the index finger and the fleshy part of the palm of the hand.

Although as we have seen the thumb is not generally employed in picking up large or bulky objects where fine prehension is unnecessary, there are numerous other instances where it is used in clear opposition to the remaining members of the hand. In holding elongated objects, as when she takes a stick or branch or when she hangs from a bar or rod and chins herself, the thumb usually opposes the fingers as it does in similar human reactions. At the later ages Gua's thumb is also separated from the rest of the hand when she holds the neck of a bottle, when she shakes hands, or when she picks up a drinking glass. She is sometimes even seen to grasp a thin surface, like the brim of a hat, by holding it between her thumb and her palm.

Object here

FIG. 4.—In a few instances Gua is seen to pick up small round objects like beans or pills between the nails of the thumb and index fingers. This maneuver is the closest she ever approaches to the more accurate thumb-and-finger prehension of the child.

There are a few instances when she achieves something resembling the human thumb-and-finger pincer movement. This happens once or twice during the final coin test when the two members are placed, each nail downward, upon opposite sides of the coin and the attempt is made to get the nails under it. It is also noted on rare occasions in a slightly different form when Gua attempts to pick up small round objects like beans. In such cases she brings the thumb and index finger together nail against nail, so that the object sought is squeezed *between the two nails*. The index finger in such a response is bent or crooked so far that its nail is nearly parallel to the nail of the thumb (see Fig. 4).

63

To say that it is structurally *impossible* for these animals to bring the tips of the thumb and fingers together, as some writers have done, is to overstate the facts, at least unless Gua's reactions in this respect are entirely atypical. There is no denying, of course, that it is difficult for the chimpanzee to pick up an object with its thumb and forefinger. It also seems likely that such reactions would not often be made by the average animal without special training, for the reason that the thumb is relatively so short the fingers must be bent or curved through a much greater distance than are human fingers in order to touch its tip. The previously discussed inability of bending "backward" the first joint of either the thumb or the index finger means that these two members can only touch tip to tip or nail to nail. As a result, the two inner or palmar surfaces of the finger pads cannot be placed flatly together.

We endeavor next to compare the coordinated arm movements of the two subjects by placing upon their heads a small skull cap cut from the crown of a felt hat. When this is first put upon Donald (age 11½ months), he tries to look upward at it and appears mystified, but makes no movement to take it off. The same procedure at 12½ months produces a slow and simultaneous upward movement of both hands followed by a grasping of the front edge of the cap and its subsequent removal by pulling it down in front of the face. The hands are moved in unison throughout this response. By the age of 14½ months he not only takes off the cap as soon as it is put on him, but he also removes it with either hand singly, and he will even put it back on his head after its removal. At 16½ months he removes it both by pulling it forward over his face and by pushing it backward. Putting the cap on after he has taken it off has by this time become a regular part of the procedure for him. At 18½ months, if he sees one of the attendant adults

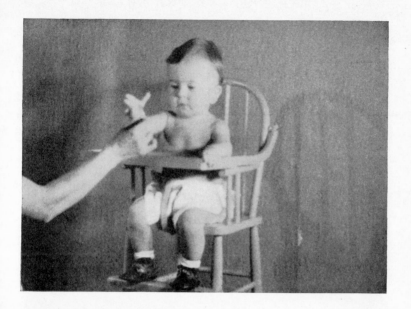

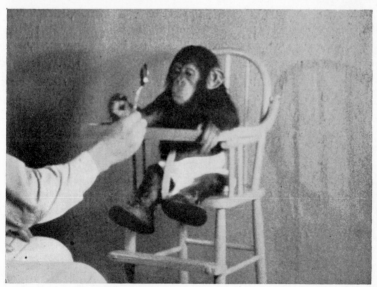

To test the tendency to use one hand more than the other in reaching, a toy or other article is held in front of the subject midway between his two hands.

Above: Gua removes the cap from Donald's head in the *cap-on-head test*. Ages: child 11½ months, ape 9 months.

Below: The all-four locomotion of the ape at the age of 9½ months.

sitting quietly with the same cap on, Donald will climb
into the lap of the sitter, remove the cap, and place it
upon his own head. Here one has the record in brief of
the development of a few simple though coordinated
responses involving the arms, neck, and head. What
will Gua do in the same situation?

Upon the first application of the test, at the age of 9
months, *she does nearly everything Donald has done by
the time he is* 18½ *months old*. She immediately removes
the cap in less than 2 seconds after it is placed on her
head, either by pulling it forward with the left or with
the right hand independently, or with both hands together. Sometimes she pushes it backward with one or
with both hands. If she sees the cap on Donald she will
reach toward him, take the cap in her right hand and
pull it from his head. At 10 months, after each removal
she waves the cap upward and downward at arm's
length in a playful manner. Not until she is 12 months
old, however, does she make the imitative response
which Donald first makes at 14½ months. She then
returns the cap to her head as soon as she has taken it
off. At 13 months when someone attempts to put the
cap on her she ducks her head and places both hands
upon her scalp in play. She will also rub or slide it back
and forth upon her head before removing it and she
still spontaneously replaces it after many of the trials.
At 14 months she takes it off and holds it out to the
observer. If she accidentally drops it while she is removing it, she at once retrieves it and puts it in the experimenter's hands.

There are further differences in the general arm and
body reactions, though less pronounced ones, which
appear when the subject is laid upon his back and a
towel or napkin thrown over his face. The response in
this case is similar to the customary infant's reaction in
playing peek-a-boo. Donald, at 10½ months, reaches
simultaneously with both hands to a point in the region
of his mouth, and pulls the towel downward upon his

chest. As soon as his face is uncovered, he is seen to be smiling. His response has been immediate, requiring not over 2 seconds. At 12½ months he starts to reach upward for the towel before it touches his face. His reactions are still made with both hands in unison and consist in pulling the towel downward over his chest and abdomen. The ape at 8 months removes the towel in about the same time required by Donald, by pulling it downward with her left hand only. She waves it back and forth after she has taken it off, bites at it, and opens her mouth in play maneuvers. A month later she responds in perhaps 1½ seconds, sometimes by pushing the towel upward from her face with both hands, sometimes by making the same reaction with one hand, and sometimes by pulling it downward over her chest with the right or left hand alone. At 10 months, unless prevented from doing so, she will raise her arms over her head in order to catch the towel before it lands there, so that by a single downward movement of the two arms she can remove it almost immediately.

If a sheet is thrown over the head of the child when he is *seated*, he tries at 18 months to remove this by alternate over-arm clawing. These reactions he occasionally supplements with simultaneous clapping movements of the hands in front of the face, which catch a portion of the sheet between them and pull it forward with less lost motion. Gua seems rather frightened at being covered in this manner and removes the sheet more rapidly, by alternate clawing movements from back to front, or by alternate lifting movements from front to back. In either case the kind of a response with which she begins is continued until the sheet is removed.

One of the most striking examples of coordinated arm and hand movement is observed in the ape at the age of 13½ months. On this occasion she attempts to seize a fly which is crawling on the floor in front of where she is sitting. Her right hand is extended with the palm in a vertical plane and is slowly moved near the fly.

She then makes a quick sweeping movement, closing the fist as she does so. Although she misses the insect, the response is well timed, accurate, and finished. The general reactions are identical with those any adult human would make in a similar situation. It may be rather extreme to consider such behavior as native— yet it is difficult to see how Gua can have learned it before her removal from her mother, because of her very young age. It is almost impossible to conceive of her having learned it during her association with humans, since the continual observation of her activity would surely have disclosed some evidence of its acquisition.

We come then to the question of the development of walking. Here is an activity which is easily observed and yet one whose explanation is a problem of much uncertainty. Does the behavior of the two subjects suggest that walking is probably a native ability? Or that it is primarily learned? Is it a matter of the maturation of nerves and muscles? Or is it a matter largely of training and of outside influences?

The answer to such questions seems to us to be that since walking, like any other activity, depends upon the use of certain parts of the body, it cannot be well developed until those parts have matured sufficiently to permit easy and accurate operation. To the extent that one can safely regard the maturation and proportions of the parts themselves as "native," walking may be so considered. But the particular fashion in which these parts are ultimately manipulated, or, in other words, the kind or style of movements which they make, are, within the limits of their possibility of movement, matters of environment and training. If such an appraisal of the situation is correct, then it should not only be possible for the chimpanzee to walk upright in a human environment but it should indeed be "natural" for her to do so, since her bodily structure

67

would certainly permit of this method of locomotion. It is to be distinctly noted in this connection that the commonly accepted "natural" manner in which these animals get about is quadrupedal, and that wild specimens have seldom been seen to walk or stand upright except for relatively short periods of time and for comparatively short distances.

Perhaps before we consider Gua's locomotion in detail, it would be well to pass in review some of the features of the development of walking in the human subject, who began this behavior while Gua was present and whose responses can be regarded as typical childlike reactions to the specific situations in which he was placed. Donald never crawled or crept, doubtless because of the fact that from the time he was able to move himself at all he was given a baby "walker." This contrivance possessed a diminutive seat somewhat resembling that on a bicycle, around which was a circular iron frame, like a high railing, which kept the child from falling off. The baby's feet could easily reach the floor and he could consequently push the device in any direction, since it rolled smoothly on small wheels and casters (the latter being pivoted) placed far enough outward at the base to prevent it from overturning.

When first put in the walker, the infant could not of course operate it at all, but he very soon learned to push it backward by extending his legs in front of him. It was about at this stage that Gua was taken into the human household. Within a few weeks the child became quite skillful and could push himself across the room either forward or backward using both feet simultaneously for any given push. He then learned rapidly to guide the machine, to turn it around, and to give a powerful shove that would permit him to coast for two or three meters. His efforts in moving the walker eventually became so forceful that he would often stand momentarily upright as he gave a great push. In such cases he would lift the entire affair from the floor, holding it as he did so by means of the railing about the seat. He thus developed a surprising speed of locomotion and could with the greatest ease overtake and catch Gua who was just then beginning to move about with any degree of steadiness. One of his common delights seemed to be to rush at the ape in this rumbling Juggernaut and laugh as she scurried to keep from being run over, often without success.

He first stood unaided for a few seconds at the age of about 10½ months or shortly after he had begun his exploitation of the walker. But it was not until he was 11½ months old that he began to show any evidence of making *alternate* leg movements in locomotion. Successive steps of this sort began to occur very rarely during the regular course of his activity in the walker in which he spent most of his playtime. But the frequency of such movements soon increased until he was making more alternate than he was simultaneous extensions of the legs. It was at the age of 12 months that he took his first steps without assistance, but as is the case with all children some weeks elapsed before he was able to cover any distance by himself. Our records when he was 12½ months old contain the following significant item: "On two or three occasions I have seen him take a step with one foot and then take another step with the same foot. What bearing does this have on the interlocking reflex view and on the 'native tendency' or 'instinct' for one foot to go before the other?" There were numerous other instances, when he was walking with the assistance of a grown-up, of his sudden bending of both knees *simultaneously* under himself, so as nearly to release his entire weight. This might of course be regarded as a sort of hang-over from the simultaneous leg movements he had been accustomed to making in the walker, or it might be taken as an indication of the lack of inherent interlocking reflexes. It may be said in defense of the view that alternate leg movements in walking are "native," that if the boy's hands were held and he was pushed backward, he seemed to have no difficulty in making appropriate alternating backward leg movements, even at as young an age as 11½ months.

He soon displayed great interest in the new accomplishment of independent locomotion, and would often cry for someone to hold his hand and walk with him. It was noticeable in the early stages of his unaided walking that he seemed to have no ready-made protective reaction, such as throwing his hands forward, when he lost his balance. This sort of thing came only slowly and after the experience of many bumps. Nor did he appear to possess the slightest conception of the necessity of avoiding the upturned edge of a rug, the shoes of his elders, or similar objects on the floor. He would walk instead directly into them and fall unless he was caught. Larger obstructions, such as chairs, he avoided without difficulty, possibly because of his experience with them in the use of the walking machine.

Lack of confidence in early locomotion found expression in a number of ways. He would walk in the walker, for example—but without supporting himself or resting against it—with greater recklessness than he would make the same movements outside of its guard rail. When faring by himself, moreover, he often moved his limbs in a stiff-legged fashion as if he feared bending the knees might precipitate disaster. He seemed also to feel the need of gripping something as he walked and if nothing was convenient he would even hang on to parts of himself. During the first few days he put his fingers in his mouth and held his lower jaw. Later he clasped his hands tightly in front of his face, each hand seizing the other with a tenseness that made the fingers white. In one instance he was observed toddling uncertainly along with the fingers of each hand pinching the lobes of the corresponding ears. Occasionally some play object, such as a rubber doll or even a small pillow, would be picked up and hugged or squeezed with a tenacity reminiscent of the drowning man and the straw.

If placed in the walker at the age of 13½ months or older, he would promptly get out and walk by himself, even though the getting out required a rather difficult maneuver of sliding downward to the floor between the seat and the protective railing. At 14 months his movements were much more efficient and he could walk with considerable speed, although there was still a certain staggering or irregularity to his gait which suggested lack of complete coordination. At 15 months he was walking on his toes, and forward locomotion seemed fully developed, while at 18 he was walking backward in his own play without assistance of any sort. The full-fledged run, if by running one means a gait in which both feet are momentarily off the ground at the same time, had not developed by the time our observations ended.

The chimpanzee, of course, was somewhat in advance of the child from the very start. She already possessed, at 7½ months, a crude sort of independent locomotion by means of which she got about in a rather uncertain manner on all fours. Her gait during the first few weeks can be aptly described by no other word than "wobbly." She would stumble, stagger, and fall down at no seeming provocation, till the casual onlooker might well have concluded she lacked the physical strength to maintain her balance. But improvement was rapid and within a month the stagger or wobble had nearly disappeared. Save for occasional falling or sprawling, she then walked steadily enough. The typical chimpanzee method of placing the knuckles on the ground with the first and second finger joints curled under the hand was regularly employed upon her entrance into the human household.

At about the age of 8½ months she developed something resembling a trot, indicative of considerably greater speed of movement. This she ultimately used to race back and forth during her play, so that the clatter of her shoes upon the floor sounded like the romping of a three-year-old child. At 9½ months she had further acquired a gallop or lope in which the two front limbs were advanced almost simultaneously and the two back limbs brought up behind them also in nearly simultaneous order. About the time she was 14 months she completed her list of four-footed gaits with a kind of stiff-legged locomotion which resembled jumping on all four feet at the same time. This was undoubtedly a play reaction. She sometimes bounced along in the most grotesque fashion, rising into the air by means of ankle movements instead of knee movements, after the manner of a clown who might depict quadrupedal locomotion. One might consider her all-four forms of locomotion as comparable to creeping in many human babies, or to the walker locomotion of Donald. These are the lowest or earliest methods which each employed.

In order to encourage her to walk upright, and to give her the full advantages which the child possessed in this regard, a special walker, built to fit her particular dimensions, was furnished Gua. Almost from the start she could be placed in this and pushed about by someone else; but the instant she began herself to move, it was always to scramble out of the device rather than to make it go by pushing with her feet. It is a curious fact that she never used this as it was supposed to be used until near the end of the nine months, when she had come to walk upright quite well without its assistance. She would then get into it, even though she had outgrown it in size, and would walk about in it as a form of play. Her ultimate conversion to its use, therefore, came after Donald had ceased entirely to ride in *his* walker, so that the immediate benefit of his example was lacking.

Almost as soon as she came to us we found it was possible to take her hands and to lead her gently about. It was also discovered that if her hands were placed at

"Walkers" are given the subjects to aid them in early locomotion. The special walker built for Gua is never used by her except as a plaything.

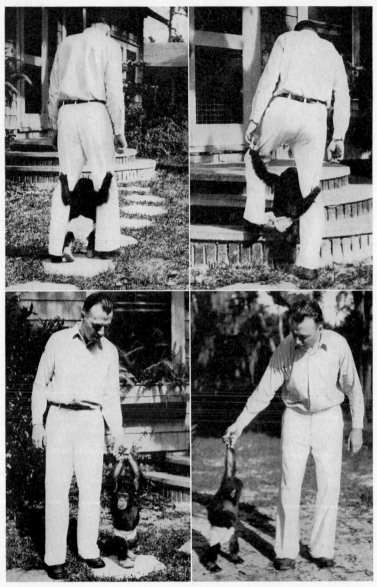

In her earliest attempts at upright walking *with assistance*, the ape clings to the trousers of the experimenter and keeps in step with him—even when it comes to negotiating a short flight of stairs. Holding her hands over her head furnishes a later method of support; and finally she will walk if held by only one hand.

convenient positions upon the trouser legs of the male experimenter she would hold tightly with one hand to each trouser and would follow along, peering between his legs, as he walked forward. She immediately adopted this method of "aided locomotion" as her own, and whenever the slightest move was made on the part of this observer she would run to him and seize him tightly. Since a step with his right foot pulled Gua's right arm and consequently the right side of her body, she usually also took a step with her right foot at the same instant, or very shortly after the experimenter had moved. The two would thus proceed at a leisurely rate, invariably in step, indoors and out, upstairs and down, in this fashion.

At first she bent forward at the hips at an angle of perhaps 30 to 40 degrees, so that although she was walking upon her feet, the upper part of her body was largely supported from above by her hands. After a little while she learned to stand in a more erect posture and with most of her weight on her feet. When engaged in this type of locomotion she could seldom entirely escape the playful advances of Donald if he happened to come rolling up behind her in his walker. On such occasions, to save her feet and toes from being run over, she would transfer her entire weight to her hands, which clung to the clothing of the experimenter. Her feet and body she would then draw well up out of danger as the wheels of the walker passed beneath her. However, when the child outgrew his walker, the ape possessed the advantage in motility. Without its assistance he was no longer able to catch and overtake her. During the early stages of his independent locomotion Gua was consequently able to run away from or around him at will.

It is worthy of note in this connection that the rate at which the chimpanzee covered ground was never much faster than the brisk walking of a human adult. Towards the end of the research she possessed but little advantage in speed over the child, whose hurried toddle was by then nearly as rapid as her own locomotion, regardless of the method she might employ.

Once, at the age of $8\frac{1}{2}$ months, she rushed to the experimenter as he started to walk away and seized his trousers in such a manner that she was facing in a direction opposite to his line of movement. The walking proceeded nevertheless, while Gua, apparently without difficulty, moved backward in rhythmic time to the forward steps of the adult. As far as we could tell this was the first occasion on which she had ever walked backward, and yet the alternating movements of the legs were made with perfect synergy, although of course with the assistance of a convenient pull transmitted through Gua's arm on the same side of her body. Here is an example which corresponds well to the instance of Donald's first backward-walking leg movements.

A further method occasionally employed to encourage upright walking in the animal consisted in our assisting her by holding both her hands over her head. Although she seemed to have difficulty in balancing when first this was attempted, she was soon able to walk quite as well with such help as she could by the trouser-leg technique. The ultimate in these aided methods was attained some time after she had passed the age of 12 months, and indeed when she had become proficient in walking entirely without assistance. She would then hold the experimenter's hand with but one of her own, usually the left, and would walk satisfactorily with this slight contact, leaving her other hand and arm entirely free. Towards the end of the nine-months period she could continue in such a manner for several hundred meters without touching her free hand to the ground at any time.

These procedures of walking by holding either to the clothing or hands of a grown-up formed by far the most important element in her walking training. Together they are comparable, we think, to what may be characterized as the second stage in the development of walking in the human infant, namely the walking with the assistance of others. It should be emphasized that the practice which Gua obtained in this regard was entirely of the "incidental" sort. That is, her reactions were direct and natural responses which her bodily equipment permitted her to make in the human environment. There was no more effort placed by the experimenters upon specifically *making* Gua walk upright than there would be in assisting a backward child to accomplish the same feat. She was, to be sure, talked to and told to "stand up" but no other rewards or punishment were given, and no systematic or forceful methods of "stamping in" the walking activity were ever employed. Many of the partial responses which she made were typically her own and were simply permitted or encouraged on our part by giving her the opportunity to make them.

There were often observed during her period of training certain spontaneous reactions which may possibly have been related to her efforts to walk, and which in some cases were much like common childlike responses. From the age of $8\frac{1}{2}$ to 9 months for example she would on numerous occasions lie on her back upon the floor and kick her feet as human babies often do. Her kicks were always made with the right and left foot simultaneously and they seemed, strange to say, to occur most frequently when her feet were encased in heavily soled shoes. Whether this was because of the protection afforded by the shoes or because of the noise made by the soles we are of course unable to say. At 9 months she would stand erect with both her hands upon her own or upon Donald's walker and would push it. In this manner she no doubt obtained additional practice. She also developed the peculiar reaction of walking by moving her feet only, but at the same time supporting the weight of the upper portion of her body on her hands which she slid along the floor in front of

75

her. On several occasions during the later months, more-over, she was observed standing while out-of-doors with the knuckles of each hand resting upon the tops of her shoes on the same side of the body. It appeared as if she were tired of standing upright and yet as if she would not place her fingers on the sand. The uneven and rough contour of the bare ground served apparently as a strong stimulus towards inducing her to walk erect when away from smooth floors. Her feet were well protected by shoes, but the skin on the hands, which was softened by frequent washing, was nearly as tender as that of a human infant. It must necessarily have been sensitive therefore to the pine needles, dry and brittle leaves, burrs, and coarse grass which were often encountered.

The record of progress of the actual upright locomo-tion in which she was completely freed of support of any kind shows that at the age of 8 months she began to stand for short periods alone, and on one occasion remained as long as 15 seconds before dropping to her hands. She was also able at this early period to make three or four steps unassisted. At 9 months she walked erect as far as 3 meters without aid and would often repeat this procedure many times during a short inter-val of observation. At the age of 9½ months she stood or walked upright fully half the time when she was out-of-doors, but not to such a great extent in the house. At the same age she also succeeded in going as far as 12 meters (40 feet) before placing a hand upon the ground. During the upright locomotion of this period her hands and arms were habitually held over her head or were extended sidewards. They would then be moved laterally in the apparent effort to keep her from falling, much as the balancing pole of a rope walker is employed.

When she was about 10 months old there occurred a peculiar and unaccountable retrogression in that she seemed once more to proceed most of the time on all fours and virtually to lose the results of her previous

In walking upright *without assistance*, the chimpanzee at first moves her arms laterally as an aid in balancing. If this balance is not maintained she falls forward to her hands at once. As shown in these pictures she is 11 months old.

Toward the last, Gua's upright walking is characterized by a strength and poise not apparent during the early months. She will even stoop over and pick up something with one hand without touching the other hand to the ground. Her arms, which were originally used as an aid in balancing, are later kept at the sides when she stands and walks erect.

splendid progress. In casting about for an explanation of this fact, we note that her food consumption had materially fallen off, which suggests the possibility that the change in behavior may have been due to a loss in physical vitality. But it was necessary, also, about this time to give her new and larger shoes, a fact which may have contributed to her lack of progress.

Some weeks later she again began to show a preference for erect walking and at the age of 11 months was once more upright during about half of each outdoor play period. She advanced so much at this time that she seldom put her hands on the ground at all when she was actually walking, but usually only before she started and after she had finished her various short trips. She was able to cover a measured distance of 13 meters (43 feet) in an erect posture, and began as well to show some propensity to walk upright while in the house. The following brief note from our written records will show the extent of her renewed progress at the age of 11½ months: "Gua walked on twos almost the entire time she was out-of-doors today."

Another rhythmic setback then seemed to overtake her and for the next few months she made little further advancement. Subsequently she found herself once more and sometimes during her outdoor play she would walk as far as 20 meters (66 feet) before stopping or touching her hands. Her erect walking at the age of 15 months was characterized by an entirely new strength and poise. She did not drop to her hands upon slight provocation. She would even stop, stoop over, and examine or pick up something with the fingers of one hand without touching her free hand to the ground, or transferring any of her weight to the hand with which she grasped the object. She would also stand upright for many minutes at a stretch. Her arms throughout this final stage were almost never held over her head and manipulated as an aid to balance, but instead usually hung at her sides.

77

In contrast to Donald's development during the nine-months period Gua was able to run in an erect position as well as on all fours. Her first recorded upright running of a few steps was at the age of 12½ months. At various times after this she was observed to run a considerable distance.

When she was 14 months old a foot movement resembling *skipping* displayed itself. This would occur only when she was holding the trousers of the experimenter, which she did occasionally till the last, and when he walked at such a fast rate or with such long strides that Gua could not possibly "keep step," as she seemed invariably to try to do. In such instances, in order to maintain her temporal rhythm with the observer, she would make a skipping hop. The skipping was done with the right foot only, her normal stride with the left foot retarding her by such an amount that the skip with the right was necessary to recover the distance lost in a complete cycle.

One of the most striking outgrowths of Gua's development in locomotion was her astonishing jumping ability, which began to manifest itself about the time she was a year old. A pertinent feature of this was that without exception it appeared to be just such jumping as a young human might attempt providing he possessed no cultural inhibitions. By that we mean that it was entirely bipedal and in no sense the quadrupedal jumping of a four-footed animal. It ultimately became a sort of play with her, so that sometimes after having discovered a particularly interesting angle for a jump or some new piece of furniture from which she had not previously launched herself, she would repeat the jump again and again, as a three- or four-year-old child might well have done.

She always stood upright as she took off, making the leap with her body leaning slightly forward. She would then land feet first, and would bring her hands to the floor only after the feet had touched. Her jumps were

78

almost invariably made from a high point to one which was lower. Thus the early jumps were chiefly from the seats of chairs to the floor, but she soon extended them to jumps from trunks, from bureaus or dressers, from overturned scrap baskets or other articles of furniture, and even from the perambulator. She would also jump from one piece of furniture to another, and occasionally from a piece of furniture into the lap of one of her startled friends. The highest leap of which we have any record was through a vertical distance of 81 centimeters (32 inches) from the tray of her high chair to the floor. This was greater than her standing height, which at the time was a little over 67.5 centimeters (26.5 inches).

Broad jumping was likewise a regular feature of her repertory. Her first broad jumps covering horizontal distances of about 60 centimeters (24 inches) she made by climbing upon the lower rung of a chair and throwing herself outward from that. Later she made measured jumps as far as 105 centimeters (41 inches) during which she dropped vertically through not quite half that distance. The long jumps of this nature usually started from the sill of an open window and ended upon a bed approximately a meter in a horizontal direction from the window. Her most astonishing broad jump was a running affair in which she hurled herself with a flying leap from the top of an outdoor porch which was raised by a distance of four steps above the ground. It was in superficial aspects quite like the effort of a professional athlete. The hands were thrown upward to a position above the head when she was in the air and were pulled downward again as she landed. Her feet touched the ground first but she fell forward on her hands immediately after landing. The horizontal distance covered was not measured but it appeared to be large.

Although jumping was not a part of Donald's activity, he early began to manifest a marked interest in and a capacity for climbing. Very soon after he had started to walk he developed the prerequisites for this behavior by learning to rise to a standing position, when sitting or lying upon the floor. At first he would reach for some near-by object with which to pull himself erect, but by the time he had attained the age of 14 months he was able to get up without assistance. A month later he had succeeded in climbing into the body of a small wagon, 23 centimeters (9 inches) from the floor, which was used as a plaything for the two. In rapid succession he then negotiated climbs to the running board of an automobile (32 centimeters), to the seat of the same car, and finally at 16 months to the seats of household chairs, 46 centimeters (18 inches) above the floor. In one or two instances he climbed from the floor to a chair, and from the chair to the dining-room or kitchen table, where he was found prancing gleefully among dishes and tableware.

Climbing downward from such objects was a task of greater difficulty, but in a few weeks he developed the capacity for this sort of behavior as well. His method from the start was to turn around and come down backward. At 16½ months he climbed to a height of 2 meters and more on a heavy carpenter's or painter's ladder of sufficient length to reach the roof of an ordinary two-story dwelling. Probably his most striking achievement in this regard was to climb up the side of his high chair (using the rungs as one might a ladder), over the arm and, into its seat, entirely unaided. This he accomplished at the age of 18½ months. That his performance in climbing was beyond the average for a child of his age goes almost without saying. His advancement in this direction is no doubt to be attributed in part to the influence of Gua, who was the leader in such activities and whose example he frequently imitated.

In comparison to the human infant's capacities for climbing, it is to be remarked that Gua first went up into the high chair, which the boy later negotiated at the age of 18½ months, when she was but 7½ months old. Her movements in climbing were always slow and deliberate so that it took her nearly as long to attain some new height as it did Donald. Shoes at first seemed a handicap in that she was unable to grasp vertical members of the chairs or other articles of furniture with her toes. But whether the shoes seriously affected her later climbing is a debatable question. The limberness of the hip joints was certainly a distinct asset in this connection for it enabled her to raise her foot to a position near her armpit, and to hook the heel over the projecting ledge which she might wish to negotiate (see Fig. 5). By the time she had reached 13 months she was performing stunts which would have taxed the capacities of athletically minded children several

Fig. 5.—Climbing upon the seats of chairs is often accomplished by hooking the heel of one foot over the projecting edge and pulling upward with the leg and the two arms.

times her age. If she could get her hands on any horizontal projection, such as a window sill, the edge of a chair, or a table, the problem of mounting to its top was, for her, already half solved. She would then chin herself, raise her right foot over the projecting ledge, and pull herself up. When she was unable to reach the ledge with both hands, she would stretch upward on her toes so as to get it with the fingers of one hand.

Having attained it in this manner she would hang by that hand, put the second hand up beside the first, and then go through the process already outlined. Whether the projecting ledge was rounded or square seemed to make no particular difference. As early as 10 months she frequently got on top of a porcelain kitchen sink, the upper ledge of which was removed by a distance of nearly a meter from the floor.

Climbing from one piece of furniture to another was also common, and if we turned our backs for a few moments around mealtime, the chances were good that Gua would make her way from a chair to the dining-room table, where she would sample the various dishes with her index finger. Whether this activity should be in any way related to the child's similar escapades upon the kitchen table, we are unable to say. It is clear, at any rate, that Gua climbed for food; and she was usually successful in getting some, while the human subject never got any even if he climbed for it. On the whole Gua's adventures in this respect were more recurrent as well as more stealthy than any climbing in which the boy ever indulged.

There was hardly an article of household furniture which she could not eventually surmount with ease. Getting even upon the backs of chairs proved literally to be "child's play," and she would also climb upon trunks, chests of drawers, and the dining-room side-board with no trouble at all. Often she would be found on top of a large dressing table observing her image in its mirror, and on rare occasions she would go up the front of a tall chiffonier, hand-over-hand by holding to the knobs of its drawer handles. The long ladder which Donald mounted, she climbed to a height of at least 5 meters, and then swung down from rung to rung upon its under side in a hand-over-hand fashion.

The methods employed by the two in going up a flight of steps were similar in many respects, although here again Gua had something of an advantage because of her greater maturation. Donald's most common procedure was to place both hands, simultaneously, two steps higher than his feet, then to lift his left foot to the intermediate step and bring the right one up beside it. Gua climbed by moving the feet alternately, the left foot going up one step and the right foot the successive step. Her hands were moved alternately in the same manner, but opposite to the feet. The whole sequence of reactions was in her case not unlike the walking of a four-footed animal, except that it was generally slower.

She climbed her first tree at the age of 13½ months. It was a small sapling about 3 meters in height, with the lower branches about ¾ meter (30 inches) from the ground. The act was begun by hanging from these branches and doing acrobatics from them. This was the first time she had ever shown any interest at all in the limbs of trees, although she had been placed in them on several previous occasions. During the climbing one of the branches upon which she was standing broke and she fell about a meter to the ground. This did not seem to annoy her, for she soon returned to the tree and went up it again, although she did not climb to a height of more than 1½ meters at any time. Shoes did not appear to interfere in the least with her arboreal agility. A few weeks later she was observed to go up another small tree in a neighbor's yard. These two were the only ones she climbed during the entire period of observation. As far as we could judge, a tree was never employed by her as a medium of retreat or protection; it seemed rather to be used as a sort of plaything upon which she could perform stunts of climbing and swinging.

Probably her most unusual feat of vertical gymnastics occurred at the age of 14 months when she chose a parked automobile as the object of attack. Climbing up the side of this, opening its door, walking upon the fenders and hood comprised part of her play activities, while on one or two occasions she even climbed upon the top of the car by using the door handle and window ledges as hand- and foot-holds.

Let us now return for a moment to the question of whether a particular kind or type of walking or climbing is inherent and so figuratively "comes out" from the inside rather than being "put in" from the outside. Our own feeling, based to a considerable extent upon the observation of these two different individuals, is that locomotion in higher organisms in all probability is "native" *in one particular and granting certain premises*. The design or structure of the bodily parts of the subjects certainly predisposed the one more readily to walk on all fours, and the other to walk erect. The longer arms of the chimpanzee, which came nearly to the ground when she stood erect, without doubt directed her toward all-four locomotion. Conversely, the relatively longer legs of the human, which would place him in a head-downward position if he stood on hands and feet, were conducive to upright locomotion, as well as the fact that he could not see in front of himself except with difficulty and discomfort when on all fours.

If we are willing to agree that bodily build is a hereditary trait, then there is no escaping the argument that walking is "native" to the extent that it is influenced by the size and proportions of the limbs, feet, and other parts. But if we prefer to adopt the technically invulnerable position of genetics and to say that bodily build or structure depends not only upon the heredity of the organism but also upon all its previous environment (both prenatal and postnatal) then we may wish to take issue with the statement that walking in any unequivocal sense is a native ability.

The same reasoning applies to the climbing of the ape. Had she not possessed the specialized musculature which was absent in the child and the enormous hook-like hands, she would probably not have achieved the progress she did. These are differences which pretty well assure us that, *if the surroundings permit*, one creature will fall into the manner of using its members in a particular way, and the other will fall into the manner of using its members in a different way.

To say, however, that the *behavior* or the movements or the activity of walking or climbing itself is inherent is, we think, going too far. This places *the act* in the semi-glorified position of an inherited *thing* or entity, a mysterious unit, as it were, within the organism. There need not necessarily be an *instinct* of walking. Instead the complex pattern of behavior which requires in some higher organisms months or even years to become entirely proficient is probably to some extent a matter of acquisition and learning based upon extra-organic stimulation. The shape and the limitation of movement of the parts necessarily set definite boundaries beyond which variations in locomotor behavior cannot be produced, as for example, wingless animals can hardly be expected to fly. But within the inflexible limits established in this way the degree of difference or change from one individual to the next, or even between individuals in two structurally different but analogous families, is quite likely in part a matter of outside stimulation. We do not mean to suggest by such a view that a human infant who matured without the positive influence of the example of other humans would necessarily fail through its own experience to walk erect. The stimulation afforded by the inanimate surroundings and by the organism's own reactions might eventually lead it to stand and walk like other humans. This conception, nevertheless, would permit the possibility on the negative side that an infant reared only among quadrupeds might incline through imitation to an all-four type of locomotion.

Were the special influence of environmental factors not significant, it is unlikely that Gua would ever have adopted bipedal locomotion to such a remarkably proficient degree as she did. Were the influence of environment not important, it is doubtful if Donald would have developed climbing behavior unusual for a child of his age. Were the environment of but minor significance, it seems to us that the kind of walking which first appears in the organism would be bound—even though incomplete—to be composed of the *same* movements which the fully grown individual eventually employs. And yet it should be clear to anyone who has carefully observed the gradual unfolding of the walking process, that the infant (whether animal or human) does not do at the start what it will do later. It makes many unnecessary or excess movements. It totters and staggers and bumps itself, not even reacting "natively" to protect itself as it falls.

All would agree that this early inefficiency is in part due to immaturity of the organism. But we think also that it is due in part to the fact that the infant has not yet *learned*, through the elimination of false movements, to walk with a finished swing. When Donald began to walk he often lifted his feet 5 centimeters or more from the floor. He moved his legs sideways at an angle of nearly 30 degrees with the median plane during the process of advancing them for each new step. In turning around he frequently kept one foot on the ground and made successive steps around it with the other. His earliest walking resembled more a caricature of certain military "goose steps" than it did the movements of the smooth and completely developed process. We do not see how a deficiency in maturation can account for the presence of such superfluous reactions. It seems necessary to postulate in addition a "lack of complete learning" to account for them.

If walking in higher organisms were entirely an instinct which simply took hold of or expressed itself in the individual by a gradual process, such partial walking movements as were made during the organism's maturation, while not thoroughly coordinated, should, it seems to us, be identically the *same* walking movements which the grown organism would eventually make. Even though fragmentary, they should at least be elements of the finished product. The fact that they are not elements, but in many cases are so very different that they cannot be fitted into the ultimate behavior pattern at all suggests to us that they are in the nature of excessive or random responses which are discarded as the learned act reaches a more proficient level.

Chapter V

THE SENSES

OUR OBSERVATIONS upon the special abilities of the two infants in vision, hearing, smell, and taste, upon the sense of balance, touch, the temperature sense, and pain, are limited in many respects. These are of necessity confined to the *reactions* of the subjects when they are presented with visual, auditory, tactile, and various other stimuli. Such observations to a considerable extent occurred incidentally during the regular course of the daily routine, although in many instances it has fortunately been possible to supplement them with the results of elementary tests.

If we begin with the *visual sense* we find ourselves at once impressed by the early evidence in Gua of a strong aversion for intense illumination. This appears to be as great as or greater than that of human adults who are temporarily "dark adapted," at least if we judge by her obvious and unfailing proclivity to play and sit in the shadow. It is particularly apparent both when photographic lights are on and from her continued avoidance of bright sunshine. If she is carried directly into an intense beam, she turns her face from the source of light or puts her hand or arm over her eyes to shade them. If her hands are held, she will raise one of her feet sufficiently to cover the eyes. Holding both hands and feet produces a persistent squirming accompanied by a half-closing of the eyelids. The child shows no similar tendency to cover his eyes or to avoid strong illumination, although if suddenly taken into bright sunlight he squints and sometimes cries.

Upper left: Gua jumps from a chair feet first, as a human might (age 9½ months).
Upper right: She climbs her first tree at 13½ months.

Both subjects go up a long painter's or carpenter's ladder which has remained near their home for several weeks. The ape (age 13½ months) attains a height of 5 meters, while the child (at 16 months) reaches 2 meters or more without aid.

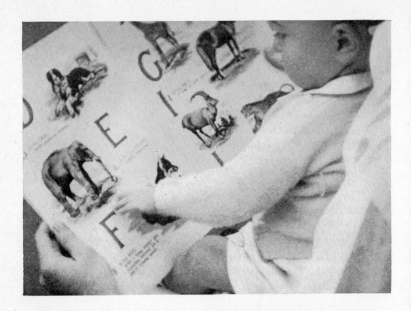

When looking at colored pictures each will point to them and scratch the surface of the paper as if to pick them up.

That the ape possesses exceptionally sharp eyesight, or *visual acuity*, and that she notices minute objects in many cases sooner and more easily than the human subject is a fact about which there can be little question. Perhaps the best indication of "seeing" or "observing" on her part is the reaction of pointing with the index finger to objects which attract her attention. It is unfortunate that she does not employ this response for distant objects, but only to indicate things that are within reach. The pointing reaction is first noted shortly after she begins her civilized existence and must consequently have been acquired by Gua without any assistance from her human associates. Similar pointing with the finger alone is never practiced with equal facility by the child during the period of the research.

The ape can sometimes be seen to point in this manner and stare intently at the most infinitesimal of insects. She will even follow an ant for a considerable distance, holding her index finger a few centimeters behind it as it crawls. Ant hills seem to fascinate her and she often sits or stands for several minutes near one, observing the activities of the members of the ant colony.

That she immediately notices new objects amid familiar surroundings is also attested by many instances, the following of which may serve as examples. Her walker breaks on one occasion and several new bolts are added to its wooden structure to give it further strength. As soon as it is returned to her, repaired, she rushes towards it like a child to a familiar plaything. Then, at once catching sight of the new bolt heads, she stares carefully at them, announcing her discovery by pointing them out.

Her further capacity for noting small objects is shown most strikingly when she is 9½ months old. She is lying on her back one morning beneath a window. The rays of the morning sun shine in a nearly horizontal line, across her body and a short distance above it. The beam, as a result, does not touch her, although in gazing upward toward the ceiling she must nevertheless look at or through it. She then seems to notice the minute floating dust particles which it illumines, for she not only stretches her hands upward so they are in the beam, but she makes grasping movements as if to seize some of the particles, and points to them with her index finger (see Fig. 6). An analogous reaction by Donald had been recorded a few weeks earlier.

FIG. 6.—Playing with the floating dust particles in a sunbeam.

For the most part, however, the behavior of the child seems to us to be less indicative of the perception of small objects or details than it is of larger general items like the activity of Gua or of the experimenters, of social situations, and of faces. Action of any sort in the ape seems to delight him continually. Before the age when he can walk by himself, if he observes her climbing, running, or playing with some object, he sits frequently in rapt attention, his arms akimbo, with fingers moving up and down in excitement, while he pants audibly in apparent interest and delight. And yet, when he is offered foods for which he has a strong aversion, he will nearly always accept them with entire disregard for their visual appearance. His rejection, as evidenced by the customary "wry face" and vocalizing,

never comes until after these foods have been received
into his mouth and tasted.

We note, in addition, that Gua shows an interest in
her own image when first presented with a looking-glass
at the early age of 8 months. At 10½ months she will
climb on to a bed and stretch upward in order to see
herself in a larger mirror which hangs upon the wall
about 2 meters distant (see Fig. 7). The same response
is made by Donald at the age of 13½ months, providing
he happens to be properly located upon the bed. The

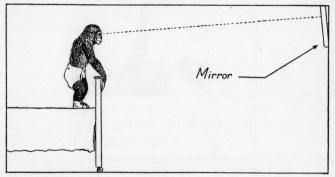

Fig. 7.—Gua often climbs upon a bed some distance from a wall mirror and gazes
at her own image.

successful completion of this act, even when climbing is
eliminated, depends to a large extent upon the ability
to stand and to stretch upward.

We show the two a motion picture of themselves.
Gua is then 11 and Donald 13½ months of age. The
projected image is on a reduced scale, being only about
15 centimeters in height. Each watches for several
minutes, but Gua is less persistent in this interest than
Donald. When the ape has attained the age of 13½
months, more pictures are presented, this time at
about half natural size. They are pictures of an experiment recently performed upon the two. At one point in
the film is shown a bit of apple which the subjects are
striving to pick up from the floor. Both watch the action

quietly for a while, then Gua climbs upon a writing desk immediately below the area where the pictures are projected upon the wall. She reaches out and touches with her finger the image of Donald's head and face. In a later scene, a moment afterward, she touches her lips to the wall in a position, which as far as we can tell, is about where the piece of apple appears in the picture. She seems indeed to be trying to pick up the apple.

She also demonstrates a spontaneous interest in the printed pictures in magazines and books even at as early an age as 10 months. This she indicates by pointing to various parts of them and usually by attempting to pick them up with her lips. We note that her attention in such cases is for the most part upon colored pictures or on parts of them, and that the sections which she touches with her lips are often vaguely similar to drawings of fruits or other edible objects. She consequently reaches towards the pictured back of a boy's head which is oval and brown like an acorn or nut. Further evidence of a somewhat questionable variety concerning her ability to see colors is offered in her attraction for flowers and blossoms of all sorts. She takes both red and blue flowers from green foliage with striking rapidity and she picks up the petals of red flowers in various stages of decay from green grass with no apparent difficulty or hesitancy. She seems particularly to be attracted to bright-colored fruits and vegetables as, for example, to red plums, lemons, strawberries, peaches, and tomatoes. At the age of 15½ months, on the other hand, she makes what we interpret to be a rather crude error of mistaking some slices of pressed gray goose-liver sausage in a rind of white suet for orange or other fruit. If our appraisal of her behavior is correct it suggests that she has in this instance confused reddish gray with some brighter color. Although chimpanzees are commonly presumed to possess excellent color vision, our own meager observations are on the whole inconclusive in this regard, because the factors of the difference in intensity or brightness of the colored stimuli as well as the influence of the shapes or patterns in which they are presented have not been controlled.

But we can at any rate compare the ability of the two subjects to perceive printed forms and pictures by showing them the same child's picture book. This contains drawings of animals in gaudy hues beside the letters of the alphabet with which their names begin. At the age of 14½ months and under, Donald's chief interest appears to be in manipulating the book by turning the pages, or tearing them if he is permitted, and inserting his thumb and fingers between the various leaves. Only occasionally does he stretch his hand towards any of the printed forms. At 15½ months his manipulative activity begins to be less noticeable and he is more inclined to sit quietly for several seconds and stare at the bright spots of color. He often stretches his hand towards a picture and rubs it either with the palm or with the fingers. Occasionally he makes a fine pincer movement of the thumb and index finger as if to pick it up. Such a reaction is particularly common in the case of highly colored shapes which stand out sharply from the background. At 17½ months he manipulates the pages hardly at all, or if he does it seems to be *in order to see new pictures*. His right hand is now continuously outstretched towards the designs and he extends his fingers to the parts to which he gives special attention. In some cases he curls the index finger and scratches the surface of the printed page with his nail as if trying to remove a three-dimensional object. At 18½ months he spends several seconds upon each picture and points to any one to which the experimenter has previously pointed. He also makes a peculiar hesitant sort of response which may best be described as a "pushing" of the palm and outstretched fingers toward the picture so as partially to cover it. One gets the suggestion that he is feeling for a projecting or raised surface. As soon

THE APE AND THE CHILD

as he has looked at the pictures on any page he is ready
to turn to a new one where he repeats his examination.

The order of Gua's reactions seems to be reversed
from Donald's in that her interest at the earlier ages is
clearly in the pictures; the manipulative tendency does
not begin to show itself until some time later. At the
age of 11 months she points to many of the pictures and
seems to try to pick up parts of them with her lips.
She even does this in the case of some of the brightly
colored letters of the alphabet. At 12 months one would
say she seems more attracted than at first by the forms,
although she still makes no attempt to turn the leaves
of the book. She looks fixedly at every shape which is
pointed out to her and usually points to it herself with
the fingers of both hands. Quite often she extends her
lips only to some particular portion of a picture. This
seems especially to be the case if the part is round,
symmetrical, or brightly colored. Thus she gives more
than usual attention to the pictured bodies of some
round pink pigs. After pointing to them and completing
the usual lip reaction, she makes as if to scrape or claw
them from the page with the fingers of her right hand.
Subsequently she slaps the page with both palms. At
13 months there is greater evidence of the manipulative
tendency in that she then actually turns some of the
pages by reaching with her left index finger to the upper
right-hand corner of the book and pulling a few leaves
from right to left. To the investigation of the pictures
she now adds the reaction of rubbing the surface of the
page with the knuckles of the first two fingers of her
left hand. At 15 months she is much more active in
manipulation, and turns the pages both to the right
and to the left by reaching to their top corners and
pulling them toward herself. She nevertheless seems to
be chiefly interested in the pictures, as is shown by her
continued efforts to grasp them with the lips. At 16
months she has supplemented her previous movements
with the grasping reaction of the hand by means of

which she attempts clearly to seize or take hold of printed shapes.

Everything, apparently, is at the start perceived as three-dimensional, and the quality of two-dimensionality is something new. This principle seems to apply to the reactions of both subjects. If Gua spills some milk upon the tray of her high chair during feeding time, she often tries to pick it up with a grasping movement of the hand. On one occasion she makes biting and lip movements against the picture of a cracker upon the printed wrapper of a box of crackers. (It happens that this is a special brand of which she is particularly fond.) As far as we can tell she has actually recognized the printed form as "a cracker" and not as a two-dimensional shape. Donald also in numerous instances attempts to pick up spilled liquids as well as the woven designs on cloth. The conclusion appears inevitable from such behavior that, although the subjects unquestionably observe printed forms, they do not at these young ages distinguish two-dimensional from three-dimensional objects.

Of their ability to perceive and act in accordance with the distance or spatial relations of objects there is good if meager evidence. From the very start of the research the child makes obvious attempts to stand at the windows of an automobile and gaze at the passing landscape. During the course of the almost daily rides of the subjects Gua comes also to adopt the same procedure, even though during the first two weeks she tends to ignore or avoid what goes on outside the machine. She is inclined at first to sleep or lie quietly upon the lap of one of the experimenters. Or if she remains awake she will play with things in the car such as the door handles, the gear-shift lever, or even with the face or hands of her adult friends. After a fortnight or so has elapsed she begins to show some interest in the distant environment by occasionally putting her hands on the window ledges and peering cautiously outside. One suspects that her original behavior in this regard was therefore the result of timidity or possibly excitement at the immediate surroundings. Her adaptation is rapid and at the age of 8½ months she has advanced so far that she will look outside the car whenever she is in it. Frequently she even puts her head through the window and holds her hand at arm's length to "catch the breeze." If a passing automobile or other near object flashes by she will duck as if something had been thrown at her. As a result of her sudden development, the corresponding interest of the child in passing objects soon appears to be less pronounced than hers, although eventually he progresses also in much the same manner

Clouds of tobacco smoke blown past the faces of the subjects cause them to halt all other activity and to look fixedly at the smoke. When this is originally done, the ape, age 14½ months, stands up and makes two or three violent arm movements through the smoke as if to stir it, or strike it, or catch it, or waft it away. Although the child at the same time follows the smoke puffs with his eyes, he makes no effort to strike or seize them. A month later, on the other hand, he will extend his arm as Gua has previously done, and will wave his hand through the clouds.

The accuracy of the ape in jumping is probably the strongest proof of her ability in distance perception. But even before this is developed, at the age of 9 months and younger, she seems to possess an uncanny capacity to avoid hitting obstructions with her feet as she walks on all fours. In passing over a tangle of electric-light wires which contain occasional loops rising 8 to 10 centimeters (3 to 4 inches) from the floor, she lifts her feet over each individual coil as if she saw it. Yet obviously her eyes are directed elsewhere by the time her feet actually pass over the wires. Such behavior does not appear to be in the nature of "treading gingerly," or of lifting the feet high at every step. Rather she seems to lift them only at exactly the right places.

Again, she is with us in an automobile as we are parked in the woods. Some men approach the gate in a fence about 200 meters distant. We observe them quietly through small rifts in the foliage and after an instant discover that Gua also is peering intently over the window ledge of the car, doing likewise.

If we pass now to observations on the *sense of hearing* we soon become convinced that Gua possesses an excellent ability to respond to faint or weak sounds. On several occasions she indicates by her behavior that she hears something when adult human ears beside her receive no stimulation. Presently, in such cases, the sound of the newsboy's bicycle or of footsteps upon sand or grass prove that she has picked up genuine sounds while they are still below the auditory "threshold" of the persons present. Reactions of an analogous sort are never observed in Donald.

We turn on a radio when the ape is standing near it and note her responses. It is the first time she has ever heard such a contrivance in her life. A man's voice is coming loudly from the speaker. She stands up and looks about herself, but not at the radio cabinet, and then begins a curious circuitous wandering, apparently in search of the sound. She goes a few feet in one direction, turns and comes back, takes a step or two in another direction, and looks behind her. Only after moving in this confused manner for a minute or more does she stop suddenly in front of the radio cabinet and look fixedly at it. Does this extremely slow orientation to the sound, at the age of 9 months, mean that the ape is deficient in the capacity to locate an auditory stimulus?

We soon have the opportunity of testing her ability in this regard and find quite by accident that she is subject, as are humans, to the so-called ventriloquist's illusion. That is to say, if a sound is made directly in front of the listener, and so equidistant from his two

14,233

ears, it may be mistaken according to the predisposition of the subject for one which comes from behind, from above, from below, or from any other point in the median plane of his own body. Conversely, a sound which comes from behind may be mistaken for one which is made in front, and so forth. The test upon Gua comes about when she enters a hall in our house about $5\frac{1}{2}$ meters long by a meter in width. She goes into the hall by means of a doorway near its middle and she then immediately turns to the right (see Fig. 8). She is looking for us and seems to be under the impression

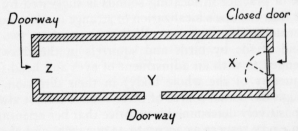

FIG. 8.—The plan of the hallway in which the first reversed sound localization in Gua is observed. The experimenter enters the hallway at *Y* and immediately leaves it through doorway *Z*. The ape, who is following him, does not enter doorway *Y* until after the experimenter has made his exit through *Z*. Apparently under the supposition that the observer has gone through *X*, Gua turns to the right instead of continuing through *Z*. When she is called from the position, *Z*, she becomes frantic to get through the closed door at *X*, reacting to the sound of the voice from *Z* as if it were coming from behind the door at *X*.

from having seen us enter the doorway a few minutes before that we have turned also to the right. As a matter of fact, we have gone to the left, so that in turning to the right, Gua actually turns her back upon us. When we call, the sound of the voice comes therefore directly from behind her. In response, however, she hurries forward to the *opposite* end of the hall, where a closed door blocks her way. We call again, and she sits down in front of the door, begins to cry and to slap it with her hands. Again and again she is called. The louder the sounds ring through the hall, the more frantic Gua becomes to get through the door at the opposite end, when as a matter of fact, instead of actually being blocked by a closed door, she has only to turn around and take a few steps to reach the caller. It is finally necessary for us to walk halfway up the hall toward the ape before she becomes aware of her error of localization and straightway corrects it.

A few weeks afterwards the child makes a similar erroneous orientation to the sound of a voice, although the conditions in his case are not exactly the same as in that of Gua. That errors of this sort may be due in part at least to the immaturity of the subjects and their lack of practice in locating sounds is suggested by the fact that the ape's localization of strange outdoor noises soon noticeably improves. Within a month or two the sounds made by birds and squirrels in the trees are attended to with an adjustment of eyes and head (and frequently of the whole body) in their direction. Although the actual source of these sounds cannot always be positively determined, we notice that her orientation is in every respect as accurate as our own, and that in most cases it is more rapid.

We undertake a little later to measure the relative capacities of the two subjects to localize a sound by marking off a square area on the ground, exactly 2.32 meters (7.07 feet) to the side. The square is placed a good distance from any building or bank of foliage so that echoes will not prove troublesome. Its center is marked with a large cross. The subject to be tested has a thick hood placed entirely over his head and tied securely behind the neck. This serves as an effective blindfold. The hood is adjusted when the subject is standing at a point about 8 meters from the square. He is then immediately carried by one of the experimenters to its center, care being taken not to twist or jar him in any way so as to produce sensations of dizziness or rotation. He is gently set down upon the cross in the center of the square facing one of its corners. The other experimenter, who has previously taken a position outside of the square but at one of the corners (without the knowledge or observation of the subject), then utters the vocal command, "Come here, Donald," or "Come here, Gua," as the case may be. Only one such command is given, and according to the conditions of the particular trial in question it may come from the subject's right side, from his left side, from in front, or from behind him. The subject then attempts to go blindfolded to the sound which he has heard, receiving as a "reward" when he gets there the removal of the hood from his head, and vocal praise and encouragement.

The point at which he crosses the boundary of the square is marked, and his error is measured in linear centimeters from this mark to the corner of the square at which the sound was originally produced. The measurement is subsequently converted by means of a simple trigonometric formula into an angular distance (in degrees). If the subject makes such a large error that he misses entirely the experimenter who calls him, he is "punished" by the added delay which ensues until he finds the person who has called. Subsequent calls are given him after he has left the square, but his "error" at that time has already been determined from the original response he made to the first call.

The conditions for both subjects are the same with the exception of the fact (1) that one of the experimenters does the calling for Gua and the other calls Donald. It is also considered advisable (2) to tie Gua's hands loosely behind her back to discourage her from removing the hood, a trick at which she soon proves very adept. Each subject is given nearly two weeks of habituation and practice before the "critical" trials of the experiment are undertaken. The final records are based on 64 separate attempts for each subject, divided equally between each of the four corners of the square, and each of the four possible directions (that is, front, back, left, or right) from which the sound can come. The subjects' ages during the course of the experiment, which requires about a month to complete, are: Gua, 13½ to 14½ months; Donald, 16 to 17 months.

Results show the general average of the errors made by Donald in these tests (computed in whole degrees) to be 40.2 degrees. The average error made by Gua is less than two-thirds as much, or 25.9 degrees. A series of "control" trials with a normal eight-year old boy, Dickie, gives an average error of 15.0 degrees. There is thus nearly as much difference between the respective errors of Donald and Gua in this experiment as there is between the errors made by Gua and Dickie. The human infant, furthermore, makes only one perfect localization, that is, one with no error at all, and he has, in addition, five reversed or backward localizations. The ape has six perfect trials and no reversals, while Dickie falls between the two younger subjects in reversal score but makes more perfect trials than either of them.

It is desired next to obtain some information upon the *sense of equilibrium* of the subjects. Yet with Donald and Gua we find it difficult to analyze with any degree of certainty the probable cause of unsteadiness upon the feet, swaying, or similar disturbances of balance. In older individuals, whose muscular and reflex equipment is fully developed, there would be less doubt. But it is possible that such behavior on the part of our two subjects may be due to immature nerve or muscle units as well as to the sense organs of the inner ear.

It is interesting to note in this connection the marked difference in the reactions of the two when we hold them one at a time at arm's length overhead, but with the stomach or abdominal side downward. Thus Donald, at the age of 12 months, will stiffen his whole trunk, arch his back, bend his head backward, and extend his legs. He usually laughs and makes no attempt whatever to hold on. But the ape, at 9½ months, responds in a totally different manner. She bends her trunk forward, puts her head down, holds the experimenter's arm tightly, and even clings as well as she is able with her legs and feet. She is clearly afraid, and sometimes cries a little. At the first opportunity she starts to climb down.

We then undertake the simple test of spinning the subjects to determine to what extent they are likely to become dizzy. The experimenter with Gua, age 9½ months, in his arms, revolves upon his heel for five or six revolutions at the rate of approximately one complete turn in 2 seconds. When Gua is set down after this stimulation, she falls to her side, or staggers if she tries to walk. Her tipping or compensatory reactions, which from general observation seem to be entirely what they should be, last within a second or two of the observer's own dizzy sensations produced by the spinning. Since both the observer and Gua have revolved in the same direction, at the same rate, for the same length of time, the conclusion seems naturally to follow that, despite the difference in organisms and the further difference in ages, the disturbances of the two continue for very nearly the same length of time. If we spin Donald (age 12 months) in the same manner he objects strenuously, holds his breath, cries, and clings desperately to the spinner. He will not be quieted for several minutes afterward so that further trials of this sort must be discontinued for the time being.

A more careful investigation of the matter is made when Gua reaches the age of 11½ months and Donald 14. The subjects are then placed in a rotating chair, which has been especially built to fit them. It will revolve freely on a ball bearing in either direction. A single strand of gauze bandage is tied under their arms and around the back of the chair to prevent them from falling out when it is spun. The subjects are then turned separately for ten complete revolutions at the rate of one rotation in each 2 seconds. Their behavior during and after this stimulation is recorded and the attempt is made to count the reflex (nystagmoid) eye movements which follow the spinning and which are related to the dizzy or giddy sensations which the subject probably experiences.

During the first few revolutions Donald exhibits signs of pleasure by smiling. As the spinning is continued his smile soon vanishes, and his grip tightens on the chair. There follows a holding of the breath, a straining of the abdominal muscles, and the resulting red face. Simultaneously with the holding of the breath, the head begins to roll (not turn) on the shoulders in a direction contrary to that of the rotation of the chair. Upon cessation of the rotation the muscles relax and the air is released from the lungs with a yell. He is much disturbed for some minutes. In a second trial, some three weeks later, there is no rolling of the head, but the subject turns his head *in the same direction in which he is being rotated*. This is a very unusual reaction and is contrary to the so-called normal compensatory response of older subjects.

Gua in her turn takes the stimulation much less violently and appears almost to enjoy it. She has a tendency to lean close to the back of the chair, to turn her head in a direction *opposite* to that of rotation (the regular compensatory reaction), and in one of the tests she extends her right arm to "catch the wind" produced by her own spinning.

Although the records of eye movements after rotation are difficult to obtain because of the activity of the subjects, they show that Donald has made 26 complete cycles of nystagmoid reactions which lasted in all for about 23 seconds (average of two trials). Gua, on the other hand, makes 67 movements which last 32 seconds (average of 4 trials). These figures unfortunately are subject to a large error, although they can surely be taken to indicate that Gua is disturbed by the stimulation longer than Donald, at least as judged by the duration and number of reflex eye movements. The responses of Donald during the rotation are difficult to explain, while Gua has behaved much as the average child might have been expected to act. Possibly the child's unusual and inverted movements are to be accounted for on the basis of the immaturity of his sense organs of balance, of the nerve processes, and of the reflex connections.

By the time the chimpanzee has reached the age of 14 months we note further that she picks up of herself a new kind of play, the enjoyment of which in human children is based essentially upon the stimulation of the organs of equilibrium. This is a spontaneous whirling or spinning. She will lift her hands from the ground, and swing on her heel about 180 degrees to the right; then she will place her hands down again, till the feet are relocated, and spin once more. The whole procedure is somewhat like that of a child whirling upon its hands and knees. It may continue for three or four complete revolutions. She will also run, upright, towards one of the rounded legs of a table which she seizes in her right or left hand as she passes. She then swings rapidly about it through an angle of 180 degrees, till she is literally thrown back in the direction from which she approached. Play of this sort is entirely foreign to Donald, who still seems at the age of 16½ months to dislike being spun or rotated even while in the arms of one of the adults.

It is often said that there are characteristic facial expressions which humans make upon experiencing certain *tastes*. We are supposed to draw down the corners of the mouth and look very unpleasant when we taste something bitter. We are supposed to "pucker the lips" at a concentrated sour taste and to cough and perhaps gag when we get too much salt. According to the popular conception we may even be supposed to smile, or at least to feel like smiling, when we taste something sweet. These impressions, even though we seldom give them a great deal of thought, have played such an important part in our colloquial language that we quite commonly speak of a person's "looking *bitter*" or "looking *sweet*" or "looking *sour*."

Just how standardized or stereotyped are the expressions of the face which are made after a given taste? If they are universally the same, are they also native, so that the first time a human baby ever tastes sweet, sour, bitter, or salt he will respond with the characteristic expression? Going one step further, since the facial muscles of the chimpanzee are essentially like those of man, is it possible that the chimpanzee also has typical expressions for different tastes and that the expressions of the animal are similar to those of the human?

In the attempt to investigate these questions, we give our subjects a number of gustatory stimuli. We are reasonably sure because of their very young ages that neither has ever before experienced more than one of the stimuli which are chosen. The first is ice, which of course strictly speaking has no taste, but stimulates only the cold and pressure spots in the *mucosa* of the tongue and mouth. At the age of 11½ months, Donald is offered a small piece about the size of a one-centimeter cube. As soon as it is in his mouth he behaves as if he had been given a bitter medicine. When a second piece is presented he turns his face away as if to avoid taking it, although he does not eject either morsel. Gua, age 9 months, makes strikingly different reactions. She first sips the few drops of cold water contained in the spoon and then of her own accord accepts the ice, which she thereupon sucks with apparent pleasure. Her lips protrude as she does this and she puts her hands up close to her mouth. There are no avoiding reactions on her part, and she takes the second piece of ice eagerly.

Because there is no good reason why she should not eat ice if she cares for it, she is occasionally thereafter given a chip or two. Within a few weeks she has developed such a strong liking for it that she runs to the ice box upon hearing the familiar sounds of the iceman, and picks up such pieces as she can find. Having obtained a morsel she will usually sit down with the ice in her mouth, and transfer it from her mouth to her right hand and *vice versa* until it is melted. She is never seen to chew ice.

Some days after they are first given ice, they are presented with a strong sweet stimulus. This is a syrup made by boiling sugar and water in a 50 per cent solution. The subjects are tricked into accepting the stimulus by repeated offerings of water in a teaspoon. At the proper moment a second teaspoon one-quarter filled with the sweet liquid is secretly substituted for that from which they have been drinking. Donald reacts to this stimulation by opening his mouth and making tongue and lip movements not unlike those of an adult who is sampling a new food. We search in vain for something resembling a smile. The facial expression is not at all unpleasant, but seems rather to be neutral than to indicate any noticeable degree of pleasure. One would say, "He acts as though he is surprised, or mystified." At length he coughs, which suggests that the stimulus is too strong for him. Quite possibly it produces a tickling sensation in the throat. When Gua is given the sweet taste she makes tongue movements similar to those of Donald and opens and closes her mouth even more than he has done. For a few moments, in fact, she may be said actually to "smack her lips." The taste is apparently agreeable to her. In one instance for a fraction of a second we observe something resembling a human smile, in that the corners of the closed lips are perceptibly raised.

The sour stimulus, a 5 per cent solution of citric acid, is not offered the subjects till some days have elapsed after they originally tasted the sweet. We cannot expect this taste to be entirely new to them since each has for some time been drinking orange juice which contains some of the same acid. The facial expression which

Donald makes is a true infantile pucker. He brings the lips together under pressure in a straight line, so that, although the face and cheek muscles are somewhat tense, the mouth goes neither upward nor downward in any of its parts. The expression might be said to be *more intense* than that following the sugar. Gua, for her part, seems to like this taste more than she did the sweet taste, at least as judged by the frequency and magnitude of the lip smacking in which she indulges. There is some slight suggestion also of an added pressure of the upper lip against the lower, and once or twice she pushes the lips together so that they protrude.

After an interval of several more days a 10 per cent solution of common salt is given the subjects. Donald responds by partially closing his eyes and raising the center of the lower lip, so the whole mouth curves down at the corners. His upper lip is mildly puffed or pouched by the pressure of the lower lip against it. It appears from his behavior as though the stimulation was more unpleasant than the sour taste, but by no means as unpleasant as we had supposed it might be. Gua in this case again opens her mouth and smacks her lips but the smacks are few and far between. It is doubtful whether such lip movements can be safely regarded as a true measure of enjoyment or pleasure. Besides these reactions the ape also on occasion forcibly raises her under lip so as to crease or wrinkle the upper one.

The bitter taste, a solution of one-fourth of one per cent of quinine, does not affect Donald at once, possibly because the location of the taste area which is sensitive to bitter is at the back of the tongue. Upon the second application of the stimulus he makes reflex movements of closing the eyes, raising the lower lip over the upper one, stiffening the spine, and violently shuddering. The experience for him appears to be very disagreeable indeed. Gua takes the stimulus without difficulty and with a much less striking reaction than Donald has made, although for an instant, she does seem to form a distinctive, unpleasant facial expression in which the corners of the mouth are somewhat downward.

It appears that Donald has been both more forceful as well as more differential in his reactions to the separate stimuli. If the responses of the two can be regarded as accurate indications of their sensitivity, it would then follow that the tastes which were used were relatively stronger stimuli to the human than they were to the animal. But any concentrated gustatory stimulus may, it is possible, be somewhat unpleasant to a human baby of Donald's age. The particular order of *dis*tastefulness for these four stimuli as measured by the behavior of the child we take to be, bitter, salt, sour, and sweet. There is some question about the relative positions of sour and sweet in such a scale because of the fact that the very concentration of the sweet stimulus has obviously been a disturbing factor for the human. In their order of *dis*tastefulness as indicated by the reactions of the ape, the stimuli would probably rank bitter, salt, sweet (?), and sour (?). Here again we are in doubt about the positions of sweet and sour, although judging from Gua's astonishing appetite for orange juice and the well-known liking of other chimpanzees for all citrus fruits, it is probable that the sour in general is preferred to the sweet.

As far as furnishing evidence of an agreement or disagreement in the type of facial expression following each taste, our results are not clear. The reader can easily see from his own observations of the accompanying photographs that there are many similarities, although there are also some differences. Donald certainly approaches closest to a smile following the stimulation of the sweet taste, and deviates furthest from it after the bitter. Perhaps we may say the same of Gua without the risk of serious exaggeration. It is worth noting also that in most cases the facial expression made by each subject is similar if not identical with that made by the same subject upon later applications of the same

In these views of the *sound localization experiment*, the subjects have been called directly from behind; they must find the caller even though their heads are entirely encased in a heavy cloth hood which serves as a blindfold. Donald turns slowly in a wide circle, while Gua swings sharply on her heel and proceeds directly to the source of the sound. A difference of this sort in the nature of their responses is rather common, and probably accounts to a considerable extent for the larger errors of the child.

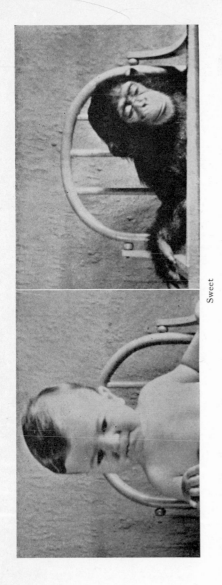

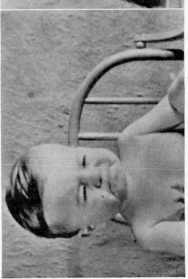

Sweet

Sour

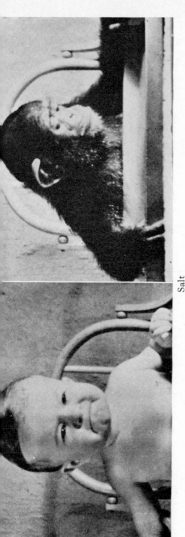

Salt

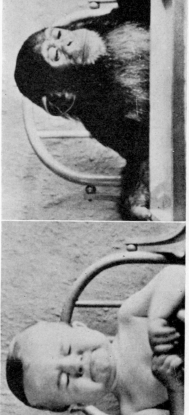

Bitter

The facial expressions made by each subject immediately after he is stimulated with *new* tastes are caught by the motion picture camera. A sweet taste was given just before the upper pair of photographs were taken. A sour taste preceded the second pair, a salty taste the third pair, and a bitter taste the fourth or lowest pair. The degree to which the facial movements are the same from one subject to the other can be observed from these pictures. During the giving of the *taste tests* the age of the child ranged from $11\frac{1}{2}$ to 12 months. Corresponding age limits for the ape were 9 to $9\frac{1}{2}$ months.

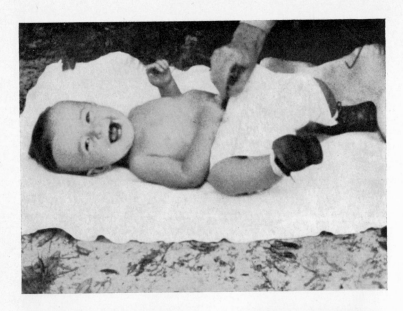

Both of the subjects will "laugh" when tickled. They are here being stimulated with the rounded end of a bone stylus, somewhat like an unsharpened lead pencil. Ages: Donald 12 months, Gua 9½ months.

stimulus. This suggests that the several expressions are typical, at least for the subjects themselves.

In observing behavior related to the *sense of smell* we find a strong suggestion that Gua employs olfactory stimuli for the identification of objects and individuals, in a manner quite different from that of humans. But she is never seen to follow a trail or a scent on the ground or on the floor and only rarely does she transport an edible object to her nose and smell it. The chief function of this sense appears to be in the recognition of individuals, or of parts of their clothing. In employing it in this manner she not only places her nose close to the object to be sniffed, but she literally buries her face in it. Occasionally, for example, before she has learned to know the experimenters visually, she will climb into their arms and sniff carefully at the chest or under the arm. Once or twice she allows herself to be taken by strangers, but following a hurried olfactory examination, she immediately squirms to get down.

At the age of 9½ months, she is seated in her high chair and presented for the first time with a (to us) sweet-smelling stimulus, such as an expensive brand of extract-of-rose perfume. According to the procedure, the bottle is to be held beneath her nose for 5 seconds. Yet long before this time has passed Gua opens her lips, bares her teeth, and turns away from the odor. She then seems for a moment to vacillate between avoiding and approaching reactions. She is obviously strongly stimulated. Upon a second trial a few minutes later she makes a more patently unpleasant facial expression, and climbs down in a hurry from her high chair. If the same stimulus is presented during subsequent months, she will turn her back, duck her head, and raise her arms and shoulders to prevent the experimenter from getting the perfume bottle close to her nose. When she is 15½ months old (not previously having smelled or seen the bottle for 2 months) she is so anxious to avoid it after the first whiff that she tumbles headlong from her chair.

The child, at 12 months, wrinkles his nose and raises his upper lip. His facial expression can hardly be called a pleasant one although he makes no move to avoid the stimulus. He vocalizes in a questioning tone. At 14 months he remains perfectly still and allows the stimulus to remain for the full 5 seconds under his nose. He looks at the experimenters and smiles. At 16 months he smiles and tries to put his index finger in the neck of the bottle. It seems safe to infer from such behavior that the so-called pleasant stimulus is more pleasant to Donald than it is to Gua.

The ape's reactions to the "unpleasant" stimulus are, if possible, even more violent than her reactions to the perfume. In this case a small bottle of tincture of asafetida is placed under the nose and held there, subject permitting, for 5 seconds. Her initial facial expression is about like that which she has previously made to the odor of roses. She is so intent at getting away from the stimulus, however, that she at once scurries over the back of the high chair, from which she hangs while she peers through its bars at the bottle. Two months later she pushes the bottle away, and rolls into a ball on the seat of her high chair, burying her face in her arms. At 13½ months she vocalizes slightly (a brief "uh") and climbs over the side of her high chair backwards. In smelling the stimulus on this occasion her mouth is partially open and the corners clearly drawn downward. At 15½ months she rushes over the side of the high chair with one wild scramble, faster than we have ever seen her perform this feat before.

Donald in his turn at first leans back to avoid the "unpleasant" odor, then protrudes his lower lip and draws down its corners, making an expression which can clearly be called unpleasant. Two months later he indicates repugnance by the same expression, by swallowing several times, and by leaning backward away

110

from the stimulus. At 16 months he pushes the bottle away from him, and at 18 months he repeats the same maneuver.

Although there is a common sort of avoidance of the asafetida between the two subjects, in one case amounting even to a rough similarity between their respective facial expressions, they by no means react in an analogous manner to the perfume. As judged from the general behavior of the two, it would appear that Gua is much more strongly affected by each stimulus than Donald is, and that the asafetida stimulates her even more powerfully than the perfume.

To observe next the responses to *contact* or *touch stimulation* of the skin we first stroke Gua's head with the stiff bristles of a hair brush. She starts each time the brush touches her. Although Donald makes no such reaction it is probably in part because he has been adapted to the feeling of a brush almost since he was born.

We then tactually stimulate the lips of the subjects by holding the end of a finger near the mouth and moving it up and down lightly against the lips. In its downward excursion it catches the lower lip, pulls it downward exposing the teeth and, as it passes, allows the lip to snap upward into place. To our surprise neither subject withdraws, but remains quiet as long as we are willing to continue the stimulation, taking it, as far as we can tell, as a sort of a caress. It is obviously not unpleasant.

A lead pencil is held lightly between the thumb and forefinger and tapped gently upon the forehead of each subject. Donald at 10 months blinks and smiles but makes no other response. Two months later he will reach for the pencil as it approaches or is withdrawn from him, but seems not to make this reaction when the pencil is out of sight above his head, in spite of the contact stimulation he receives. At 14½ months an abrupt change is apparent, for he then looks upward at the first tap, smiles, and reaches accurately for the pencil at the exact point where it is touching him. There is no noticeable development in Gua's responses to this stimulation, since they are about as accurate at the start as Donald's are during the last application of the test. She will sometimes hold her hands over her head so the pencil cannot strike her, or she will open her mouth in a sort of smile and extend her hand for the pencil before it touches her head.

Soon after she has come to us it becomes apparent, furthermore, that she can reach to almost any part of her body and scratch it with a precision approaching that of the human adult. This fact is ascertained after she has been bitten in several places by ants. Their bites leave small inflamed spots which permit an easy check on the accuracy of her scratching. In contrast to this performance, Donald at the age of 12 months makes only an indiscriminate rubbing movement upon his face, regardless of whether he has a mosquito bite upon his temple or his chin. At 14 months he is still unable to locate the bitten spot although his accuracy is much improved. Observed in his attempts to scratch insect bites upon his forehead, his movements at this age are often directed to positions 3 centimeters or more from the inflamed points. He seems, in addition, to make no typical scratching movements with his finger nails as Gua does, but turns the back of his hand towards his face and rubs the sensitive area with his knuckles. Part of this marked behavioral difference in the two organisms is certainly to be ascribed to the structural variation of the length of the arms.

We subject this ability to a specific though elementary test by touching each individual at the same bodily points with the blunt end of a pencil. If the child is so stimulated in the middle of the back, his only reactions at 12 months are to arch his spine away from the stimulus and to smile. It is not until he is 18½ months old that he accurately localizes the point touched by placing his hand behind him and moving it upward approximately to the stimulated region. His responses are much the same if we touch the tip of his right or left ear, if we similarly stimulate him on the shoulders or if we touch the top of his head. At 18½ months he reaches with considerable accuracy to all these points but not at 16½ months or younger. And yet the very first time the test is tried with Gua she touches directly the area which is stimulated within a little more than a second. Her original performance is altogether about as good as that of Donald some six months later. The only inaccuracy, a minor error in reaching for the ear points, disappears by the time she attains the age of 11½ months.

In spite of Gua's early proficiency in scratching and reaching, there is no evidence of the "picking" or "skin searching" reactions common to the lesser monkeys and in general to most captive chimpanzees. Of course the little animal is at all times so scrupulously clean that, strictly speaking, she never has anything for which to search. There are but few observed responses which can be even remotely associated with such activities. In one instance she is seen to point to the scab of a sore upon her knee and attempt to pick it with the nail of her left index finger. Again, during the final month of the research, she seems to discover for the first time, that Donald's hair possesses possibilities as a plaything. She will therefore run her fingers through it, occasionally seizing some of the hair in her fist. Or she will pat his head, sometimes with considerable vehemence. If on the other hand, we rub Gua's skin, or scratch or manipulate it in various ways, she will lie contentedly absorbing this attention as long as it is given. To what extent these reactions are genetically related to the systematic skin searching of older specimens, no one, of course, can say, although it appears to us that the assumption of such a connection is rather doubtful.

It is very clear, nevertheless, that she is extremely sensitive to such stimulation as usually produces tick-

ling in humans. If touched in the abdominal region she
will rapidly draw her legs and arms over the sections
stimulated, as older children might "cover up" in such
cases. Moreover *she will both smile and laugh on such
occasions.* The laughter consists in a series of exhalations
of the breath produced by tensing the abdominal muscles and releasing the air rhythmically from the throat.
The tempo of the rhythm is rather more rapid than that
of most human laughter, and the separate syllables are
often not vocalized, but are simply breathed or "whispered." At other times of less frequent occurrence they
are definitely vocalized in a deep guttural sort of sound.
The mouth in all such instances is opened and the teeth
are partly exposed, although the lips are hardly drawn
upward at the corners by a sufficient amount to enable
anyone not well acquainted with Gua to recognize the
expression as one of laughter. What is here and later
referred to as "smiling" consists of the same playful
facial expression employed in laughing, but without
the accompanying exhalations.

As a result of this responsiveness we find it possible
to examine the two to discover, if we can, their relative
sensitivity to tickling as well as the kind of stimulation
which is most effective in producing tickle reactions.
We cannot be certain whether either of the organisms
actually experiences a tickle sensation, and so we must
compare them entirely with respect to their behavior.
In Gua the reactions which seem to us to deserve the
name of "tickle responses" are (1) laughing, (2) smiling
with the accompanying behavior either of rolling away
or of trying to ward off the stimulating object with her
arms or legs, and (3) smiling and putting her hands to
the spot stimulated. Since the child at these ages apparently possesses no reactions of "covering," avoiding,
or reaching for the stimulating object, the only "tickle
responses" in his case are (1) laughing, and (2) smiling.
The stimulating objects are a small ostrich feather
about 25 centimeters in length for mild stimulation,

and the rounded end of a bone stylus in general dimensions about like an unsharpened lead pencil, for strong stimulation.

The results show that Donald does not smile or laugh if strongly stimulated under the arms, anywhere on the head, upon the soles of the feet, upon the hands, or on any part of the limbs. But he is sensitive if stimulated on the abdomen (particularly pelvic area), the back (particularly lower portion), and in the neck region. To the mild or feather stimulation he appears to be sensitive, in addition to the areas mentioned, upon most of the arms, legs, soles of the feet, cheeks, and especially upon the erogenous zones on the inside of the upper thighs. He gives no evidence of similar sensitivity when touched with the feather upon the forehead or the scalp.

Surprising as it may seem, there can be little question about the fact that, in terms of reactions, the chimpanzee is "more ticklish" than the child. Contacts of the right sort upon almost any part of her body, even on the top of the head, will elicit laughter or smiling, and playful avoiding or "covering" responses. For strong stimulation the most sensitive places appear to be: the abdominal and chest areas (pelvis especially), over the spinal column (particularly lower part), neck region, under the arms, on the soles of the feet, and the palms of the hands. To gentle stimulation she will react in a similar manner when touched at any of the same points, and also if touched upon the legs, cheeks, face, and head. It is possible that her generally greater responsiveness may be due in part to her hairy coat which may induce such sensations of tickling as human hairs are often known to do.

The most significant development in the ticklish behavior of the subjects during the nine months is the increasing sensitivity of Gua toward the end. She is frequently observed in the process of tickling herself, and laughing as a result. This is usually accomplished by rubbing the spine or the back of her neck against a projecting edge or corner of furniture. Occasionally she will even stimulate herself with her fingers by reaching behind herself to the same general areas.

During the later months her self-stimulation seems to expand so as to include the touching or rubbing of the erogenous zones and ultimately of the genitals themselves. She is probably given added impetus in the development of this sort of behavior by the rubbing of her diaper and other clothing upon these organs. She will frequently laugh during such stimulation although by no means regularly. The self-tickling of the back, neck, and other areas of the body continues to be a common method of producing laughter up to the end of the research.

It appears also that Gua is especially *sensitive to temperature changes*, although no comparative tests of this sense can be conveniently undertaken. She will refuse her food on many occasions, particularly during the early months, if it is a little too warm or a little too cold. In this respect she seems to be more fastidious than the human infant. She is similarly disturbed by variations in the temperature of her bath, although she makes fewer screaming and avoiding reactions to water at higher than atmospheric temperature than she does when cool or cold water is directed upon her. Each subject will awaken at night if he is cold, and the human seems to be affected in the same way if he is too warm. It is suggested from such incidental observations that the chimpanzee may be the less disturbed of the two by higher than average temperatures, but more disturbed by those which are lower.

An unusual instance of her withdrawal from a warm object occurs at the age of 11½ months. She is observed at this time to make an exploratory mouthing reaction upon the handle of a stove which feels only comfortably warm to the experimenters, and whose estimated temperature is about 45 degrees centigrade. Yet, as soon as her lips touch the handle, she recoils and rapidly retreats to the other side of the room looking back at the stove as she goes and licking and pursing her lips.

The behavior of the ape when she receives a bump or other hurt is usually something of a paradox. She never vocalizes in *pain* quite like Donald, who will frequently cry for several minutes. Even when she does "oo-oo" or scream for a few seconds in situations which appear painful, we are always in doubt whether her reactions are prompted by actual pain or whether they are fearful responses produced by a new or shocking stimulus. Her crying in such instances is almost never of more than momentary duration. She is certainly much less sensitive than the human baby to the ordinary round of scratches and falls, and even open cuts do not seem to cause her any serious annoyance. Possibly her relative indifference to such minor injuries is in some way to be related to her general muscular toughness.

Suppose for comparison we try pulling a wisp of hair on the forehead of each of the subjects. We find at once that Donald can easily be induced to vocalize in a sort of a whine or moan, but that Gua will make no outcry even though we pull very hard. She will instead reach for the experimenter's hand and attempt to push it away. If it cannot be readily moved she may seize his wrist in both of her hands and pull with a strength which must exaggerate the unpleasantness of her own sensations.

In spite of such behavior, there is other evidence which suggests that she may possess an acute sensitivity to pain in certain special respects. If soap is allowed to get into her eyes during a bath, she will reach for the eyes with both hands, rub them frantically and scream. Once in some unknown manner she received a deep cut in the membrane upon the inside of her lower lip. It was obviously a source of considerable discomfort, especially when she took acid substances into her mouth. When first given orange juice after she had gotten this hurt, she retreated sharply and put the back of her hand to her lips in a defensive gesture. She subsequently refused to touch any more orange for forty-eight hours after the initial unpleasant experience.

She was also able at an early age to localize the painful areas upon various parts of her body, and, by the time she was 10 months old, she customarily did so whenever she received a severe bump. In one such case, after falling upon her face and striking her lips a sharp blow, so that it appeared she must have bruised herself, she sat up and fingered them with both hands, pulling them away from the teeth. She also moved the lips by pouting and pursing them. Another time she fell upon her back from a chair, and at once stood up and put both hands over the region struck. On a third occasion she sat down forcefully and immediately thereafter put both her hands over the genital swelling. There was no vocalization in any of these instances. It was not until Donald, on the other hand, had attained the age of 13½ months that he even began to rub the affected parts after a fall, and it is doubtful whether his "pain localization" during the nine months ever became any more accurate than his localization of touch stimuli. At no time did the subjects receive any intentional instruction in this sort of behavior, through either manipulation or example.

Chapter VI

PLAY

BY FAR the major part of the waking time of the two subjects was consumed in activities which can be classified only under the heading of play. Even when we occupied them with experiments or tests, their behavior in all but a very few of these soon became to a large extent a sort of play in which the measurements themselves were taken as something of a game. The liking for playful activity and companionship was surely as basic in the case of the ape as it was with the child, and each was almost continually playing—except when very hungry or very sleepy—either by himself, or with the other, or with elders. If we left Gua alone for a moment she would immediately pick up some toy or play object such as a piece of paper or a stick, a doll or a string of wooden beads; while in moving from one room to another a similar trinket, the favorite of the moment, was almost sure to be transported with her. When no regular playthings were available she would adopt whatever was handy to her use by playing with the furniture, draperies, rugs, or other convenient articles. After the subjects had been living together for a few months and had become close companions, their interest in playing with one another was so strong that one of them could often not be induced to eat his meals while the other was playing, so great was the impulse to get down and play also.

Less than two weeks after Gua had first been introduced to a high chair she discovered, as human babies do, the joys of dropping things from its height to the floor. She was thereafter addicted to the habit not only of holding objects over the edges to hear them clatter, but of deliberately throwing them down and then peering over the sides after them.

She played with her feet quite like a child, by lying on her back and examining them, often slapping her feet with her hands. If her shoes were on she would play with them in the same manner—or sometimes with the dangling shoe laces. A similar sort of play consisted in the swinging or kicking of one or both feet, when she was seated, against the rungs or legs of a chair so as to bang them rhythmically. At the age of about 9 months she further developed the peculiar reaction of raising the left foot to a height of about 10 centimeters upon each step. She would thus stamp across the floor with an irregular clatter if she seemed to feel particularly like a romp. Quite frequently during her play behavior she would open her mouth in the same smiling manner which she employed when she was tickled. The drawing back of the lips with the teeth partly bared thus became a typical playful facial expression.

Another of her characteristic play gestures was to raise the arms simultaneously over the head while she held the toy or other object with which she might be playing in her hands. The object was then usually placed behind her head; or if it happened to be in the nature of a cloth or string, it would be put around her neck or draped over her shoulders. On frequent occasions she would adorn herself with larger or heavier articles in the same manner. Thus she would sometimes place a blanket or a piece of clothing over her shoulders and drag it around with her; she would put small branches containing foliage upon her back and similarly carry or trail them; or she would wrap herself in hanging tree moss or in rags by putting them behind her back and holding them with both hands in front. She would thereupon walk upright with a train following in her wake, towards which she would gaze with a play smile, moving usually in a wide circle as she did so.

Nothing of an exactly similar nature was ever observed in the behavior of the child.

An odd form of self-play common to both subjects was the getting wholly or partially inside of wooden or pasteboard packing boxes, bushel baskets, cupboards, and even pots and pans which were large enough to permit them to sit. No doubt this is related to that play of older children directed towards the building of huts, digging caves, getting in closets or in similar protected and out-of-the-way places. Gua carried the behavior further than Donald in that, besides sitting and playing in such objects, she would often go underneath larger boxes and baskets when they were inverted. She would even walk about on all fours when completely covered by them. This altogether bizarre sort of behavior proved quite astonishing to the onlooker who might behold a basket or cardboard packing box move jerkily from place to place, bumping its way from one piece of furniture to the next, without obvious motive power. Once when she was 15 months old we were astonished to see her thrust her head entirely inside a hole in a soft pasteboard box and walk, both upright and on all fours, in this improvised helmet.

Play based upon the stimulation of the organs of balance in the inner ear was likewise of frequent occurrence in the activity of the ape. Under this classification should be listed her jumping, whirling, hanging from doors as she pushed them to or fro, rocking in a rocking chair or baby rocker, and swinging from ladders, branches, or from the hands of grown-ups. Although she was at first somewhat averse to being swung by others she soon adapted to it. The child on the other hand was always more backward in such activity and could seldom be swung without a resulting disturbance and crying. His only spontaneous efforts in this direction consisted of his rocking in a rocking chair or in a children's rocker.

During the first two weeks in civilized surroundings the ape selected as playthings from the household environment such objects as pencils, fountain pens, a string of wooden beads, the top of a talcum-powder can, the glass top of a perfume jar, the celluloid top of a boudoir powder box, books, magazines, newspapers, a fly swatter hanging from the wall, toothbrushes, a hairbrush, a comb, the perambulator to push, the walker to push back and forth, pieces of cloth or clothing, the fringe of rugs, the hanging corners of table cloths, buttons on clothes, legs of tables and chairs, swinging handles to furniture drawers, shoe laces, and electric lamp cords. Other articles which she was offered but which she refused were the rubber doll, which made a noise when squeezed; a small wooden dog, 12 centimeters long by 10 centimeters high, on wheels; and a teething ring with a bell on it.

This catalogue of self-appropriated toys was soon augmented by the addition of such items as a leather harness used to hold Donald in his high chair or perambulator, the experimenters', Donald's, or her own shoes, a toy automobile of the child's about 8 centimeters long made of soft white metal, and anything that hung from above, as lace curtains, the tassels of shade cords, and particularly women's skirts. She began also at this time to play with ash trays, small pillows, rubber balls, and the small children's rocker in which she and Donald could rock back and forth.

By the fourth month of our observations the number of preferred playthings, although still increased, had become fairly well stabilized. Donald, as well as Gua, at that time accepted nearly all the articles listed, so that *in toto* they may be taken as a fairly complete inventory of the items in which each of the subjects ultimately showed a play interest. These included, besides the objects already mentioned, such things as rag dolls, blocks, sticks of wood both large and small (matches, toothpicks), a small wagon, string (rope,

tape measure, bath-robe cords, leather belts), tools
(hammer, screw driver, pliers), a coil spring, keys on
key ring, the rubber doll (formerly rejected by Gua),
rocking chairs as well as other chairs (pushed and later
climbed upon by both subjects), small articles of furniture in addition to chairs (as magazine rack, end table,
waste-paper baskets, stools), pictures on wall, toilet
articles (mirror, nail file, scissors, safety pins, hairpins,
etc.), and dried leaves, branches of low bushes, acorns,
twigs, sand, and stones. There were in addition one or
two articles which Donald selected but which Gua did
not play with. In this category belongs the broom which
was a favorite of his although she seemed to fear it.
Conversely pictures hanging upon the wall, which she
sometimes tilted or swung were completely beyond the
reach of the child even at the maximum of his climbing
ability. And he showed only a minor interest in the low
branches to which she seemed strongly attracted.

The properties which for the ape seemed to determine
the original selection of playthings were:

1. *Hardness or Toughness*. Hence things which
could be chewed, or pounded or handled roughly without being destroyed. It is possible, of course, that this
quality itself was not so much a primary requisite as it
was a function of the durability which objects long
played with by the chimpanzee must necessarily possess.
On the other hand, her tendency to chew and bite demanded at the start something which would resist the
teeth.

2. *Novelty*. Anything new in her experience, unless
it was definitely an object to arouse fear, was preferred
to something which was not new. Bright or shiny objects
usually proved particularly attractive. Given two toys,
one of which she had seen before, the newer one, other
things being equal, would always be accepted.

3. *Movability or Portability*. This seemed to be an
almost indispensable quality and predisposed Gua to
the selection of articles small in size, which could be

more readily carried and manipulated. Large objects like the perambulator, chairs, etc., were not played with till she had been about them for some time, doubtless because she had to learn in what ways they could be used as playthings. Swinging or hanging things fastened at the upper end and strong enough to support her weight were particularly favored. The only items which by any stretch of the imagination could be called "immovable" playthings were the solid legs of tables or the wooden or glass knobs on drawers upon which she occasionally chewed or swung.

4. *Quietness or Silence.* This characteristic was one which seemed to be rigorously demanded only at the start. It appeared then as if objects which made a noise were feared and consequently avoided. That sound in itself was not necessarily disliked, however, was evidenced by much of her very noisy play which frequently consisted of pounding articles on the floor, lifting up and dropping the tray of her high chair, or of hammering the bottoms of pots and pans and of an inverted metal scrap basket with her hands. It was when something made a noise—particularly a strange or new one which to all appearances was not clearly understood—that it was shunned. Hence things which jingled, or squeaked, or rattled, and at first things which rumbled upon the floor, were let alone. But as their particular kind of sound became more familiar, they might ultimately be accepted.

The ape's superior strength was no doubt responsible for the great degree of boisterousness and destructiveness which characterized part of her play. After some months in the human surroundings she picked up the habit of seizing an article of furniture high enough upon its structure to upset it, and then walking or running away so as to pull it over upon herself. As it started to fall she would dash out of the way to safety, allowing it to tumble with a crash to the floor. This behavior, we think, probably started accidentally when

124

she first began climbing upon chairs without regard for their center of gravity. Later she extended it from chairs to scrap baskets or boxes, and even to a small end table whose balance was none too secure. Beyond occasionally overturning a scrap basket, Donald did not follow her very far in such activity. But this was rather irregular. For if one of the subjects became interested in some particular form of play, the other was quite likely to take it up, provided it continued long enough. In such a manner they both developed the habit of attacking a certain piece of wicker furniture about which and upon which they played, so as to pull out and break off small pieces of the cane from it.

Probably one of the most astonishing and genuinely childlike forms of non-social or self-play in which Gua ever indulged, was to occupy herself with the moisture of her breath which had condensed upon the window pane. She would make marks in the fogged area with the nail of her index finger and also with the end of the finger itself. Of course her tracings had no particular direction or shape; yet the very fact that she would draw them in this fashion was in itself, it seemed to us, an unusually high type of behavior, comparable probably to early scribbling in children. It cannot be said that she deliberately blew her breath upon the pane for the "purpose" of making marks, as our observations suggested that the presence of the mist there was incidental to her previous looking through the window. The well-developed tendency to point her finger at new or strange objects no doubt predisposed her to this kind of reaction. Her age at the time was 13½ months.

Attention to shoes, we think, was likewise never directed specifically to untying them with the object of getting them off. It seemed rather, in the case of each of the subjects, to be a more generalized interest in the shoe strings as playthings. Gua would habitually poke or pull the loops of the strings with her index finger, and seldom if ever made a serious attack upon the shoes themselves, as for example by biting them. She was about as interested in someone else's shoe laces as she was in her own. The child, particularly at the younger ages, was also attracted by this kind of a stimulus and was observed at 10½ months both to pull at Gua's laces and to try to get her shoes in his mouth. One of the favorite forms of play of each subject toward the last was to pick up the shoes of adults from the closets and to carry and push these to various parts of the house. They would play, both together and separately, in this fashion.

The first evidence of anything vaguely resembling a child's playing in the sand appeared in Gua at about the age of 11 months. She was then seen to sit with her legs apart in a private roadway and rake or scrape away the surface of pine needles of which it was composed until she had reached the sandy surface beneath. This she clawed further by making finger or nail marks in it. Within three months she had reached the stage where she would pick up sand, and let it run through her fingers. Since her palms were usually damp with perspiration a thin film of sand almost always adhered to them following such play. She would often, as a result, touch the sand remaining upon the palm with the tips of the fingers of the opposite hand and so wipe it off. The human during the same period would pick up handfuls of sand and carry it about with him, frequently spilling much of it upon himself. He would also sit before a sand pile and pat it, claw it, and allow streams of it to run through his fingers. Subsequently both of the subjects learned by themselves to dig holes in the sand, although those which Gua made were never deeper than approximately 10 centimeters and about large enough to admit one of her hands.

Once during a play period when the ape was about 14½ months old one of the experimenters became engaged near by in the act of relining the court for an outdoor game with powdered slaked lime. The chimpanzee was apparently attracted by the fresh lines, or by the clouds of white dust which she soon discovered could be raised by disturbing them. Presently she stood upright upon one of the lines and shuffled along it for a good 2 meters scraping and kicking at it with her shoes. She was dissuaded from this play only by vehement objections from the linesman and she went back to it like a rowdy boy as soon as his back was turned.

The following excerpt from our notes shows in detail the reactions of the two upon being presented with their first mechanical toy:

March 24.

This toy is a tin goose about 15 centimeters long, upon which sit Mother Goose and a cat. When wound, the body of the goose sways backward and forward upon enormous webbed feet. This has the effect of bringing the head to the ground in a simulation of pecking and also, when the contrivance is placed upon a level surface, of producing a jerky sort of locomotion, like hopping.

Donald—Goose first drawn from box and placed on floor in front of him unwound. His expression becomes very serious. Looks at it, then picks it up slowly and examines it. This is done several times by holding the toy either by the goose's head or by its tail. Frequently it is turned over and the various parts looked at. He puts it down of his own accord, in one or two cases, on its feet. When it is wound his general reactions seem to be little different from before except that he reaches towards it as it moves away from him or crawls after it if it gets out of reach. He seems, one would say, anxious to get his hands on it and examine it, so that he is not content merely to stand by and observe its gyrations. There is no evidence of fear, nor of joy or amusement. Throughout, the seriousness of the expression is surprising and he seems to be motivated chiefly by curiosity and the manipulative impulse.

Gua—Looks for a moment at the toy when it is withdrawn from the box, then hastily retires and peeks from behind a chair about 2 meters distant. Presently her courage seems to return and she comes back, touching it hesitantly with the tips of her fingers on the tail, on the beak, and on the cat which rides in front of the figure of Mother Goose. She then seems interested in "tasting" it or in biting various portions. The conical yellow hat on the figure of Mother Goose is a special attraction in this connection, but she also, after having (no doubt inadvertently) knocked the toy on its side touches her lips to the brightly colored skirts of the Mother Goose figure. I notice that whenever I extend my hand towards the toy she speedily retreats to the safety of her first peeking place where she eyes it cautiously. When it is wound, she becomes more wary than before and is inclined to remain a good distance away and only to rush towards it in a moment of great courage, after which she usually retreats again. On two occasions after sudden approaches of this sort she gets down close beside it with her left ear not more than 12 or 15 centimeters away as if listening to the ticking. Her position in these instances is that of resting on her elbows, chest downward with the forearms crossed beneath her. After a few seconds she moves her left elbow gently towards the toy and tips it over, immediately thereafter rushing away. It appears almost as if she is afraid to touch it with her hands when it is moving and that her elbow in these cases is a safer point of contact. There is no vocalization but she seems clearly delighted (or should one say "thrilled"?) with the experience as evidenced by her increased activity and the fact that on one or two occasions she jumps up and down and stamps her left foot. Both of these responses suggest emotion—usually, though not always, I take it, of a pleasant or playful sort.

Among the activities which may be classified as social or *cooperative play*, since they require the assistance or participation of other individuals, perhaps their early interest in the faces of adults is the most elementary. Both subjects, if laid prone upon the lap of one of the experimenters, would usually extend their arms upward to the countenance above them. Gua would reach toward us and play with parts of human faces immediately after she had come to us. As a rule her attention was directed toward the mouth, into which she would insert one or more fingers if permitted. When the lips were closed she would even endeavor to open them by forcibly pushing the fingers between them. She soon discovered the pliability of the lower lip and seemed to enjoy its manipulation so greatly that she would pull the lip downward with the index fingers of both her hands, and hold it there and examine it while it was in this inverted position. The principal feature of attraction for Donald, however, appeared to be the projecting nose, which he would seize in his fist, occasionally placing his thumb into one nostril as he did so. Having obtained a secure hold in this manner he not infrequently thereafter would push and pull the nose so as to cause the head of the victim to roll from one side to the other.

Gua's fondness for putting her finger in people's mouths found no exception in the case of her human playmate. And since the child seemed to enjoy biting or chewing fingers, an action to which the ape offered no serious objections, the two soon developed a remarkable sort of teamwork. Gua would point her finger towards Donald's face and he, at such a signal, would lean towards it, open his mouth, and bite it. This when Gua was 9½ and Donald 12 months old.

Apparently noticing also Gua's propensity for picking up small pebbles, acorns, or pieces of dirt from the ground or floor with her lips, Donald, by the time he had reached the age of 14½ months, would often assist her in carrying out such designs. His method was to stoop over and pick up some such object himself with the thumb and index finger. He would thereupon extend it towards Gua who would remove it from his fingers with her lips. A similar and equally ingenious reaction on the part of the ape occurred when she was 12½ months old. She had been playing for some time with a large spoon when Donald suddenly entered the room. Acting as if she had been "seized with a new idea" she ran to Donald holding the bowl of the spoon towards him about on a level with his mouth. When he obligingly responded by opening this aperture, she immediately thrust in the spoon.

The development of something resembling a game of tag in which the subjects jointly took part was observed as early as a month and a half before Donald could walk. Preliminaries for this sort of play probably began when the child, in his walker, first chased Gua and she, to avoid being run down, would then dodge behind furniture or one of her adult friends. Ultimately, the behavior became less serious upon the part of the ape, and after Donald had abandoned his walker entirely the two would frequently continue in chasing frolics of this sort for many minutes at a time. Usually in such cases Gua still played the part of the pursued while the child acted as the pursuer. Except for the first month or two, she seemed to be able to keep well out of his reach and would remain just far enough away to act as a continuous incentive. On some occasions the game quite obviously was started by the ape who would suddenly seize some plaything which Donald held and run with it. In this manner she seemed to entice him into following her. During such activity, Gua, for the most part, would open her mouth in her usual play smile, while Donald was generally found to giggle, smile, pant, or pleasantly vocalize.

After barely two months of human association, the little animal was observed on several occasions to lie upon a bed and alternately pull the covers over her face and then remove them. This behavior seemed originally to be spontaneous, for it was not aided on the part of the experimenters by any known example or direction. The movements were in all essentials quite like those of the human baby playing peek-a-boo. Some months later, as an outgrowth of the tag which the subjects played, they developed a special form of peek-a-boo which demanded the cooperation of a second individual. Gua was the first to acquire this activity. She liked to be chased by friendly adults as well as by

Their general reactions to blocks are similar in that each will examine them, throw them, and put them in his mouth. Differences in manipulation and in the ability to construct small towers are not observed until the later months.

Lower left: A favorite plaything is a children's rocker in which they sit both singly and together. Gua is soon able to get in and out of this by herself and learns to rock it some time before the child can do so.

Lower right: The rotating chair used to test the sense of equilibrium (see page 102).

(*Facing p.* 130.)

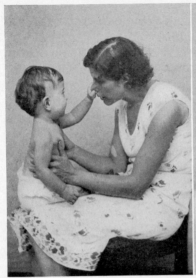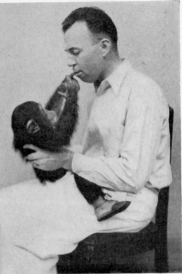

An early interest in human faces is demonstrated by each. The child usually reaches for the nose while the ape is attracted by the mouth.

"Playing ball" by rolling it back and forth constitutes one of their more advanced games. They are assisted in this behavior by verbal directions from the experimenters. Ages at the time of this picture: Donald 18½ months, Gua 16 months.

Donald, and when trapped behind some piece of furniture she would put one eye out from behind this obstacle and peer at her pursuer. If he showed signs of approaching she would then move quietly to the opposite corner and peek stealthily around it. This back and forth, corner-to-corner, procedure came eventually to amount to a sort of peek-a-boo in which the pursuer was trying to surprise the pursued by catching her face to face, while the pursued in turn was trying to avoid such a climax. Donald, who soon also adopted such play, responded somewhat as Gua did except that he would look from behind the protective piece of furniture with the exclamation "Bah!," doubtless intended for "Boo!."

Among their further forms of cooperative play should be mentioned the behavior of handing an object to one of the experimenters and then receiving it back in return. When first we noted that there seemed to be any special tendency to play in this manner, Gua was 11 and Donald 13½ months old. The completed responses were always accompanied by the verbal commands, "Now you give it to me" and "Now you take it" or "Now, I'll give it to you," on the part of the adult. This sort of "give and take" might continue for a dozen or more cycles before either of the subjects tired of it.

Such activity was easily extended a few months later to a simple game of ball playing, in which the subject would sit with legs spread apart on the floor, a few feet from one of the observers. A brightly colored rubber ball about 15 centimeters in diameter, would then be rolled from one to the other, accompanied by the statements, "Now you roll it to me" and "Now, I'll roll it to you." The "rolling" of the child for the most part consisted of "dropping" although because of the position of his legs, the ball would usually bounce in the proper direction. Gua's difficulty, on the other hand, seemed to be in releasing the ball from her hands, possibly because her long curved fingers made this an awkward sort of response. The two ultimately not only surmounted these difficulties, but would sit and play ball together with no assistance from outsiders except verbal directions, and the occasional retrievement of the ball when it bounced out of their reach.

Seizing and taking playthings from the human subject was a reaction which Gua displayed as early as her ninth month. If she took a fancy to something he possessed, the direct solution of simply taking it offered no difficulties whatever. Originally the boy did not seem to object to this behavior, but subsequently he would enter strong vocal opposition and finally he began to hold tightly to the toys the ape attempted to purloin. By the time Donald had attained the age of 13 months, he retaliated with the same type of activity and would take things from Gua nearly as frequently as she did from him. It was noticeable in this respect that anything she was carrying in her mouth seemed to be attained by him with ease, possibly because he twisted it or in other ways made it difficult for her to hold. At 15 months his grip had become so strong that he was not often bested by the animal. The additional trick of turning his back abruptly, if she reached for what he had, became a further effective defense against her raids. It is noteworthy that, despite play of this sort, neither of the subjects exhibited any behavior which could properly be considered hostile or resentful towards the other. The ape's reactions at first appeared to be a straightforward means of obtaining something desirable while later, one would say, they served more in the nature of definite invitations for play.

Although the play of the chimpanzee was thus in many respects strikingly childlike, there was one aspect in which it differed significantly from that of Donald. This concerns the *exploration* and *manipulation* of new objects with which the subject may come in contact, or, if you will, with his curiosity over and tendency to examine things for their own sake. If the child, even at the age of 10 months and younger, was presented with some strange article or new toy, he would gaze fixedly at it with the closest attention. He would shift it from his left to his right hand and back again many times, turning it over as he did so and studying it in great detail. During such operations his face seemed to be a very screen upon which the expression would change from instant to instant. One fancied he could see bewilderment, surprise, interest, and delight. The infant would smile, look from the object to the countenance of one of the experimenters, turn the object over, look to the face of the other experimenter, smile again, pass the object from his right to his left hand, all the while intently examining it. Such a procedure might continue for a minute or more, during which he would be definitely exploring the new article, through sensory avenues of touch and vision, and occasionally by biting and mouthing it as well.

Although such behavior was not entirely lacking in Gua, its presence was by no means as common nor its development as advanced. It is possible, of course, that her deficiency can be ascribed in part to the early difference in general motility, since the ape was never forced by her own incapacity for locomotion to remain fixed in one place as Donald was. As a result her explorations were more likely to be concerned with such gross activities as peeking behind doors or looking into drawers or scrap baskets.

No doubt, also, a part of her inadequacy in this respect is to be explained by her relative inattentiveness. This is easily brought out by the simple expedient of tapping an empty drinking glass with a spoon before the two subjects so as to produce a clear musical sound. At 10½ months the child suddenly becomes perfectly still and looks towards the source of the sound. He subsequently turns to the face of one of the observers, then to the other, and finally back to the glass. His attention may be held as long as 15 or 20 seconds by a single stimulus of this sort before he again resumes his spontaneous activity. Yet the chimpanzee at 8 months looks towards the glass only for a moment, and almost immediately turns to other things. Two months later the response of the child is much the same as it was at first, except that he now smiles in an interested fashion as he looks from the glass to the faces of those near by. The ape at this time gets up, walks to the glass, and tries to drink from it.

Again the reactions of the subjects towards a strange workman, whose activities outside the house cause Gua, 14 months, and Donald, 16½, to climb on a chair and look out of the window at him, may be regarded as typical. They stand side by side in this manner with occasional pounding by one or the other upon the window pane. After a few moments the ape tires and gets down, while Donald remains for a much longer time, apparently greatly interested in what is going on before him. In a similar manner the human will stare with close attention while a package is being unwrapped or the grate of a stove shaken down; or he will watch the process of peeling apples or some other culinary operation for minutes on end. But Gua can seldom be attracted by stimuli of this sort.

The apparent result of the child's more careful observation was soon to be seen in the manipulation and use to which he put many of the articles that fell into his hands. He would, for example, pick up the small rubber doll with which they both played and squeeze it repeatedly, causing it to produce a shrill whistle. And yet Gua, who ultimately took the doll, would never squeeze it unless specifically directed to do so, except towards the very last of the nine-months period. Again, if given a pair of pliers he would take one of the handles in each of his hands and open and close them. The ape, who reacted in the same manner only occasionally, was more likely to hold one of the handles in her hand

and chew on some part of the other one. Perhaps the most striking example of such differences consisted in the child's manipulation of Gua's walker, which he adopted as a plaything at the age of 17 months and which for a few weeks appeared to be his favorite toy. He learned by himself to push and guide this as well as to back it up. Of course for months previous to Donald's acquisition the ape had dragged or pulled the walker about by herself but for the most part in a rough and boisterous manner, and frequently without regard to whether it was right side up, on its side, or upside down. The human, on the other hand, always went to the back and pushed it front first, a distinction which the chimpanzee had never consistently made. He would even right it by himself so that it rested properly upon its wheels before he attempted to roll it, and he seemed carefully to back away from and avoid obstacles in his pathway as well. Sometimes of his own accord he would indulge in further constructive play by picking up small toys or other objects, placing them upon the walker, and pushing them about as on a wagon.

During the last few months, it is true, Donald's advancement in the examination and manipulation of objects was not quite so pronounced in many respects as it had been earlier, although it was still clearly apparent. The change in this regard resulted both because Gua developed into more of a manipulator herself, and because the boy's attention seemed largely to shift from new objects to new activities, of which climbing (self-manipulation?) was probably the most important. At about the age of 13 months Gua seemed to take a renewed interest in familiar objects, possibly because many of her early fears were by then thoroughly dissipated. She was observed on one occasion to examine a felt hat with as much care and attention as the child some months earlier had studied new toys. Once during this period she picked up a toothbrush which she studied and passed from hand to hand quite as the human had done on earlier occasions. At the age of 14 months Donald spontaneously turned the leaves of magazines, without apparent regard for the pictures in them, but chiefly, it seemed, for the manipulative interest. Gua herself soon thereafter found that books could be similarly handled and when she was 13 months old she would in turn open their pages if given the chance. Each of the subjects discovered the telephone as an object of attraction and would make his way to it whenever the door of the room in which it was situated was open. Each as well would put his hand upon the small crank used to signal the operator, although Donald usually succeeded in turning the handle better than Gua. The first time one of Gua's human friends spoke to her over the telephone, she started, put her hand to her ear, looked at the receiver, and pushed it away from her. Under like conditions the child also pushed the receiver from his head but without so obvious a shock of surprise.

In order to trace the development of the exploratory and manipulative responses to a single object, the subjects are periodically presented with an ordinary watch, the classic stimulus for which human infants are supposed to show a strong fascination. The watch is held by its chain and offered to the individual tested or dangled in front of him. It is originally shown to Donald when he is 15 months old. He turns it over and over in his hands and examines it with considerable interest. Occasionally he looks up at the experimenter during the procedure and smiles. When the watch is placed to his ear he momentarily inhibits breathing and soon thereafter attempts to move it to the ear himself. His localization is so poor, however, that he misses the entire *pinna* and instead places it upon his head or neck behind the ear. At 17 months he comes at once if the watch is held out to him. He also seems at the same age to notice its parts for the first time, by pointing out the hands and stem with outstretched fingers,

and by turning the knurled winding screw. He continues
to inhibit breathing when the watch is placed to his ear
and although we put it over his left ear, he takes it
himself and tries to put it on his right ear. His localization as before is very poor. At 18 months he succeeds
in placing the watch accurately over the ear at the start,
without any clue from the experimenter. He is still
interested in examining the parts. Oddly enough, he
tries once at this age to put the stem in his mouth,
although he has never previously done so.

When similarly tested at 12½ months, the ape attempts to put the watch in her mouth upon every possible opportunity. She is a little hesitant about having
it placed out of sight against her ear, but eventually
she permits such contact, whereupon she partially,
though not entirely, inhibits her breathing. She soon
seems to lose interest in the whole procedure and goes
away of her own accord. At 15½ months she runs towards
the experimenter and climbs in his lap as soon as he
displays the watch. She still attempts to bite or mouth
it and makes no effort to move it toward her ear. She
begins at this time a new kind of play, namely the
swinging of the watch like a pendulum, from its chain
which is securely held by the experimenter. At no time
does she devote any special attention to the parts or to
carefully examining it. Throughout most of the test she
"smiles" in typical play fashion.

We turn now to what may be characterized as *imitative play*, in that the subjects for the most part picked
it up, without definite instruction, from the behavior
of one another or from their elders. Because of the
reputation of the chimpanzee as an imitator, the observers were on the alert from the start for the appearance of this sort of behavior. And yet, strange as it may
seem, imitation in Gua was clearly less pronounced than
in the boy, or at least it did not manifest itself to as
marked a degree within the ages which the ape was

under our charge. The greater tendency of the human subject to imitate should probably be connected with his superiority in the exploration of objects and with his correspondingly keener observation of all that went on about him. One might have predicted from the known differences in attention and observation that the child would be better able to reproduce the acts which he saw.

Typical reactions in this regard: If given a hairbrush when under a year in age, the boy would place it against his head and make crude brushing strokes. A little later he would close each dresser and chiffonier drawer which he found open in evident imitation of his adult associates, and he would similarly push a broom back and forth upon the floor. He learned to shake hands, moreover, not as Gua did by merely extending her right arm, but with a genuine pumping movement of the hand which he received. On one occasion during his seventeenth month, when he came upon his mother sorting a bushel of oranges by placing some in one box and some in another, he immediately took part in the job with great enthusiasm by toddling from one box to the other carrying an orange at each trip. He was also discovered at about the same age prancing back and forth across the room with his hands joined behind his back. The purport of this behavior was at first a puzzle until the experimenter who was with him discovered that, in a moment of deep concentration, he himself had been striding in the same manner with hands clasped behind him. These and similar mimetic reactions seem to have been called forth largely as spontaneous play gestures.

The child's development of a rough sort of mauling play, which he directed towards Gua, we took also to be something of an imitation of her coarser play tactics. For the most part, he would undertake this mauling by seizing her in both his hands, whereupon he would pull or press her down upon her back, frequently hugging her during this maneuver. If she started to walk

138

away he would hang on tenaciously, sometimes walking after her upon his knees while he clung tightly to her clothing. It was our clear impression that Gua, and not Donald, got the worst of this wrestling, although for the most part she took it resignedly enough. Donald seemed greatly delighted and would laugh throughout almost the entire performance.

Both were enormously interested in being carted or wheeled about not only in the perambulator, but also in a diminutive express wagon which served as one of their toys. They became so attracted to this wagon that upon its mere sight Gua would often climb in and wait to be pulled, while Donald attempted the same act long before he could climb well enough to complete it. After he had been lifted into it Donald would hold tightly to the sides of the wagon, and Gua, who was usually behind him, would throw both arms about the boy in a bear hug which protected her from falling.

The effect of imitation first began to be apparent in this play when Donald at the age of $15\frac{1}{2}$ months, upon seeing Gua climb into the wagon, would take the part of one of his elders, pick up the tongue of the wagon, and begin pulling his playmate about. Although Gua could also accomplish the same thing it was not observed that she ever did so without the previous encouragement of one of the observers and often even some slight assistance in starting the wagon.

The slapping and pounding of doors, windows, and certain flat articles of furniture by Gua, while not entirely mimetic, appeared under some conditions to be largely so. If Donald went to a small radio bench and hammered its seat with his hands to produce a metallic drumming sound, the chimpanzee was beside him in an instant doing likewise. She would also open cabinets and cupboards, probably as a result of her observation of others, and during the later months she needed no encouragement to put a hairbrush to her head and make brushing movements like the child.

When the two were 11½ and 14 months old respectively they developed the habit or fad of removing the contents from partially opened drawers. The actual opening of drawers subsequently became a regular form of play with Gua (but not with Donald) and she often threw her weight skillfully against them so as to succeed with drawers which were difficult to operate. This behavior did not become highly proficient until the ape was more than 15 months of age. But when it did, anything she might find, from powder puffs to motion-picture film, was not safe from her pillaging.

A good portion of their handling of the perambulator was likewise of an imitative nature. Hence Donald early took hold of the two upright supports of the handle, and standing (in his walker) with a hand upon each, he would push the whole carriage across the room. The same reaction appeared somewhat later in the ape, her original interest in the perambulator being to climb into and out of it, and to swing and hang from its handle. At 13½ months Donald learned to rotate the wheels of the carriage when it had been turned on its side or end either by Gua or by the experimenters. His movement of the wheels apparently attracted the chimpanzee, who would consequently observe Donald in this activity, sometimes going so far as to seat herself upon his lap while he was so engaged. Frequently also she would pull or bite at the tires in the apparent attempt to duplicate his performance. It was several weeks before she finally succeeded. In the meantime the child on some occasions was seen to attempt to bite the tires during such play, as Gua had done in her attempts to imitate him.

Each was much interested in typewriters, and during the last few months would go to one whenever it was within reach and pound the keys with his fingers, in this case demonstrating a common tendency for its manipulation. It is impossible to say which of the two first exhibited this behavior, since they were originally observed doing it within a few moments of one another. Gua would even climb on a typewriter stool and seat herself properly before the machine, moving her hands simultaneously up and down upon the keyboard. According to our records, they first imitated the motions of a typist at the respective ages of 13 and 15 months. At that time they had both seen a typewriter operated from time to time for more than five months.

Probably the most convincing proof of the child's superiority in imitation was his direct mimicry of the ape herself. Since Gua was the boy's only intimate companion of comparable age, the human subject picked up a great deal from her in this incidental manner. Indeed, the situation in which the two lived together as playmates and associates was much like that of a two-child family in which Gua, because of her greater maturity and agility, played the part of the older child. With the added stimulation thus afforded, the younger child in such situations usually learns more rapidly than would otherwise be the case. It was Gua, in fact, who was almost always the aggressor or leader in finding new toys to play with and new methods of play; while the human was inclined to take up the role of the imitator or follower.

A pertinent example was the discovery by the chimpanzee that the upholstered seat cushions of a davenport were removable. She found this out apparently by first inserting her finger in a crack between one of the cushions and the frame of the davenport. Her hand and then her arm finally followed the finger, and by lifting the cushion after the insertion of these members she ultimately got her whole head beneath it. It was thereupon completely overturned and so removed from its allotted position. As the cushion fell to the floor it was jumped upon and slapped; the depression left by it was entered and jumped upon. Donald, who had quietly observed the original performance, assisted Gua to remove the cushion the second time (after it had been replaced) and then did his own part towards sitting upon it and climbing into the depression it left.

There were other instances of his performing at once an act in which the ape had just previously been engaged. Thus, when she lay on the floor and peeked under a closed door behind which something interesting was taking place, he would often do likewise. On one or two occasions, when Gua appeared holding the trousers of the experimenter and walking between them, the boy almost at once seized them in a similar manner, although his taller stature and larger head made it difficult for him to stand in the same relative position. Crawling, which was never of regular occurrence in the development of his walking, he learned by imitating Gua, long after he could possibly have had any use for it, since he then walked upright without difficulty. In some cases, when Gua dropped to all fours in the house, he would get down upon his hands and knees and crawl after her.

His capacities astonished even those closest to him when it became apparent that he was also vocally imitating his playmate. Such behavior was first observed during his fourteenth month in the reproduction of her "food bark" or grunt. This call was characteristically given by Gua if some particularly desirable tidbit, usually a piece of orange, was in sight but had not yet been obtained. The vocalization of the ape under such circumstances may be described as a series of guttural grunts about one-half second each in duration, of low (baritone) pitch range. The vowel sound in which this tone was produced was like the "u" in "duck" or "buck," sometimes changing to the double o of the words "book" or "wood." Such grunts were initiated through a release of air held under pressure by the soft palate. Donald's imitation, instead of being single-syllabled like Gua's, was usually two-syllabled and somewhat higher in pitch, although it was repeated many times in the same manner and under the same conditions. It may be written as "uha, uha, uha" or "uhuh, uhuh," the second syllable being longer in duration as well as accented more strongly than the first. Whenever an orange or other desired food was observed and barked for by Gua, Donald would usually take up this imitative call. In fact, on several occasions he picked up an orange by himself and ran to the experimenters with it grunting "uha, uha" or "uhuh, uhuh" as he approached.

A form of behavior to be mentioned in connection with imitation is the continual biting and chewing of the chimpanzee subject. Possibly one should classify this as a subhuman or infantile type of play. Certainly it was partly exploratory and manipulative in nature. We frequently felt that the mouthing reaction of the ape should be compared, as a bit of exploratory behavior, to the continual sniffing of dogs or perhaps to the persistent gnawing of a young puppy. There were times when it seemed impossible for the little animal to go for many minutes without having something in her mouth "to play with." Pieces of paper or cardboard, pieces of string or thread, buttons, needles or pins, match sticks, rags, pencils, blocks, spoons, or kitchen utensils, and if out of doors, stones, twigs, leaves, sand, acorns, pine needles, or other articles of a size and weight to be handled and lifted easily would soon be rolled about by the lips and mouthed. If nothing convenient was available she would often prepare something by scraping bits of paint from the furniture, by chewing or breaking ends from a wicker chair, or even by tearing strips or small pieces from bed sheets.

Quite likely such behavior is to be related, as it is in the young human, to the process of teething. But its unfailing persistence made one wonder whether the diet of the ape could be deficient in certain necessary salts, so that she was forced by her appetites into continually sampling the objects about her. The fact that her tendency to bite and chew would periodically strengthen and weaken seemed particularly to support such a view. On the other hand, Gua seldom actually ate the things which she placed in her mouth, more often rolling them around or feeling them with her lips. This fact points again to the extreme sensitivity of the mouth and lips as a tactual organ. It appeared at times as if it was no more possible for her to refrain from touching things with the lips than it is for the young human baby to keep his hands from attractive objects.

It is to be especially noted that, when articles were placed in the animal's mouth, they were held or chewed often with one end exposed, much after the manner of a man who goes about with a match stick or toothpick, or even a cigar, protruding from his lips. Perhaps it will occur to the reader at this point that a considerable number of humans during this civilized age regularly pursue the practice of mouthing, chewing, and manipulating quantities of tobacco and chicle. If one does not wish to compare the behavior of the ape to that of the humans, he may prefer to compare the humans to the ape. At any rate such an interesting similarity is hardly to be overlooked.

We made two attempts to introduce Gua to chewing gum as a possible substitute for the other articles she was inclined to accept. The first was when she was less than a year in age. All went well on each occasion until she removed the gum for examination, whereupon its adherence to the hairs upon her lips and to her fingers called for an abrupt cessation of the procedure.

Biting reactions, analogous to those of Gua, were of course common in Donald likewise, as is the case with all young babies. These would fluctuate somewhat in frequency with their most common occurrence before the eruption of new teeth. Examples may be found in the child's biting at 11 months the edges of tables within his reach, of his picking up leaves and placing them in his mouth at 12, of his subsequent scraping of window and door screens with his teeth as Gua had done some time earlier, and of his tendency at 14 months to put paper into his mouth. Instances in which the boy bit individuals, sometimes with considerable strength, are also not lacking. At near the age of a year he would occasionally chew at the shoulder or arm of the person who was carrying him, and at 15 months he bit the thigh of one of the experimenters so severely that deep impressions were left by the teeth.

The precise extent to which such behavior on the part of the child was due to some inner stimulation and the extent to which it was imitative of Gua is of course difficult to say. The examples already given we have regarded as probably non-imitative. There are others in which the degree of imitation is quite likely greater, and some about which there can be no question at all. Never at any time did the human possess as pronounced a tendency to make the hand-to-mouth reaction as the animal, although the recurrence of this response following its earlier disappearing strongly suggested the influence of Gua's example. At 14 months he was occasionally caught attempting to bite or scrape the wall with his teeth, one of the ape's most objectionable habits. Sometimes this reaction would appear in the child shortly after the animal had been similarly engaged, but more often it came quite without her immediate example. Further instances of clearly imitative biting or mouthing behavior in the child were his picking up of a stick and transporting it to his mouth, just after Gua had done the same thing; his occasional efforts (at 16 months) to pick up crumbs with his lips from the tray of his high chair, even though his finger prehension was then excellent; his attempt (at 16½ months) to put sand into his mouth (which is common with many babies); his occasional carrying of small objects from one place to another (as a spoon or a wooden block) by holding them in his teeth; and his efforts (at 18½ months) to chew a shoe with which he happened to be playing.

145

Chapter VII

SOCIAL AND AFFECTIONATE
BEHAVIOR

CERTAINLY the relation between play and social behavior is an intimate one, since play in its advanced forms demands the presence of a playmate or companion, of partners or associates with whom to play. One could reasonably consider the question of *playmates*, therefore, under the heading of play. This might well have been done in the present instance, were it not for the fact that the choice and treatment of play companions are connected also to the more general question of the friendly and antagonistic responses of the subjects to other individuals of all sorts. It is because of this latter relationship that we take it up under the discussion of social behavior.

The human infant served as Gua's most intimate playmate for nearly nine months and she in turn filled a similar role with regard to the child. It is safe to say, we think, that Gua was the first playmate Donald had ever had, aside from his parents. He correspondingly became the first playmate of the little animal, excepting only her mother, with whom she lived during her earlier cage existence. The initial reactions of the subjects toward one another should for this reason be of particular significance.

From the moment they first entered each other's presence there was evidence of curiosity and interest on the part of both. The interest seemed to be more marked in the case of Donald than of Gua. When they were seated side by side, the human reached for the ape and touched her, although at that early stage she

146

would make no corresponding advances. They were not subsequently brought into close proximity for several days, but continued to eye one another from a distance. Donald, as before, seemed to persist in this behavior more than the chimpanzee. As soon as they had been moved together for the second time, she immediately *extended her lips in a series of exploratory kisses* which touched the child upon his face and lips. At first he seemed startled but made no avoiding reactions and subsequently cooed his pleasure.

The following selections from our notes indicate the further progress of their acquaintanceship.

July 5.
Donald placed in baby pen. Gua is on floor outside of pen. She goes towards him, reaching through the bars with her right hand. *They hold hands.* Donald seems delighted. She touches him gently on the abdomen with her closed fist. He gets hold of her hair and pulls it. She reaches through bars with her right hand, and extending her index finger she touches his hand lightly. She loses her balance while sitting and falls on her back . . . . Donald soon afterwards falls likewise from a sitting position to his back, and cries.

July 10.
He stands in his play pen holding the rail. He is apparently so delighted when she approaches that he lets go with one hand as if to reach for her and nearly loses his balance. He laughs with almost every breath. . . . Gua goes to side of pen. Donald falls down, first to a sitting, then to a lying posture. He is picked up and placed again in a sitting position. He leans forward towards her so far that he then falls forward. Raises his head while lying prone and looks through the bars at her. She reaches in to him, pulls his head down and kisses it. She touches his face and hands. . . . Both seem to be very interested and striving to get nearer to one another.

July 11.
He is so excited he pants, vocalizing at each exhalation. He repeatedly stands up in his walker and then sits down again stamping his feet in this manner. He seems to like to see her fall down and invariably laughs aloud when she does. She is very active, moves rapidly and awkwardly, and prob-

ably falls oftener than usual. She moves towards him, bites at the counting balls on his walker, and pushes the walker with her hand. He reaches for her head and touches it. He evidently attempts to go after her in his walker as she moves away but jumps up and down in his excitement and pushes the walker backward instead. He cannot push it forward very well as yet.

July 13.

They are placed on a bed together. Donald reaches towards Gua. She "smiles." Seems very complacent and friendly. He puts his finger in her eye.

He then gets upon his stomach and while in this position he slides himself backward by pushing with his hands. He accidentally slips off the bed by this means before he can be caught. He is not hurt but cries loudly. Gua appears terrified at the noise and excitement and although she utters no sound she rushes to me and buries her head in my lap.

She continues to kiss Donald frequently on approaching him. This is usually the case when she climbs up in his high chair, making contact with his bare foot which she kisses.

Each of the subjects served as a strong stimulus to the other, who was electrified into action, so to speak, by the presence of his playmate. Exercise and romping were almost continuous when they were together, but as soon as either was distantly removed, the other would at once become quiet and relatively inactive. This common tendency towards greater activity when they were with one another was a condition which persisted throughout the period of the research.

As examples of the mutual attachment which grew up after their initial meetings, it may be pointed out that Gua almost always, if not prevented, would make her way in some manner to the child. She would go to him if he was in his walker, climb into his lap if he was seated in his high chair, and frequently sit upon his foot or his leg if he was on the floor. She would stare after him when he was carried from the room, and frequently she would even follow him away from the protection of those who cared for her. If he had not yet awakened from his nap when she awoke from hers, she could hardly be kept from the door of his room, to which she would go and, during the later months, which she would often open. Sometimes she would lie prone with her face upon the floor and peek with one eye through the crack beneath the door.

Once, during an unavoidable absence on the part of the two observers, the subjects were left at home taking their noonday naps in charge of a maid who was new and somewhat strange to Gua. The ape, then 10½ months of age, awakened before either of the experimenters had returned. A report of her activities as obtained from the attendant is as follows: When Gua awakened and found herself alone with the strange person she began screaming and ran from one room to another as if in search of a familiar face. Her cries aroused Donald, to whose door she had not yet gone. Immediately upon hearing the noise he made, she rushed to the door of his room and hammered on it with both hands. When she was permitted to enter, she became quiet at once and remained in the presence of the child without further disturbance.

On another occasion about two weeks after this incident, when the subjects were playing beside one another in the same room with both the adults, one of the observers without warning accidentally upset a chair. This made a sharp clatter near Gua as it struck the floor. Instead of running towards either of the grown-ups—a reaction to be expected under such circumstances—Gua rushed to Donald, threw both arms around him and hugged him tightly, crying the while.

The human infant, for his part, learned to say "Gua," which he pronounced "Gya," a few days after he had first seen the ape, and this became for some time thereafter the most frequently employed word in his vocabulary. He would go to her if she did not come to him and invariably seemed to enjoy feeling or touching her. It was clear, however, that he did not relish her handling of him to the same degree, and frequently he made avoiding reactions when she attempted to do so. Although he would not always come when called, the stimulus of either of the experimenters carrying Gua was one which for some months he could not well resist.

When they had been acquainted for about one-third of the observation period it began to be apparent that Donald would frequently cry when Gua screamed, particularly if he was present and could observe her behavior while she actually emitted her cries. Quite possibly this was a fear response to the loud and piercing noise, although the sound was certainly one which by that time should have been familiar. Some three months later, if Gua was placed on a chair and required to stay there by way of punishment, Donald would run to the chair, stretch his arms upward, and embrace her. Gua usually reciprocated in such instances by putting her head on the child's shoulder and one or both arms about him. There can be little doubt that this was a genuinely affectionate reaction on the part of the chimpanzee, as evidenced by similar behavior in caged specimens of like age towards one another. And it was probably of the same nature on the part of the human subject, whose age at the time this sort of activity began to show itself was nearly 17 months.

Not long after the first occurrence of these responses, Donald began to toddle to Gua as soon as he was dressed and put down on the floor in the morning. His first act was then to greet her by stooping forward and hugging her. The same procedure would usually be repeated whenever she had been screaming or even if she had only been scolded. The little animal in her turn began about this time to take what appeared to us to be a protective attitude towards the child, particularly if the two were out of doors. When they held hands as they walked together, it was Gua at first who did the actual holding. If their grip broke for an instant, it

Their pleasure in riding in any vehicle is readily apparent and rides in the perambulator form a regular part of the daily routine. When preparations for a ride are being made the child often runs to the carriage and hangs upon it, while the ape climbs in and sits down in her allotted place.

The hugging of one subject by the other, particularly at times of scolding or punishment, is a common occurrence during the last months.

The ape's attachment to her older associates is shown by her rushing toward the experimenter with arms outstretched. The picture to the left was taken two days after her removal from her mother; that to the right one week later. The standing postures are only momentary and occur as she raises her hands from the ground to grasp the observer.

was she again who stopped, waited for Donald, or went after him and seized his hand in hers, although the child became the aggressor in this act at a little later date. When Donald would cry she would run to him, and if he was being carried by someone she would often slap the holder.

Although they had several contacts with other children during the nine months, these were never very intimate or prolonged. It appeared, in general, that each preferred children somewhere near his own size. In fact, after the novelty of Gua's association had worn off and Donald had become a little older, he would play with other young humans with about the same enthusiasm which he directed towards the ape.

Her second close association with a child playmate other than Donald occurred about six weeks after she had been in the civilized environment. When the new acquaintance, a little girl of 3½ years, named Martha, entered the play group, Gua ran to her, followed her, smelled her, and hugged her. There was little difference in the behavior of the animal towards Martha from that towards Donald, at least after the first friendly gestures had been completed. At times the ape seemed even more interested in Martha than in Donald, possibly because of the older child's greater agility, or possibly again because of her newness in Gua's experience. After a very few moments Gua and her new friend were sitting in the children's rocker, holding hands and otherwise playing together.

The reaction of the chimpanzee to children who were older and bigger was, as a rule, quite different and seemed to depend to a large extent upon the behavior with which they received her. All too frequently it was the tendency of pre-adolescents to point their fingers at her and giggle, which seemed at once to draw aggressive and antagonistic responses from Gua. In such instances she would usually rush at the affected children, emitting threatening dog-like barks as she did so, and she would slap them on the shins if they had not already dashed beyond her reach. She would then herself retreat in haste. An exception was made in the case of Dickie, an eight-year-old boy whom Gua had met on several occasions. With Dickie she was very friendly. She would hold his hand, play and romp with him without any evidence of antagonism. But then there was never any tendency on Dickie's part to run or dodge away from Gua or to laugh at her in a high-pitched giggle.

With regard to adults, Gua's reception was much more timid and distrustful than that of Donald who save in the last month or two appeared willing to be openly received or carried by anyone. Becoming acquainted with Gua, on the contrary, was for the most part a long and arduous process, subject to many possible pitfalls before true intimacy was attained. She might even become belligerent if she were forced too much. For almost the first third of her civilized existence she usually avoided all human adults with the exception of the experimenters. She would make no additional contacts herself, but would only "accept" after a long time the advances of those who sought to cultivate her.

Her hand-shaking when she was introduced to new acquaintances was a continual illustration of her shyness. She seemed to try to respond correctly when told to "shake hands," but often she acted as if she could not overcome her fear. The result in the case of strangers was that she often made a sort of compromise reaction which consisted in advancing rapidly and slapping the extended hand with such speed that her own hand could not possibly have been seized. She would then dodge backward to a point of protection behind one of the observers. Persons whom she knew she would approach more leisurely and she allowed her hand to rest in theirs till it had been appropriately shaken. There seemed to exist a regular progression of steps between these two extremes which might be considered as measures of the degree of her acceptance of different individuals. The longer she would permit her hand to rest without withdrawal in that of the one who was shaking it, the more could that person regard himself as her friend. As time went on she became generally more amicable towards everyone, so that when the human subject had reached the bashful stage at 15 or 16 months, the ape in some cases would receive newcomers with almost as little reserve as he did.

An unusual fact in this connection was that, with but one or two exceptions, she became acquainted more quickly and appeared to be more at ease with grown women than with men. The same sort of tendency, oddly enough, was at one time apparent in Donald's behavior as well. Between the ages of 11 and 12 months he would cry when a strange man approached, although he made no similar response to the presence of strange women. Whether this could have been due in any degree to the shorter average height of the female stature, to the milder voices, or possibly in Gua's case to the less curious interest which women seemed to exhibit, we are unable to say. As far as the ape was concerned it appeared to us that *the skirts* of the women had something to do with her reactions. She was strongly attracted, it will be remembered, to swinging, hanging, and waving playthings from the start, and the dangling garments of her women acquaintances proved no exception to the rule. There seemed as a result to be a play attraction for her in the case of women, which men did not possess. At any rate, she was prone to take hold of, hang upon, and handle women's clothing. In this way she ultimately developed the unusual and often embarrassing habit of lifting the hems of their dresses and putting her head underneath them. In one instance she was observed to make an analogous exploratory gesture with a man's trouser leg, by pulling the cuff of the trouser away from the ankle and bending down so she could look upward. It is possible that this type of behavior is related somehow to the play activity of covering or concealing herself beneath boxes and bushel baskets.

In line with the child's less wary approach to human beings, he seemed for the most part to accept animals as well with somewhat greater freedom than the ape. He would originally go toward any cat or dog which did not make threatening noises and if permitted, he would pet or maul it. He was also observed at 15 months to toddle towards cows and apes in cages with equal curiosity and lack of fear, although it is true he maintained a safe distance between himself and the animals. He frequently chased small domestic pets if they would run from him and on more than one occasion was observed making his way with outstretched arms after a large butterfly.

At first Gua appeared similarly to have no fear of animals and would approach dogs several times her size. When originally presented with a neighbor's cat she kissed it and tried to put her finger in its mouth. Birds and squirrels also interested her, and she would frequently sit quietly gazing into the trees at them. When she was 11 months old, however, her whole attitude appears to have changed suddenly as a result of an unfavorable encounter with one dog, a very small puppy which at that time was about one-third her own size. Upon first seeing this animal she rushed toward it, presumably to investigate, but the dog became frightened and ran. Gua at once took up the chase as she would a game of tag, until the puppy, which was momentarily cornered, snapped at her. She backed away screaming and thereafter clung to the experimenter. All subsequent friendly advances of the previously terrified puppy were of no avail, and from that time onward Gua seemed to be generally afraid of nearly all strange animals. She became so cautious, in fact, that she could not even be led by the hand to within 4 or 5 meters of such docile creatures as chickens, cows, and farm horses. But toward older chimpanzees at the Experiment Station she displayed no such aversion. Whenever permitted she would approach their cages and touch their extended fingers.

We seek to examine the reactions to animals a little closer by offering the subjects a live beetle, 2.5 centimeters in length. Although the ape, age 12 months, observes it closely, under no circumstances can we induce her to do more than touch it with the tip of her index finger. She will make physical contact with it only in a touch-and-go manner similar to that which she employs in shaking hands with strangers. Donald on the other hand at 14½ months picks up the beetle and examines it with deliberation.

Some months later we show them a cage of laboratory white rats. But this time, to our great surprise, it is the child who appears afraid. He is strangely interested in other things when we bring him close to the rats. If one of them is taken out of the cage and placed upon the ground, he cries. If it is offered to him he yells. Gua likewise cannot be induced to approach the cage, and if a rat is held out to her she runs and cries, "Oo-oo." Neither of the subjects has ever previously been close to a white rat and probably has never even seen one before this time.

How can we account for this behavior? Of course, as far as Gua is concerned it might easily have been predicted, in view of her then known aversion for strange and unknown animals. The child's reactions, on the other hand, are difficult to explain unless they are merely sympathetic responses to Gua's general avoidance. But this does not seem likely, because Donald is shown the rats first and although Gua does happen to be present, she is quiet and maintains a [discreet distance until her turn to be tested has arrived.

We discover soon after this test that the child is now more cautious than he formerly was when confronted with many animals which he used to approach without hesitation. There seems consequently to be a rough similarity between the behavior of each of the subjects if it is considered in broad perspective. Although neither has shown any fear for the first few months, they both appear later to shun too close a contact with unknown members of the animal group. In Gua's case, moreover, the avoiding behavior can be positively identified with a minor attack upon her by one small dog. Since there is a definite event in Gua's history to which her change in behavior can be attributed, it is quite possible that some similar though unknown factor has caused the analogous change in Donald.

There are, nevertheless, a few animals which Gua does not shun, even after her unfavorable encounter. These are domestic pets in the neighborhood, which she knows well will avoid her. She will definitely pursue a certain cat, if it comes within her sight, and she will continue to scramble after it with great bravado, even though her progress in the chase is hopelessly slow. This is strangely similar to her reactions to older children who point at her and giggle, and who back away from her when she goes toward them. It thus appears that toward organisms which are afraid of her or at any rate which retreat when she approaches, she will manifest aggressive and threatening behavior. Organisms which are themselves aggressive will at once be avoided by her. And organisms which display neither aggressive nor timid behavior, but which are very large or unfamiliar, are quite likely to be sedulously avoided as well, at least to the extent that she will not approach very close to them.

That the primates in general are thoroughly social animals is evidenced by the numerous instances of specimens pining away in solitary captivity, of their adoption of animal companions of various sorts, and of their living in the jungle in bands or groups. Our observations seemed to indicate that Gua not only sought social contacts, but that she was absolutely *dependent* upon them. This dependency might be said to be of two sorts, the first of which, a *physical* dependence, is like the dependence of the human baby. That is, she needed at the start the same general care and attention, the same precautions regarding food, and the same sort of carrying. To be sure, the relatively greater maturity of the ape modified her physical requirements to some extent. In being carried, for example, she assisted the carrier by holding on much better than Donald did, and if very hungry she would in a way forage after her own food, even though much that she ate under such circumstances, particularly when she was very young, was likely to be indigestible.

The second, a sort of *psychological* dependence, must surely have made life harder for Gua than it was for Donald. This consisted of an intense and tenacious impulse to remain within sight and call of some friend, guardian, or protector. Throughout the entire nine months she was much more dependent in this respect than the child. Whether indoors or out, she almost never roamed very far from someone she knew. To shut her up in a room by herself, or to walk away faster than she could run, and so leave her behind, proved, as well as we could judge, to be the most awful punishment that could possibly be inflicted. She could not be alone apparently without suffering, whereas Donald would frequently play by himself if no one was about. When out of doors he would sometimes wander entirely away from home with a care-free abandon unknown to Gua. If left in the house with a stranger, the chimpanzee seemed, at least during the first several months, to be caught between the horns of a terrible dilemma. On the one hand she would not permit herself to be touched or to get too close to the unknown individual, and on the other hand she apparently did not dare to be left without his protection. The result was that if he should move from room to room, Gua would tag along at a respectful distance, crying or "oo-ooing" miserably as she went.

Quite possibly, of course, a good part of this behavior, at least at the start, was occasioned by the emotional shock suffered by the little animal when she was taken from her mother. It is not incredible to suppose that her impressions at that time were similar to those of a human child of one or two years if it suddenly were placed among fearsome creatures from whom it had always before been protected by bars. Her behavior certainly suggested such an analogy, particularly during the first day or two, for she was then not quiet or at ease unless she could bury her face in our arms and so shut off outside stimulation. In the beginning, moreover, she could not be placed in her bed unless she was already sound asleep, and if she later awoke in the strange surroundings, she would scream until picked up. Although she subsequently adapted to the procedure of being put to bed, it was several weeks before she would relax and close her eyes unless she could maintain physical contact with the experimenter, as for example by holding his hand.

For some time also she showed similar evidences of anxiety when required to sit alone in her high chair. Indeed one of her most difficult problems was to remain in her chair while the adults were eating. Usually she would respond to vocal commands when told to sit down but her patience was sorely tried, and towards the end of the meal she frequently began to whine or cry. Her behavior was not unlike that of a young child who nags and frets to leave the dining table before his elders are ready to get up. Often she would only relinquish her efforts to climb down when the experimenter placed his hand or arm upon the tray of the chair. Her reactions were thereupon either to hold his hand in one or both of her own, or else to rest her head upon it.

Her strong dependency was responsible, no doubt, for her fear of being shut away by herself. This led to an early understanding of the mechanism of door closing and a keen and continual observation of the doors in her vicinity. If she happened to be on one side of a doorway, and her friends on the other, the slightest movement of the door towards closing, whether produced by human hands or by the wind, would bring Gua rushing through the narrowing aperture, crying as she came.

Although her original attachment to those about her was for the first few days somewhat indefinite and generalized, in that it was directed to anyone who would pick her up, it rapidly became specific to the male adult of the human household. In this respect there seemed to be a transfer of dependency from the little animal's mother to her newly adopted parent. The new fixation was probably hastened by the fact that Gua was cared for almost entirely by this observer. Her attachment became so strong that she had been in the human environment for fully a month before she would let go of the trouser legs of her protector for any length of time, even though he might sit quietly at a table for as long as an hour. Almost without respite she clung to him in one way or another. If through a temporary lapse in her vigil he should succeed in taking a step or two away from her, it would surely precipitate a frantic scramble after the retreating trousers, to which she would thereafter hang on determinedly.

If the experimenter was absent for a few hours she would pick up some article of his clothing, which she apparently identified by both smell and vision, and this she would drag around with her as a fetish of protection until his return. The particular garment which she seemed to prefer in this connection was an old suit of khaki coveralls which had been worn by this observer for a few days after the separation. Occasionally, if it was necessary for him to go away, the leave-taking could even be accomplished without emotional display on the part of Gua if the coveralls were given her before the time of departure. Such behavior of substituting a memento for the object of her affection persisted only during the first few months.

When viewed over a long period of time, Gua's affection could be seen to fluctuate, if we judge by the variations in the closeness of the contact which she maintained with the experimenter. She was intensely devoted to this individual throughout the entire period of the research, although perhaps somewhat less so at the end than at the beginning. And yet, in spite of its general ardor, her attachment would wax and wane in a slow irregular rhythm. After a brief sickness, during which her dependency necessarily increased, Gua behaved again for some weeks almost as she had at the beginning, even though she was then many months older. She was similarly more and then less attracted to certain of her other acquaintances (although of course to a relatively minor degree), depending perhaps upon the amount of temporary attention which was shown her by them.

During her fifteenth month, when she seemed to be in an "accelerating" phase of her cycle of affection for the chosen experimenter, she would scream and rush after him whenever he opened the door of the house. If left behind, she would run from one window to another pounding upon them and wailing, quite regardless of the fact that her two other good friends, Donald and the remaining observer, were still in the house with her. Upon his return she would suddenly scream (with joy?) and rush towards him with hair on end and arms outstretched. In the same stage of development she began to cry again to be carried by the individual of her preference and nothing would calm her till she had her way.

The first clear evidence which the child displayed of anything in the nature of a special preference for a single person appeared at the age of about 16½ months. He would then fret for his mother and toddle after her when she went from room to room. Although her departure from the house usually left him for a few moments in a state of disturbance, he would presently become quiet and return to his play. Upon the occurrence of sounds of her returning he would go any place in the house to greet her. It need hardly be added that his receptions were much less vociferous than those of the ape.

In spite of the fact that Gua's affection for the second observer was by no means as strong as it was for the first, after a few months the chimpanzee *did* seem to regard her as a sort of substitute protector. As a result, the ape would usually cling to her when the other adult was well out of sight. On one occasion in the fourth month of the observations it became necessary for the chosen experimenter to go away for about a week. Almost immediately after his departure Gua transferred her affections to the remaining observer, to whom she seemed quite as attached in a few days as she had previously been to the absent member of the group. But upon his return she rapidly reverted to her original attachment.

There was no apparent reason for the blind affection of the little animal, which would even cause her to attack her lesser friends in her loyalty to the greater ones. Thus, during Gua's sixteenth month, if the preferred observer made threatening movements towards the non-preferred, Gua would assist by barking and bristling to the attack of the latter even to the extent of using her teeth. If the non-preferred, on the other hand, should threaten or slap the preferred it was again the non-preferred whom Gua attacked, this time apparently in defense of her chief. Surely no patriot, even though governed by the precept "My country, right

161

or wrong" was ever moved by a more zealous devotion than that which Gua displayed towards the person of her choice. But it should be added in fairness to the ape that she would also threaten relative strangers who raised a hand against the non-preferred observer or against other members of the household.

She soon displayed such docility and *cooperation*, no doubt as an outgrowth of her high degree of dependency, that she proved to be an easier experimental subject to handle than the child. As a result the making of bodily measurements became comparatively simple in her case, whereas it was always a most difficult task with the human infant. Since the ape, in addition, could be placed in almost any position and would allow her muscles to become limp when in our hands, her reflexes could also be more easily elicited. She was superior to the boy as well when it came to taking unpleasant medicines, and she would lie quietly and permit argyrol to be dropped in her nose time after time, while Donald made a trying experience of the same treatment. The process of dressing and undressing proved an additional department in which Gua herself furnished excellent assistance. She would lean forward and bend her head as an aid in slipping a suit of rompers over it, she would put her arms in open sleeves which were held before her, and she would push mightily to help the experimenter in getting her shoes on. The child, who was helpful to some extent in such activities, hardly proved to be as adept as the ape. At mealtime, moreover, she would lower her head to the side of her high chair for us to tie her bib. She began assisting in this manner fully six months before the human was observed to make similar reactions.

As might be suspected from this generally cooperative attitude, her responsiveness to vocal commands was likewise more immediate and more consistent than Donald's. In one sense she could therefore be said to obey better than he did. But such a statement needs qualification, for the reason that the duration or effect of any particular command seemed in most cases to be only momentary with Gua; whereas the child would usually refrain from an undesirable act for a considerable period after he had been warned against it. Suppose that the ape was engaged in biting or scraping the wall with her teeth. When told to stop, she would desist on the instant, although a moment later she might resume the same activity, only to stop at once when forbidden a second time. This cycle of activity-command-cessation might be repeated over and over again within as short a period as five minutes, the actual interrupting or inhibiting of the forbidden behavior in such a case seeming to have no lasting influence upon Gua. Although Donald, on the contrary, could only with difficulty be induced to stop an activity in progress, when once he stopped there was usually no immediate tendency to repeat. Since he was less responsive to vocal commands, he had more often to be forcibly prevented from doing prohibited things, whereas a word from the experimenter was more likely to produce the desired— even though only temporary—effect with Gua. That she showed a greater ability to react to vocal commands can be accounted for on theoretical grounds by the greater number of times she was corrected, and consequently by the more frequent repetitions of the inhibitory behavior which she went through.

It soon became clear that Gua would obey the voice of the chosen experimenter as she would obey that of no one else. On rare occasions she would ignore entirely everyone but him. One of the most difficult and prolonged "obedience tests" to which she could be put furnished ready proof of this fact. This consisted in our commanding her to remain seated upon a stool or chair while we left her alone in a room by herself. The task proved a serious ordeal for the subject. It was one which she never wanted to do and through which she would often whimper until we returned. Apparently torn between the impulse to obey and the impulse to follow she would sometimes get down from the chair after we had gone and look cautiously after us. The moment she heard us returning, however, she would scramble back into her place and be waiting innocently as we reappeared. She could seldom be induced to respond in this way for more than a few seconds by anyone except the preferred observer.

It was our impression concerning the obedience that the act itself was probably not the item of consequence *from the point of view of the ape*, but rather that her behavior was modified only *to satisfy her superiors*. Providing she responded according to their immediate requirements, what she did subsequently seemed to be a matter of no relevant moment. It appeared then as though the specificity of each act was lost to her and that the trouble was simply a matter of being "in bad with the boss." Certainly one could hardly expect individuals of the ages of Gua and Donald, to possess much in the nature of a conception of the rightness or wrongness of their acts. Neither subject was ever observed, after having commenced some form of forbidden activity, suddenly to inhibit the act "as if from memory" of previous directions, or from the ethical influences of a developing "conscience." The only cases of inhibition without immediately preceding vocal commands were when the furtive glances of the culprits revealed they were under the close observation of their elders.

The occurrence of behavior which was not openly sanctioned came eventually to be fairly common in each of the subjects, although it was more prevalent in the ape than it was in the child. In Gua's case the genetic development of this sort of slyness can be traced step by step. At the age of $8\frac{1}{2}$ months, she became interested in road maps kept in a pocket of the door of the automobile in which she traveled almost daily, and it was her habit to remove them on every convenient opportunity. Admonitions against this were usually only temporarily effective, although they did cause her to regard us closely before touching any of the maps. In one case she extended her right index finger slowly towards the maps, then turned while her hand was still outstretched and looked at the experimenter as if almost to ask his indulgence. A withering scowl upon his part immediately caused the withdrawal of the finger, but again for only a few moments, when the entire sequence was repeated.

She soon thereafter fell into the manner of looking at us before putting her teeth upon furniture or walls. She might even go so far as to have her mouth open and her face within a few inches of the plaster, then glance momentarily in our direction and, if we were watching, inhibit the act entirely. This behavior later developed to the stage at which a slight movement on the part of the one in authority, even before he directed his gaze toward Gua, would cause her to desist. But if the experimenter was sitting quietly beside her, although without attending to her, the forbidden act would often be performed without the least compunction.

At a subsequent period she would deliberately go behind objects to escape observation when some secret sin was about to be committed. She had been repeatedly cautioned against putting any of a new set of brightly colored blocks into her mouth. On one occasion at the age of 11 months she carried a block behind a small piece of furniture, and then stooped low and peered beneath it, with the block poised a few inches from her mouth, before she began her chewing. Having discovered the experimenter peering likewise beneath the furniture and in her own direction, she removed the block in haste from before her mouth. A few months later found her going behind trees and bushes, or turning her back directly upon the observers, to put sand, leaves, or stones into her mouth—all of these reactions being taboo. She was at that time frequently caught removing the evidence of her error the minute we suddenly turned in her direction. In more than one case, when she had stealthily scooped up a mouthful of sand, she would sit down hurriedly if surprised by one of the experimenters and stick out her tongue. She would thereupon wipe the sand from it by moving the palms of both hands in rapid alternation in a downward course over the tongue. The fingers would close with the passage of each hand in a manner which a human might employ in trying to scrape a hair from his tongue.

Undercover behavior of this sort, while by no means as common in Donald, was observed on numerous occasions. In one instance, at the age of 16½ months, he started to pick up a fountain pen although he put it down immediately when cautioned to let it alone. A moment later, while the experimenter's back was turned, he began to reach for the pen again, but withdrew his hand hurriedly as the experimenter suddenly faced towards him. Not a few of the combined acts of the subjects, when such acts were regarded as improper, would also be performed surreptitiously. A case in point is the biting of Gua's fingers by Donald, and her cooperative response of inserting the fingers into his mouth. This behavior, which was well known to both of them to be prohibited, would be interrupted in the process of consummation providing either subject became aware of serious outside observation.

The foregoing facts should demonstrate clearly that each of these immature organisms possessed the capacity, at least in an elementary fashion, of understanding simple social situations. To what extent this was based upon the general behavior of the individuals involved and to what extent it consisted in an actual interpretation of human facial expressions must certainly be largely a matter of conjecture. Each of the subjects, as previously mentioned, showed an early play interest in the human countenance. That Donald as well as Gua was sensitive to changes in the facial expression of his elders was shown by the fact that he could be made to smile when less than a year of age if someone smiled at him. And yet, oddly enough, he would also smile if distorted expressions of other sorts were made for his benefit. Gua, in her turn, would respond to changes in facial appearance by stopping whatever was occupying her at the moment and looking fixedly at the altered countenance. Sometimes she would stretch her hand towards it and insert a finger in the mouth—naturally the most mobile part of the face. She could also be induced to protrude her lips preparatory to kissing at the presence of protruded lips before her. Reactions of this sort suggest that facial expressions themselves soon became a focal point in the environment of the subjects.

As a further indication of an elementary sort of social perception, one may turn to the peculiar change in Gua's behavior which amounted to a strutting or showing off the minute she confronted Donald. This was a common occurrence for several weeks after she had first met the child. She would become more active, would bravely let go of the experimenter, and might even wander a short distance away from him. She was then likely to demonstrate her prowess by hanging with one arm from some convenient article of furniture while Donald acted the part of the appreciative audience. At such times she was noticeably less dependent and less afraid to be by herself, she would attend chiefly to the child, and often seemed almost to swagger as she went past him. Such *exhibitionism* before the human subject soon passed, so that before long the most obvious result of his presence upon her seemed to be simply to stimulate play. On later occasions Gua's tendency to perform before sympathetic audiences with which she was well acquainted was remarked by persons other than the experimenters. In this respect she was somewhat more advanced than the child, who did not begin to display behavior which could be regarded as analogous until he reached the age of 16½ months.

Chapter VIII

EMOTIONAL BEHAVIOR

AS THERE is no real distinction between cooperative play and other forms of social activity, so also is the line very thin between social and emotional behavior. Indeed, we were led into the topic of affection in the preceding chapter although this is certainly a phase of emotional activity and is usually discussed as such. Emotional behavior, in common with nearly all other behavior, is so basically social that there are strong grounds for the oft repeated statement, "All psychology is social psychology." In this section, however, we shall confine ourselves for the most part to a survey of those responses of the subjects which can be grouped under such typical rubrics as fearful, angry, jealous, or joyful reactions.

Whether Gua (or any other subhuman organism) ever actually experienced the inner impressions which are commonly called mirth, enjoyment, sorrow, anger, fear, jealousy, disappointment, and so forth, no one, of course, can positively determine. It is not our object or desire to set up either a negative or an affirmative postulate in this regard. The important consideration here is the behavior itself, a series of objectively observable facts about which there can be little dispute. But it is almost impossible to talk or write about the human-like activity of which the chimpanzee was capable without employing many of the common "human" idioms of our language. And this, unfortunately, is all too likely to expose one to the criticism of anthropomorphism, or of "reading into" the responses of the animal more than those responses *per se* indicate. Against such criticism we can only say that it is our aim throughout this report to render a careful and complete description of what actually took place, with only such interpretative additions as are absolutely necessary for a clear understanding of the results and an elucidation of the point of view. Let us proceed first, then, to those activities which appear to us to be related to the so-called *pleasant emotions*.

The earliest occurrence of the rhythmic exhalations corresponding to human laughter was observed in Gua at the age of about 8 months, while Donald already possessed a full-fledged laughing response considerably before the research was begun. For some time after its first appearance, Gua's "laughter" was distinctly unvocalized and was of the general nature of a series of rapid pants except that the inhaling half of the panting cycle was absent. The only adequate stimulus for this response seemed at the start to be a tickling of the sensitive zones. It was thus a question whether the chimpanzee ever made use of such a reaction in any situation in which actual physical contact was not essential. If this proved to be the case, the reaction could be said to bear only a rudimentary relation to human laughter and might better be described not as laughter at all, but rather as a mechanical reflex response to tactual stimulation.

That such an interpretation would not adequately account for the facts became apparent by the eleventh month of the ape's life. At that time she began now and then to vocalize her exhalations in sounds which were not unlike the guttural laugh or chuckle of a man. Soon she began to laugh in this overt manner *in situations in which no "contact" tickle stimulation was present*. Specifically, these were of three sorts.

The first were situations in which she was spun or whirled. One of her arms would be held by the observer who would then revolve upon his heel so that Gua moved in a forward direction around him while centrifugal force carried her outward in a wide circle. She would draw up her feet, stretch her free arm out radially to catch the breeze and often she would laugh almost without stopping as long as the rotation continued. In such cases there was obvious stimulation of the labyrinth—one of the surest laugh producers in children two or three times the age of the ape.

The second of these situations involved threats of tickling without its actual accomplishment, as when one would thrust his finger towards the belly of the ape and make appropriate "tickle" sounds. At times, in fact, she was so responsive in this way that it was difficult to place a stethoscope upon her chest for the purpose of obtaining her weekly pulse record. She would not only laugh at the contact of the instrument, but even when we simply moved it towards her. Obviously such instances were of a more purely psychological nature than those of the first type. After Gua's thirteenth month they became the commonest stimuli which could be employed, aside from the actual tickling, for inducing laughter.

The third of the laughing situations were cases of spontaneous play between the two subjects in which no interfering experimenter took the slightest part. Laughter under these circumstances was noted but rarely, and only when Gua was 14 months and older. In a typical example she is chased by Donald around a large wicker chair. The boy himself, as he trots after her, is laughing continuously and presently the ape as well begins a series of short vocalized chuckles. It is hard to believe that such a response from either subject can result from the stimulation of any particular sense organ. Certainly the turns about the chair are much too slow for a special labyrinthine effect. It appears, indeed, as if the childlike excitement of the chase is producing such effects. In our opinion, this behavior *suggests* that the chimpanzee can appreciate "good fun" as well as the human infant, and that under proper conditions, it can express its appreciation in an analogous manner. If such observations have never been previously reported, it may well be that caged chimpanzees, like caged men, are unfavorably situated for the production of spontaneous laughter. If this response, on the other hand, besides being partly reflex, is also modifiable through learning, it is possible that other observed specimens have never been afforded the same opportunity of developing it which Gua possessed.

That the little animal also behaved as if she was capable of a feeling of relief was evidenced by the audible sighs she would emit at the end of some difficult or trying situation. When finally picked up from the floor or from her high chair after she had been reaching her arms towards the experimenter and crying to be taken up, she would frequently produce such exhalations. She would also heave these sighs when permitted to leave the toilet or the nursery chair following an unusually long trial. And their occurrence when she clambered into our arms upon our return after an absence of several hours was very common. Occasionally they were noted even at as young an age as 8 months, although they were observed much more frequently as time went on.

Probably the best examples of the production of the sigh of relief appeared during the later months when Gua was punished, *or often simply scolded*, for biting the wall, making an evacuation error, or committing some similar *faux pas*. She would thereupon utter "oo-oo" cries and try to run to our arms. The most effective turn which could be given the punishment at that instant was for us to push her away or hold her at arm's length. This treatment would invariably precipitate more severe outbursts of wailing and screaming, which would only subside when we signaled our willingness to receive her. The vocalization would then change to a higher pitch and a very rapid rhythm of "oo-ooing" and she would at the same time rush towards us with arms outstretched. She would not only cling to us but would pull herself upward to our shoulders—at all odds getting her face somewhere near our own. The next reaction was the kiss of reconciliation. If we acquiesced and responded to her invitation in this respect she would then heave her great sigh, audible a meter or more away.

The act of kissing for Gua was originally, no doubt, an exploratory response and was well developed when she first came into the human surroundings. Probably it became in part mimetic as well and certainly it was not discouraged by the experimenters. It began soon to possess not only an affectionate significance, but seemed in addition to serve, as in the example just given, for a symbol of "forgiveness." She would kiss and offer her lips in recompense for small errors many times a day. Her frequent and effective use of this reaction leaves little doubt, in our judgment, as to her actual understanding of it. The only adequate interpretation which these observers can conscientiously make is to say that she seemed disturbed over having lost favor and sought in this manner to compensate for her deficiency. Her reactions would indicate a strong impulse to set matters aright or to "be forgiven" and her screaming and travail with accompanying attempts to come to us would continue until she had succeeded. Thereafter she could be put down again and would play, but unless the ritual had been satisfactorily completed she would not be quiet or turn away until it had, or until some other climax had superseded it. Her behavior in this regard is all the more remarkable in view of the fact that the spontaneous use of affectionate gestures does not usually begin to appear in the human infant until about the eighteenth month. Although Donald had acquired some elementary affectionate responses shortly before he reached this age, he possessed no reaction as expressive or as meaningful as the kisses of the ape for many months after the termination of the research.

Nor did the child display behavior corresponding to the chimpanzee's sighs of relief. Unless we assume that his cessation of crying when he was picked up, a characteristic which Gua also possessed, is significant in this respect, there is nothing in his activity which is similar to hers.

Among the so-called *unpleasant emotions*, fear, or at least the objective activity of fear behavior, proved for the ape to be by far the most important and of the most frequent occurrence. Probably the commonest of her fear reactions consisted of running from the fear-inducing stimulus (often screaming at the same time) and of rushing to the experimenter for protection. This is very similar to the boy's avoidance of a fearful object, to his clinging to the adults when carried close to it, and to his crying or whimpering. Although these about complete the category of responses in the human subject which could be taken to mean, "He is afraid," the ape was by no means as limited in her fear reactions. As we have seen, emotional urination and defecation were common when she was seriously affected. Moreover, she would bite if cornered or trapped by something strange or fearsome, as by an aggressive dog or an undesirable object suddenly thrown at her, from which it seemed she could not at once escape. Her hair would bristle or stand on end in cases of extreme fear, and her legs or even her entire body would tremble on some occasions. But in view of the fact that the trembling which was observed invariably appeared during her early contacts with water, there is a legitimate question whether it was part of the general fear response or outright shivering (conditioned or otherwise) from coldness. Probably one of the most distinctive features of the emotional behavior of the chimpanzee is the tantrum, from which Gua was in no sense immune. By most observers of these animals such reactions are described as "temper tantrums" and are often interpreted as explosive paroxysms of rage. As a result of our close contact with Gua, however, we feel that in her case it would be more accurate to call them "fear tantrums," since the situations suggestive of anger in which they occurred were relatively rare. By far the most frequent occasion for the appearance of the tantrum was when she was left alone or when conditions were such that it was momentarily impossible for her to get into the protecting arms of one of the experimenters. Of course an occasional tantrum would occur when she was whipped or scolded, but tantrums of this variety were usually of a milder sort and even these were more suggestive of the fear or pain of failure than of the bitter resentment of anger. The situation preceding the sigh of relief which has already been described may be considered a typical example.

In the more violent type of tantrum, such as that which resulted when we ran away faster than Gua could follow, she seemed to become "blind with fear" and would utter a series of shrill vibrant screams which could sometimes be heard for a great distance. These would contain, as they progressed, more and more of the guttural element, until finally the windpipe would close entirely from a glottal cramp. During the screaming she would run without definite direction and with decreasing acceleration. Occasionally she would bump headlong into bushes or other obstacles, which we take as evidence that she did not observe where she was going. As the cries became more guttural and her speed continued to decrease, the arms would be held outward at a progressively greater angle, causing the head gradually to approach the ground. About coincidentally with the glottal cramp she would fall prone to the sand and literally grovel in it, seeming then to be past all control, so that when she got up a moment later, her mouth, nose, and often her eyes would be filled with sand. Needless to say, protruding hair, urination, and defecation always accompanied an outburst of such turbulence. In some cases she would roll upon her back during tantrums of this nature, but since they usually occurred when she was running after us on all fours, this was not likely to be the case.

The principal stimuli for eliciting fear responses during the first few days following Gua's separation from her mother seemed to be (1) "loss of support," that is, her falling from a sitting or standing position, probably because of immature postural reflexes, and (2) being left alone. There were no doubt other situations which would have been effective at this early date, although special additions to the list were discovered only after further acquaintance. When she had become better adapted to her new surroundings the sudden approach of strange persons or objects, or peculiar and sudden lights, sounds, and contacts apparently formed the largest group of fear-inducing stimuli. The suddenness or abruptness of the occurrence of the stimulus seemed to be particularly important in this connection. Hence, as we have previously noted, the sound of a pistol shot and of slamming doors would almost always bring out fear or startle reactions in Gua but less often in Donald. Similarly the noise of strange bells or of low flying airplanes and even the sudden whir of wings from a flock of birds were disturbing influences. Once a loud noise like the firing of a shotgun occurred in the woods about 200 meters from where Gua was playing. She started, made a sharp and audible intake of the breath, and seized the observer's legs at once. The abrupt flashing of excessively bright lights in the eyes of the two subjects usually caused a rapid retreat upon Gua's part and a subsequent avoidance of the light-producing mechanism. There was no corresponding fear reaction to this sort of a startle stimulus in the case of the boy. The use of force in new and strange situations, as when Gua was first introduced to the mysteries of a toothbrush, or when she was held by main strength upon the stadiometer, was also an effec-

175

tive means for producing fear reactions, at the beginning as well as throughout the entire period of research.

Toward another group of stimuli, distinctly not of a forceful or startling nature, the ape displayed a persistent and in some cases a strange aversion. Fire, seen through the open door of a stove, in bonfires, and also in lighted cigarettes and matches, was generally avoided, although with no great show of terror unless she was very close to it. She would approach and examine both unlighted cigarettes and matches and originally she evinced no fear at a lighted match, but would subsequently run from us if we held one. To the best of our knowledge she was never burned by actual flame. A pipe, whether lighted or not, was never an object of fear to her, possibly because the "fire" therein was not usually visible. Donald seemed to show no hesitancy in approaching fire, although he avoided hot objects, as Gua did, once he had been hurt by them.

Perhaps the most unusual and at first glance the most puzzling of Gua's fears was her peculiar terror in the presence of toadstools. This was accidentally discovered during an out-of-doors play session when we plucked a large toadstool, whose top was about 15 centimeters (6 inches) in diameter. The ape, then 11 months old, at once began to cry and to act very oddly indeed, the cause of her behavior being for the moment unknown. It was soon found, however, that if the toadstool was offered to her or if we approached her with it, she would scream and run. If the person holding it would then pursue her she could be chased continuously in this manner, and would scream whenever her pursuer got too close. Defecations were frequent under such circumstances. When she was picked up by someone who secretly held a toadstool, and then shown it, she would either scramble down or bury her face in the arm of the carrier as if to escape the sight of the thing. If she chose to remain in his arms under such conditions she would shrink as far as possible from the object of her fear and cling to her protector with excessive muscular tenseness.

Such behavior was by no means specific to one single plant or to any special variety of toadstool, a fact which was disclosed on later occasions when Gua was led to both small and large growing samples of different kinds. She was found invariably to back away and cry, and refused even to touch the chosen experimenter (unless coercion or trickery was employed) providing he carried specimens of these plants. If he held them as he walked away from her she would follow only at a respectful distance, frequently whimpering as she proceeded.

Here is an interesting and mysterious bit of behavior! Does it not appear that the animal possesses an instinctive fear of fungi of this sort, which protects her from eating the poisonous varieties? There is not the vaguest possibility, it seems to us, that during the first $7\frac{1}{2}$ months of her life Gua can have *learned* to be afraid of such things, if she has ever previously so much as seen one. There has, furthermore, been no secret opportunity to acquire a specialized fear of this sort during her life with humans, since she has been under observation for practically every waking moment. That such a fear is peculiar to the chimpanzee subject alone is demonstrated when Donald is offered the toadstools under like conditions. He immediately grasps and manipulates them as he does any new object.

Seeking to discover whether the animal's reactions to these plants can be based upon scent, we wrap some toadstools loosely in a paper. The ape, who has not witnessed the procedure of wrapping, is then offered the package. She accepts it without the slightest show of diffidence, and even starts to chew part of the paper. But when the package is unwrapped before her, she backs away apprehensively and will thereafter have none of the paper or its contents. Apparently she is stimulated only visually by the toadstools.

Thirteen chimpanzees at the Experiment Station are thereupon tested to find out if this is a general reaction common to the species. Three of the subjects are mature males, six mature females, two are adolescent females, and two are "children" whose ages are about three years. The method is to coax the subject to the wire of his cage, then suddenly to produce a toadstool from behind one's back and offer it to him. As control stimuli, stones, a handful of hay, a short stick, and pine cones are used. In only four of the cases do the animals make avoiding responses to the toadstools which they do not make to the other objects as well. Two of those which indicate a special fear of the toadstools are adult females and the other two are the three-year-old youngsters. The aversion to toadstools is hence by no means a reaction which is characteristic of the chimpanzee at large.

Our interpretation of the whole matter would then be as follows: The chimpanzee is in general wary of *the strange* and *the unknown* either (1) natively or (2) because of learning to be so from the earliest influences it gets from its surroundings or from its mother. Toadstools serve as objects sufficiently peculiar to be avoided by some of the animals. Probably the reaction to any other objects equally queer or strange in these animals' experience would be the same. In order to account for their behavior it is not necessary, therefore, to postulate responses specific to the toadstool itself. The two important facts which support this interpretation are the more violent reactions of the infants than of the adults, and the tendency of many of the subjects to be less seriously affected on later presentations. But it is to be noted in this connection that Gua herself avoids both plucked and growing toadstools $2\frac{1}{2}$ months after her original fright—or as long as any specimens can be found in the woods. It is quite likely that her reactions would have remained essentially the same throughout the entire period of the research.

There are further examples in Gua's subsequent history which suggest that the toadstool fear is simply a special case of the more general fear of unknown objects. For instance when we appear attired in a pair of blue trousers which the ape has never seen before, she avoids us meticulously, and cries as she does so. It then develops that she will come to us if we stoop over so she can grasp us above the waistline, but that she will not touch the offending garments at all. She will even run away if we walk towards her, and when the trousers have been later removed and are offered or thrown towards her, she dashes from them with a scream.

At 13½ months upon encountering an old pair of brown leather gloves she displays reactions of a similar nature. Her fear in this case is ultimately turned to good use by the simple expedient of placing the gloves on top of a bureau where Gua occasionally climbs to examine her reflection in a mirror. The minute her eyes come above the level of the bureau top she spies the gloves and gets down in haste. Identical avoidance is exhibited at the age of 15 months to the remnants of a flat and rusty tin can which she discovers during the course of her outdoor play. In view of such responses it now seems possible that Gua's strong aversion for the odors employed in the *smell tests* (Chapter V) may have arisen from the very strangeness of these peculiar and unknown stimuli.

It is difficult to reconcile behavior of this sort with the ape's obvious preference for new toys. Of course the visual appearance of the toys was for the most part markedly different from that of the objects avoided since brightly colored and shiny playthings were generally preferred. The circumstances under which the new object was originally presented may also have been influential in determining the later reactions to it. In many cases it is to be noted that the new toys were handled by Donald in Gua's presence, while the offending stimuli, after their character had been determined, were often unfortunately thrust forward in a manner which in itself may have appeared threatening. And yet, one can hardly overlook the fact that the child made no avoiding reactions to the same objects thrust forward in the same manner. Nor can one ignore the fact that there were certain *new* playthings which the ape shunned for several months, among which have already been mentioned the rubber doll and a teething ring. No doubt her avoidance of some objects and the acceptance of others depended in part upon the way in which the balance happened to swing at the start. Subsequent developments in many cases may then have added momentum to the initial chance direction which the reactions had already taken.

For the most part the child possessed few, if any, similar aversions at least of as great a magnitude and severity as those of Gua. He did, however, appear strangely frightened by the sight and sound of persons plunging or diving into deep water, while this behavior seemed to leave the chimpanzee quite unaffected.

It has frequently been supposed in this connection that these apes are incurably afraid of water and will shun large bodies of it; yet there was no clear evidence of such an attitude in Gua. In the beginning, it is true, she showed but little liking for her bath and if her head went under the stream of the faucet or if she was momentarily submerged, she appeared terrified. But her adaptation to the new medium was nearly as rapid as it was to other features of her environment, so that before long she would enter the heavy torrent of a shower bath if simply called by the experimenter. When first she was carried into a large swimming pool she seemed slightly disturbed and it appeared to us as if she tried to get down from the shoulders of her supporter and walk upon the surface of the water. After a few moments in this situation she was more at ease and would slap her hand upon the water and play with it somewhat like a human baby.

Again, when introduced to a small circular pool about two meters (6 feet) in diameter and twenty centimeters (8 inches) deep, she drank a great deal of the water and tried to grasp a small stream which trickled into the pool as one would seize a stick. At the age of 10 months she would sit and play in this same body of water—although not quite as enthusiastically as the child. She would furthermore stand or walk in the water without contact with anyone else, and on one or two occasions she was induced, after some wailing, to enter the pool herself and move through it to the opposite side where the experimenter was calling her.

Her adjustment in this respect, even though incomplete, seems to us to argue against the presence of a fixed or native fear of sizable bodies of water on the part of the chimpanzee. In our opinion Gua's general reactions were probably determined in part by her gradual introduction to the new medium. A more violent procedure such as throwing her bodily into water beyond her depth would quite possibly have conditioned her against it at once. It seems reasonable to suppose, nevertheless, that an animal like the chimpanzee can never become an adept swimmer because of its muscular and bodily solidity, which probably give it a higher specific gravity than that of the average man. These animals should consequently find it more difficult to remain on top of the water than humans do, and many specimens in their natural state may soon learn as a result to stay away from water of any depth.

Both subjects displayed what might be called *anxious behavior*, if obvious preparations were being made by the grown-ups to leave the house. It was noticeable that fretting and crying under such conditions were exhibited by Gua only when the person of her preference was arranging to go. The child, on the other hand, was more inclined to whimper when his mother got ready, although also occasionally upon similar activity on the part of the other experimenter.

While the ape was more agile than the child, she was at the same time more *cautious* and seemed to avoid objects, even in her climbing, until she had become quite familiar with them.

No doubt the chief stimulus for *angry behavior* is the failure to get what one wants, or an interruption or restraint, either permanent or temporary, in some specific reaction which has already been started. Although Gua, it seemed to us, was not particularly prone to this type of activity, she would occasionally have tantrums which were without question in the nature of angry responses. In the early days, before her attachment for her human friends had thoroughly crystallized, there was noticeable a certain *negativism* which was possibly a precursor to later angry behavior. Thus she occasionally refused to accept new playthings which were given her even though for the most part she showed no fear or avoidance of them unless she, so to speak, "found" these herself. Her later aversion for new foods may be considered as another example of this trait.

Among those responses which were more definitely suggestive of anger, or at least of *irritation* or *impatience*, was her pounding or slapping with one or both hands upon the tray of her high chair or the tray of her nursery chair. In such cases she was literally restrained by not being permitted to leave the chairs. The forceful throwing of one object after another to the floor as these were placed successively upon the high-chair tray, we took as evidence of her refusal to accept conciliatory advances on our part. The threatening bark of resentment was occasionally made to her lesser friends when she was prohibited by them from eating stolen foods, from pilfering, or from indulging in some similar unethical satisfaction of her appetites. A sort of nervous scratching which seemed to occur chiefly in situations likely to be unpleasant or irritating was also a common sort of emotional response. When she was required to remain for some time before photographic paraphernalia it seemed often that she could not contain herself, and she would "oo-oo" and begin to scratch herself with one or both hands either upon her head or any part of her body. In a more violent outbreak which ultimately led to a tantrum, we have seen her beat her head against the sides of her crib, while she cried to get out. Once she was observed to place her closed fist in her mouth and bite her knuckles hard enough to break the skin! But reactions of this sort were almost never observed after the first few weeks of her presence in the human home.

The same, we think, can be said in general of the temper tantrums themselves. Of course there were tantrums a-plenty throughout the entire nine months, but as this report has already revealed, it seemed to us that only rarely could such outbursts be accurately interpreted as true "temper" tantrums. The problems facing the experimenter in such situations should be apparent from the foregoing descriptions of emotional reactions. So little is positively known in this complex and bewildering field that the direct observer of emotional activity is in constant danger of going beyond his facts. The question of exactly what kind of emotional behavior is being witnessed resolves itself very largely into a matter of interpretation, in which the stimulus situation itself plays all too important a part. We are too likely to define the behavior in terms of the stimulus, and to say that the organism behaves angrily because we have done something to it which we think should make it behave so. Or we may say it behaves fearfully or jealously simply because we notice its activities change when it is in *what appear to us* to be fearful or jealous situations.

The interpretation of angry behavior on the part of the child was especially difficult since it was almost impossible to say when he was crying bitterly whether this was from fear, pain, anger, or from some other cause. Only on one occasion was there anything resembling a true temper tantrum in Donald's behavior. In this instance at the age of 11 months he stiffened his back and screamed. Whether such a reaction could have been in part imitative of Gua's frequent outbreaks it is difficult to say, although it never recurred thereafter.

Mild anger or perhaps *disappointment* was suggested in the human by the time he had reached 14 months, by his suddenly sitting down upon the floor, leaning forward upon his hands, and crying in a low-pitched voice. The specific instances in which this was noted were when it seemed that he was not to be permitted to go riding in the perambulator or when his food was being prepared but through some delay he was not immediately given it. When Donald was taken by his mother in the perambulator but Gua on the other hand was left behind, the ape in her turn would also indicate disturbance or disappointment, but hardly anger. During the later months when she had become more accustomed to being away from her best friend she would run to the door and try to open it, then climb to a window and stare after the retreating carriage while she whined pleadingly. In view of her almost insatiable desire to ride and her tendency to get into the perambulator and wait whenever any suggestion of going out had been made, there can be little doubt that she was definitely affected by the failure to be taken, even though the chosen experimenter remained at home beside her.

Jealous behavior was more frequent in Gua than in Donald, although it never formed a very important part of the emotional activity of either subject. During the early months he laughed when one of the adults played with Gua, and seemed to have no necessary impulse to participate of his own accord. Later it was noticeable that he would more often go towards the scene of activity, and that sometimes when Gua put her hands upon his walker or climbed upon his high chair, he would push her away. At the start as well he permitted her to take things from him without objecting. By the time the child was 16 months of age they seemed each to want the same toys and would frequently tussle over a single play object like two squabbling children.

As early as her eighth month Gua, for her part, would push Donald's hands from her walker when he reached out and grasped it, and she seemed soon thereafter to prefer the boy's walker to her own. She appeared similarly on many occasions to select the things with which he was playing or had previously played in preference to other toys. When Donald was spoken to or attended by others, Gua always rushed to the spot, and actively edged her way into the proceedings. If this could not be done by pushing herself between Donald and the person attending him, she would slap the legs of the latter, or even pull at Donald's clothing. Sometimes there was further evidence of jealous behavior when one of her grown-up friends displayed affectionate behavior to another without similarly noticing Gua at the same time. In such instances she would occasionally attack the recipient of the embraces with slaps and rarely with her teeth. And yet, in spite of such examples, Gua's jealousy was never very conspicuous or troublesome. Providing the two subjects were treated as any two children near the same age are treated, that is, providing they were shown the same attention, and petted and talked to together, there was nothing striking or unusual in Gua's activity which would stamp her as radically different from a child in such situations. Her anger was never of an aggressive sort, nor did her jealousy appear to be so either, excepting in the affectionate situations mentioned.

Bashfulness or embarrassment, first appearing in the boy at the age of about 15 months when he would grin and look sheepish if asked to perform in some way before strangers, found no recognizable counterpart in the ape.

With reference now to Gua's emotional background, to her attitude, or to her disposition and temperament, it may be said that almost from the start she seemed willing and ready to do whatever was required of her. Aside from her early negativism regarding new toys, her dislike of new foods, and her uncontrollable fears, there was no evidence of opposition or deliberate resistance to any part of the training. She seemed to try to do whatever was wanted if it was clear she understood, as evidenced by her responsiveness to vocal commands, shaking hands with strangers, and her general willingness to cooperate. She was sometimes mauled and even hurt during the various procedures and still she offered no opposition. One would say in everyday language that she was very good-natured.

There can be little doubt in this connection that her ruling emotion was fear. In those rare instances when she did object to the treatment accorded her it seemed usually to be because she was afraid. She resented handling by strangers and on occasion she might bark threateningly at them, or bite. But in our opinion there is a strong possibility that this behavior also was based ultimately upon fear. That is, she became terrified and bit defensively. There was little of the vicious or malicious about her to those who knew her well. She was usually amenable enough to her best friends and seldom made anything stronger than sly or mischievous attempts to resist them.

According to our observations, she possessed fewer inhibitory responses than the human subject. She was thus a creature of more violent appetites and emotions, which swayed her this way and that, seemingly without consideration of the consequences. Examples are her intense and almost unquenchable thirst; her frantic

hunger when she had missed a meal or two, which would
often lead her to gulp her food with such rapidity that
much of it would spill; her inability to restrain bladder
and bowel evacuations in disturbing situations, and
the consequent emotional significance of these responses; and her intense affection for those who cared
for her, at times amounting to an uncontrollable passion
which nothing but physical contact, including embrac-
ing and kissing, would satisfy. She seemed to follow her
ruling impulses with little permanent regard for re-
straining circumstances. In this respect she was coarser
than the child and more elemental in her motives.

Chapter IX

LEARNING

IT IS WELL-KNOWN that the abilities of the chimpanzee for acquiring manlike methods of reacting are remarkable. Nearly everyone, no doubt, has seen animals in either theatrical or cinema performances who could eat like humans, dress and undress themselves, ride bicycles, skate on roller skates, smoke cigarettes, or perform similar astonishing feats. The significant fact about this kind of behavior is that probably with few exceptions such acts are learned as stunts or tricks and are performed only at stated intervals in response to special stimuli, signals, or cues which are given by a trainer. For the most part, then, they cannot be considered incidental acquisitions which develop naturally from the everyday surroundings of the theatrical chimpanzee, for these animals of necessity spend a good portion of their lives in cages, in crates, or at the end of a leash or chain.

But in the present research, it will be remembered, we set an inflexible requirement which opposes in many basic respects the methods employed with "trained animals." Neither of our subjects was to be systematically drilled in any behavior which is learned *incidentally* in the normal course of the upbringing of a civilized human. Of course there were certain specific experiments set, in which the rates of learning of the two were compared, but organized trial-by-trial training in the development of common childlike responses was pursued to no greater extent than it is with any human baby. We wished to find out under these general and, if you will, lax conditions how much the subjects *with-*

out undue pressure or specialized methods would pick up by themselves from their surroundings and, if possible, the manner in which they would pick it up. There were, to be sure, a few minor variations in the treatment accorded Gua and Donald which were demanded by their own differences in structure and behavior. It was furthermore necessary in introducing the ape to the human environment to deal with her as best we could to hasten her adaptation to it. Although some may choose to regard these things as serious infractions of the conditions of the investigation, they involved no regularized or systematized training, as the following survey will show.

Since Gua had never previously been out of sight or call of a larger protecting organism it was natural that our initial contacts should be made through her need for assistance and care. From the moment of her separation, therefore, her wants were satisfied by the male experimenter, who thus substituted, so to speak, for her mother. The little animal seemed at times to have considerable difficulty in accepting her new guardian. At the start his visual appearance must have served as a disturbing stimulus, for she would rest quietly in his arms only when her back was facing in his direction. She was inclined, as well, to resist many initial advances with bites. But fortunately these were never very damaging and in a few days had become so mild that they appeared to be in the nature of exploratory or feeling responses.

She was obviously comforted by the swaying motion of the body when she was carried. In fact, it seems probable that her strong attachment for this experimenter—certainly a necessary step in her "taming"—was considerably advanced by many preliminary hours of carrying. In a surprisingly short time she had so completely transferred her fixation from her mother to the human adult that if she lost sight of him for a moment she became greatly upset. It was a common occurrence during this early period for her to start walking away and, since her back was then towards the experimenter, to "lose" him entirely. She would thereupon walk faster, become terrified, and scream. Sometimes in such instances the observer was only a few steps away, but the din which she herself set up apparently prevented her hearing his voice.

Soon she would permit manipulation of her hands and limbs and would sit on the shoulders of her new acquaintance holding tightly to his hair. By the third day she frequently fell asleep in his lap and would pull at his clothing to be taken up when she was tired. The progress from then onward was rapid. Diapers were initially put on while she was under the soothing influence of the observer's body movements. A bib in the same manner. She was similarly placed in her high chair or her nursery chair only when actually supported by human arms. All such advances were gentle and gradual and never at the start was she forced or whipped. If Gua insisted on having her own way, she had it, but eventually by some other method or after a suitable delay, the desired end was usually achieved. One procedure which was found to be particularly effective might be called the sleeping technique. This consisted in placing the animal in the desired situation while she was in a sound sleep. Difficult ends were in some instances attained by this method, which eliminated the possibility of emotional outbreaks or of biting. She was so adapted to many of the unwelcome features of the new environment. The use of this procedure probably compensated to some extent for the failure to begin Gua's human training at a younger age.

By the end of the first week she was continuously dressed in diapers and shoes, and on one or two occasions she had been clothed in a romper suit as well. Within the same period she began to sleep in her crib (although at first without a full equipment of bedding), and she was regularly fed from a spoon and a cup in her high chair. By the end of the second week she permitted the cutting of her finger nails and before the fourth was over she was daily submitting to the application of a toothbrush.

She had been in human surroundings about a month and a half when she originally mastered the operation of a swinging door in the dining room of her new home. Not long after this initial development she would stand up and push it quite as skillfully as a human adult. The boy did not learn to open the same door until a month after Gua had done so; but he was obviously handicapped in this performance because of his walker.

The chimpanzee released a door latch by turning the door knob at the age of 10 months. Her first success in such a task was accidental, however, since she was hanging by one hand from the knob at the time so that the torque-like pull of her weight on one side of the handle caused it to turn. Just when accidental door opening, which thereafter became quite common because of her increasing tendency to hang upon door knobs, gave way to deliberate door opening, it would be difficult to say. For some months Gua was more likely to cry, or to lie down on the floor and look beneath a door, to put her fingers under it, or to slap it, than she was to manipulate the knob itself. The child never succeeded throughout the entire nine months in releasing a single door latch, possibly because of the shortness of his reach. He would, nevertheless, touch the knobs with his fingers and rattle them almost whenever he approached one.

By the time the ape had attained the age of $13\frac{1}{2}$ months, she was observed to unlatch the front door of the house in a manner which appeared anything but accidental. This she accomplished by climbing upon a small piece of furniture beside it, reaching from the furniture to the knob with her right hand, and turning the knob successively to the right and to the left by extending and flexing her arm. As soon as the latch was released she pulled the door open at once. Tests made after these observations by shutting her in a room by herself disclosed that she could then open almost any door in a moment and wasted no time in attacking the knob. On one occasion some time later, when a door was locked, she hung from the knob with both hands, raised her feet to a level with her hips, and began jumping against the door as if to force it open in this manner.

The unhooking of the window screens which were hinged at the top and held by a single hook at the bottom she performed at the age of 10½ months. There were two methods she employed upon the hooks, involving respectively the use of her teeth and of her index finger. Every so often she would fall about 2 meters to the ground outside the house from the sills of windows whose screens she had loosened. Screen doors she first unfastened at the age of 11 months and after that hooks of any sort seemed easy for her to manipulate. She would subsequently open from the outside an unhooked screen door, whose handle was too high for her to reach, by inserting her finger nails in the crack between the door and its frame and pulling the screen towards her. On several occasions Donald was observed similarly to put his fingers in the cracks of doors and of screens, but his reactions were never productive of the same results which Gua achieved. The unhooking of screen doors was also a task which was beyond him, although toward the end he succeeded in unfastening certain of the window screens.

Instances of typical psychological "conditioning" were observed in both subjects, at relatively early ages. The child developed such a response to a muscular or kinesthetic stimulus when 11½ months old. The response grew out of his habit of dropping objects over the side of his high chair and blinking or winking from the noise they produced upon hitting the floor. When the conditioning was complete, the winking reaction occurred *before the actual sound was made*. The infant winked, in other words, before the object he dropped had struck. In such instances the movement of the hand in releasing the spoon apparently functioned as a substitute for the sound in eliciting the lid reaction. Probably the child's self-training in this sort of a conditioned response had been in progress in the neighborhood of two months when it was initially observed. The total number of trials he had made must therefore have ranged somewhere between 50 and 100.

A similar case, first noted in the ape at the age of 10 months, is related to the procedure of brushing her teeth. The prickliness of the bristles of the toothbrush was apparently not pleasant and would cause her to draw back the lips from the teeth and the gums. Conditioning eventually developed to the mere sight of the brush, which would then call out the reaction of opening the lips even before the bristles had come in contact with them. Since the daily brushing of the teeth had been in progress at that time for about nine weeks, the number of repetitions of the stimulation before the response was first observed was probably somewhere near 60. The laughing reaction of both subjects at the threat of tickling is another example of the early conditioning of each.

That Gua had also formed a connection between electric-light switches and the illumination of the electric bulbs themselves became apparent when she was about a year old. The occasion for this observation was when one of the experimenters placed his hand upon a switch but for some reason did not immediately operate it. The chimpanzee was seen to follow with her gaze the movement of the hand towards the switch and then after a moment to look towards the light fixture, even though it was not yet illuminated. Since there was no direct stimulus which could have caused her

to look upward, the entire response must unquestionably have been a result of previous learning.

Within two months after this incident the operation
of light switches of the toggle or throw type came to
be one of Gua's regular accomplishments. The response,
which she picked up without instruction or assistance,
consisted in hooking the index finger over the movable
part of the switch and pulling it downward. Imitation
was no doubt important in her acquisition of this reaction, as it was for the child, who mastered the same
operation a day or two after Gua had done so. Yet
neither could extinguish the light by pushing the
switch upward for more than a month, when Gua alone
achieved this result. Donald tried frequently, but he
was never successful, probably because his hands and
fingers were not sufficiently sturdy.

The child proved, on the other hand, to be much
superior to the chimpanzee at the game of pat-a-cake,
for Gua was here a hopeless failure. Toward the last
she would slap the extended hands of one of the adults
when told to pat-a-cake but she never learned to respond with typical handclapping. Her inability to
acquire such a simple reaction is all the more surprising
in view of the fact that she was given almost daily
opportunity for such play for several months, while
the human infant was not so persistently encouraged.

Miscellaneous observations of this sort are obviously
conflicting with regard to the relative learning ability
of the two subjects, so that we must turn to more precise experimental techniques in order to throw light
on this important comparative problem. In this connection it is to be noted that probably the most exact
and certainly the most persistent training through
which the average human baby is conducted is in learning to control the bladder and bowels. Such training is
begun usually at the age of less than a year and may
continue as long as three or four years. If properly

managed it is an invariable, methodical, day-and-night procedure which few subsequent endeavors in the life-time of the individual can equal in either regularity or extensiveness. Here, then, should be an excellent field in which to compare the learning abilities of the two organisms, without modifying their ordinary childlike surroundings or conducting them through unusual or irregular processes of training.

The method which we at first planned to employ was to place the subjects upon their respective nursery chairs (or on the toilet) only at prearranged times. These were to be upon awakening in the morning or from any naps taken during the day, after each meal, before going to bed, and approximately every 45 minutes to an hour in between. It was soon decided, however, to allow the proposed intervals to be modified by the demands of the subjects themselves. If, for example, the subject should void 35 minutes after the previous trial, the nursery-chair sittings which followed would be spaced a few minutes less than this or at about 30 minutes apart. The actual frequency of the responses hence to some extent governed the spacing of the attempts. This method had the effect of correct-ing for physiological changes within the subjects themselves so as to make the interval used correspond to the ability of the organism, even though this ability might vary from time to time.

While the subject was seated upon the nursery chair, the words "chair-chair" were repeated at approximately half-minute intervals, until a response was made. If there was no success within 10 minutes, the subject was removed and the trial recorded as a "failure." Records were kept to the nearest half minute of the time required for each response, as well as of the "errors" or evacuations made by the subjects when they were not upon their respective nursery chairs. Throughout the nine-months period of training in both bladder and bowel control, nearly 6,000 responses of the ape were tabulated, of which a little over 1,000 were errors. The child, in his turn, reacted more than 4,700 times, of which about 750 were errors.

Each subject was praised verbally by being told he was "a good boy (or girl)" following a success. Punishment in the form of confinement upon the nursery

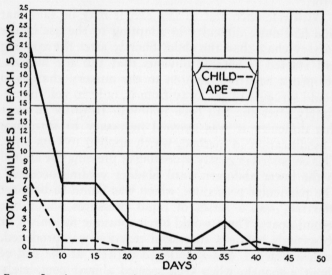

Fig. 9.—Learning curves covering the first 50 days of the bladder training. A "failure" in this case consists of the inability to make a voiding reaction within the arbitrary limit of 10 minutes which constitutes a trial. It will be noted that the child has fewer failures than the ape throughout, and that he adapts to the situation more rapidly than she.

chair (up to the limit of 10 minutes) also served as an incentive to perform the required reaction and so to win release. Each was scolded furthermore when he made an error, and was told he was "a bad boy (or girl)." The training was begun within the first few days or, to be precise, when Gua was exactly 7½ and Donald exactly 10 months old.

It should be noted at this point that there are three distinct steps into which the results of evacuation training of this sort can be divided. The first is the positive learning of the use to which the nursery chair (or toilet) should be put. The second may be called a negative learning of withholding or inhibiting the reaction until the proper time and place have arrived. The third is the definite announcing of the need by telling others about it within ample time to avoid an error.

With reference first to *step one*, it may be said that Gua had more difficulty in adapting to the use of the nursery chair than the child. Shortly after the training had started it became obvious that the ape had developed a negative reaction to the nursery chair, and would struggle to get away from it, only to void immediately after she had been removed. In order to meet this difficulty it was deemed necessary to introduce a modification in method, which applied to Gua only. This consisted in gently squeezing or pressing the animal in the lower abdomen until bladder voiding occurred. The particular procedure, which was found to be most effective, was a series of rapid pressures about one second apart. These would often continue for only 5 or 10 seconds before a successful reaction was produced. Such a practice was abandoned entirely at the end of about a month, when Gua seemed almost completely to have overcome her negativism.

But her progress was noticeably slower than Donald's, even in spite of this assistance. Thus after 15 days the boy almost never failed to respond when placed upon the nursery chair, while Gua continued to make failures up to approximately the thirty-fifth day (see Fig. 9). The average time required for the subjects to respond once they had been placed upon the chair was, during the first two weeks, a little over 2 minutes for the child and a little over 5 minutes for the ape. The difference here is partly to be accounted for by the fact that the animal's average response times for this period include 35 failures (that is, 35 periods of 10 minutes each). The boy on the other hand had only about one-fourth as many failures within the same interval. If we eliminate the failures from the computations, it appears that Donald responded on the average during the *first* two weeks in 1.61 minutes, and Gua in 3.35 minutes. In the *last* two weeks the response times of each were very close to zero.

Both subjects had practically mastered step one, that is, they had learned well the use of the nursery chair within six weeks, so that little attention was given to this phase of the learning after that time. At the end of this period Gua would usually void her bladder whenever she was told. On some occasions, in fact, she seemed to be so impressed with the function of the nursery chair, that she would urinate at the mere sight of it, or when she was in the process of being placed upon it, but before she was fully seated. A glimpse of Donald responding in the same manner, or the words "chair-chair" intended for Donald but overheard by Gua, would often cause her to make errors, sometimes seemingly in spite of her own efforts to the contrary.

The second step, consisting of the development of inhibitions strong enough to postpone the response until the proper moment, is obviously much more difficult than the first step and requires longer and more careful training. The child at the start had had no previous experience whatsoever in this regard. Yet much to our astonishment, it soon became apparent that the ape, even at the age of her removal from her mother, had already made a start towards evacuation control! Her early progress was clearly demonstrated in the first few days of her association with humans. For in spite of her fear of being left alone and in spite of her liking to be carried, she would squirm and wriggle to the ground when she needed to make a bladder or bowel response. She seemed to know that she must get down and go away by herself. Such training must in some way have been imparted by the mother, although the exact method by which it came about is not known. It is possible that the mother held the infant at arm's length when she was very young, and pushed her away as she grew older, during the voidings.

Although Gua started her human evacuation training with an advantage not possessed by the child, she had also some serious disadvantages which far offset this apparent benefit. One of these as we have seen was the emotional character of many of both her urinating and defecating reactions. She would sometimes make several errors a day, all of which were unquestionably of an emotional nature. Another important handicap may be traced to the probably reduced number of sweat glands which she possessed and to her related tendency to drink large quantities of water for the sake of coolness during warm weather. This condition worked doubly against her, since the lack of the sweat glands eliminated a considerable source of water exudation which the child possessed, while her more frequent drinking gave Gua a correspondingly greater intake of water. Each of these causes naturally contributed to a more rapid filling of the bladder than was the case with Donald.

In the hope of assisting the chimpanzee to overcome these special difficulties a further modification in procedure was introduced. This consisted in slapping or whipping her with the bare hand following an error, a method which was employed only very rarely with the child. But regardless of the increased motivation which we sought to develop by such physical punishment, Gua failed to demonstrate any superiority over the boy in the acquisition of voiding inhibitions.

The generally greater propensity of the animal for evacuations is shown by the fact that she urinated on the average from 17 to 31 times a day, while the child's corresponding record ranged from 13 to 23. The ape defecated, moreover, from 4 to 7 times daily, while the human infant reacted similarly usually only once and almost never more than twice in 24 hours.

As is the case with children, Gua's bowel control developed much more rapidly than her bladder control, so that by the end of the fourth week she seldom defecated when away from the nursery chair, except in emotional situations. It is nevertheless to be noted that emotional defecations were at no time entirely eliminated, although emotional bladder voiding seemed eventually to be overcome. The child's progress in bowel training was much less marked than the chimpanzee's, but his errors at the start were also less than hers because of the relative scarcity of his defecations. His possibilities of improvement were consequently more restricted.

Oddly enough, there was no consistent tendency on the part of either subject to decrease the number of daily evacuations as the training progressed. Fluctuations and variations in the number of daily voidings, which were common enough, seemed to depend at least as far as bladder is concerned, upon factors which at first glance may appear irrelevant. Of these, the external temperature was probably the most important, particularly with the ape. Because a high outside temperature increased the amount of water which she drank, it also increased the number of her urinations. And yet, such a relationship did not hold in the case of the child. For even though he might similarly consume more water during warm weather, by far the major part of this was released in the form of perspiration, so that his bladder voidings actually decreased during high temperatures and increased during low.

The time of day also proved to be a significant factor in this regard both for Donald as well as Gua. The urinations were less frequent in the early hours than they were in the later ones. Possibly this condition was related either to increasing fatigue as the day progressed, or to the tendency of the intestines to become full and resulting internal pressure against the bladder itself. It was noticeable in Gua's case, moreover, that

discharges of the bladder were more likely to occur
following violent exercise than during periods of relative
quiet. This again may be related either to the momentary fatigue of the chimpanzee or to the generation of
heat within her body and the consequent need for
expelling as much of this heat as possible by whatever
means. The trials were adjusted to meet such require-

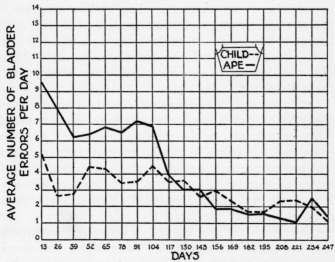

FIG. 10.—The learning of the subjects in the inhibition of bladder voidings is
graphically depicted in these curves. The progress of the training in units of 13 days
is represented along the base line, and the average number of errors per day is shown
on the vertical coordinate. An "error" is a voiding made while the subject is not
upon his nursery chair or on the toilet. During approximately the last half of the
training the subjects are about equal in the number of their daily errors, although
more of these are bed-wetting errors in the case of the child than they are in the
case of the ape.

ments as soon as they were clearly recognized. Allowance
for the diurnal variation, for example, was customarily
made, during Gua's twelfth and Donald's fourteenth
month, by spacing the successive attempts of each subject
about 45 minutes apart till 10 A.M., then 30 minutes
apart till noon, and 20 minutes apart after lunch.

Regarding the actual rate of progress in bladder
training, we see that during the first 13 days, Gua made
an average of nine urination errors daily, while Donald

made a little over five errors *per diem* within the same period. The number of errors made by the ape remained consistently higher than that of the boy till more than 100 days had passed. At that time the performances of the two became practically equivalent, with about four daily errors each. From then onward until the end of the research, although the errors decreased to around two a day, their number at any given period was nearly the same for each of the organisms (see Fig. 10). But it is to be remarked that although the error curves are similar for the last half of the experiment, from 75 to 100 per cent of the errors made by the child within the last 130 days were bed-wetting errors. These occurred during sleep or at the moment of awakening, either in the morning or from daytime naps. Sometimes for a period of fully two weeks the child made no bladder errors whatsoever which were not of this category. The ape, on the other hand, had relatively few errors of the bed-wetting type, and within any specified fortnight there were never more than 26 per cent of her errors which occurred during or immediately after sleep. If we include bed-wetting, therefore, the two are seen to be about on a par for the last part of the experiment, although the ape learned more slowly at the beginning; while, if the sleeping errors are eliminated, the child becomes superior to the ape throughout the entire nine months, in spite of the employment of physical punishment following many of Gua's errors.

It is interesting to note, particularly during the early stages of the training, that if the experimenters went away and left the chimpanzee with someone else for a few hours, the effect of her previous progress seemed largely to be lost for the next day or two. No doubt the shock of the temporary parting, the relatively large number of emotional evacuations which ensued, and the possible inability of the stranger to handle Gua in familiar ways were responsible for such lapses.

We come then to the *third step* in evacuation control
or to the anticipation of the voiding by a sufficient
margin of time to communicate with or "tell" someone
about the impending discharge. The earliest instance
of anything which at all resembled a definite attempt
to indicate his needs occurred in Donald at the age of
about 13 months, when he was observed to fret and
place his hand over the genital region. Within the next
two weeks he also developed a vocalized grunt which
he occasionally used. This was a two-syllabled "unh-
unh" uttered not necessarily *to* any individual nor even
in front of anyone. It seemed rather to be a more or less
haphazard warning, which was thrown out at random
as a signal for what was to follow. At first it occurred
in cases of defecation only and then infrequently in
cases of urination as well. But unfortunately, this initial
progress disappeared entirely about the time the child
began to be proficient in walking. Later, during his
nineteenth month, a second development of these
anticipatory warnings occurred. He would then tell
his elders in about one-third of the cases of impending
bowel action. Yet this was not quite as good a performance as he had given for the space of a few weeks some
five months earlier.

In Gua's behavior there seemed to be a more lucid
picture of the genesis of the anticipatory warning, for
it was clear that she understood the nature of the requirements long before she was able to fulfill them. By
the time she had attained the age of 11½ months, she
would frequently cry, "Oo-oo," if we happened to catch
her while she was urinating. But she seemed quite
unable to arrest the process, even though we might
approach with threatening voice and gesture, and she
would continue to cry as the act was being completed!
At about the same time she began to "tell" us when
she had finished her voiding and was ready to be removed from the nursery chair. She would begin her
announcement by "oo-ooing" very low at first, and if

we paid no attention, by crying more loudly. Not long afterward she would cry the instant she saw we had discovered one of her puddles upon the floor. Often not a sound was necessary on the part of the observer by way of scolding but a mere pointing to the spot would call forth whimperings from Gua. Later she would run to the experimenter "oo-ooing," place her head in his lap, and so "tell" him immediately after she had made an error. It appeared indeed as if she was fully aware of the wrong she had done, but that she was still not entirely able to anticipate it.

In this way she first began to give spontaneous signals *after* the act instead of *before* it. But the presence of any communication, even though in the wrong temporal position, we took to be promising. The first sort of observable behavior which began to precede the evacuation with reasonable regularity put in an appearance at about the age of 11½ months. Curiously enough, this signal was probably of an entirely involuntary sort, for it consisted in an abrupt increase in the frequency of the urinations when a defecation was imminent. It was as though the ape, unable to inhibit both of these activities, had chosen the lesser of two evils. At any rate, her need could usually be correctly predicted by this means.

By the time she reached 13 months she had begun to make use of three more pertinent signals which were employed either separately or in combination. These possessed more the appearance of definite anticipatory responses. The first comprised the holding of the genitals, an act which was accomplished by covering them either from the front or from the back. The tendency to resist internal pressure by applications from without, which is common enough among human children, found its direct counterpart, therefore, in Gua. One or both of her hands, and occasionally even one of the feet might be used in this maneuver. Usually she was walking when she gave such a signal, quite often in the direction of one of the experimenters. If she employed her foot (which was rarely) she would press it against the genital region while she hobbled grotesquely along on her two hands and the remaining foot.

Not infrequently she would cry or "oo-oo" as she approached in this fashion. It was then an easy and natural development to employ the crying as a signal by itself without the accompanying covering of the genital region. She made such obvious progress in this regard that we list the crying next as the second direct means of advance communication which she employed. It could be relied upon in numerous instances. And yet, there were so many stimuli which would elicit the typical chimpanzee "oo-oo" that it was often difficult to detect when this sound served exclusively as an evacuation notice.

Her third early method of announcement was to interrupt all other movement, run at once to the experimenter, grasp his trousers tightly, and look up at him. It seems surprising in this connection that neither of the subjects ever attempted to signal by going to the nursery chair, by pointing to it, or by leading the experimenters in its direction.

There was never any special signal which Gua employed consistently at the expense of all others, although the holding of the *genitalia* seemed to predominate. By the conclusion of the research, the ape had supplemented her three original methods with further additions, such as the slapping of the genitals with the palms of the hands, climbing into the experimenter's lap and looking up at him, refusing to eat when food was offered, and being very restless and continually on the move when held in the arms.

In the last two months, she frequently succeeded in telling us by these various methods in advance of as many as one-half of both the bladder and bowel voidings she would make during a single day, although the general average was closer to one-third or one-fourth of the times. This was clearly superior to the performance of the child, whose less regular anticipatory warnings applied, for the most part, to bowel action only. But unfortunately such figures are spuriously affected by the lack of confidence of the observers in Gua, and they do not as a result indicate the true capacity of the subject. Even after she began to tell us, it was our practice to take her to the chair at stated intervals, providing she did not signal beforehand. One or two attempts to leave her entirely on her own had readily demonstrated that she was not sufficiently self-reliant to signal us on every occasion. In cases, therefore, where she was taken without a previous signal, it is possible that the announcement might have been forthcoming had she been permitted to wait a little longer.

After completing our survey of the results of this extensive training, we may still find ourselves in doubt as to which of the subjects is the better or the faster learner. Possibly the question is too complex to be disposed of in such simple terms. The issue is certainly confused in this instance by the important physiological differences in the individuals, which considerably increase the number of evacuations made by the ape both under normal and under emotional conditions. If we are inclined to ignore these factors, we may say that in adaptation to the use of the nursery chair and in the development of inhibitory reactions, the child proved superior despite the added motivation which changes in procedure gave the ape. The latter, on the other hand, seemed to be superior in the development of anticipatory reactions, although the child originally started to announce himself at a calendar date about two months in advance of the animal's initial attempts.

Further evidence, which appears necessary before we arrive at a final conclusion, may be obtained from specific learning experiments undertaken during the later stages of the observations. In these we endeavor to set the subjects clear-cut problems too difficult to be solved immediately and to trace the course of their activity as they master the separate tasks.

The first may be called the *hand-in-loop* experiment. Its equipment consists of a twisted cotton rope about 3 millimeters in diameter and 50 centimeters (20 inches) long. The rope is tied at one end to a stake driven all the way into the ground. At the free end of the rope a simple slipknot is fashioned, so as to leave a projecting "tail" 5 centimeters (2 inches) long, which when pulled will loosen the slipknot. The loop in the slipknot is then placed over the subject's left wrist and pulled taut. The experimenter withdraws and observes him from a point of vantage to see if he can release himself from the trap. Tests of this sort are begun when the subjects are 11½ and 14 months old respectively and continue, except for a few unavoidable omissions, at the rate of one trial a day for several weeks.

Surprising as it may seem, we observe that Donald in his very first trial attends to the knot itself, seizes the projecting tail in his right hand, gives it a good pull, and so removes the loop from his wrist. It has not taken him more than 30 seconds for the whole procedure. Although it may seem unlikely that a complex act of this nature could be accidental, we are forced to accept such an interpretation when it turns out that the next 8 trials are all total failures. In these cases the subject is allowed 5 minutes in which to release himself, and if he does not succeed in that time he is removed and the trial recorded as a failure. Throughout certain of the unsuccessful attempts there are crying and fretting. In others there seems to be something in the nature of a stolid sort of waiting, without continuous effort towards a definite solution.

Gua, for her part, fails in her first attempt, yet on the second she also contributes a surprise solution by biting at the knot and pulling it loose with her teeth.

She requires only 35 seconds to free herself. A significant difference develops at this point, for Gua makes only a single additional failure, namely on the eighth trial, in the entire 28 trials which are given her; while Donald has a total of 10 failures.

After the fifth trial we transfer the experiment to the shelter and protection of the house, since it appears that the damp ground may prove unhealthy for our subjects. The cord is there fastened through the center of a rectangular piece of wooden flooring roughly 1 by 1.5 meters in size. This change does not seem to affect the performance of the subjects, except to increase Gua's time of solution by a small amount upon the first indoor trial.

We may sample their attack upon the problem by selecting a so-called poor trial and a so-called good trial from the record of each.

Donald—Trial 7, November 27.
This trial is a failure. He stands perfectly still looking at me as I retreat. After one minute he still does not move, although presumably I am out of his sight and observe him only at some distance around the edge of a doorway. When about 2 minutes have elapsed he begins to attend to the wrist, waving it in the air and pulling at the cord with his right hand (3 minutes). He falls down, jerked by the string as he starts to move away. Begins to cry and fret (4 minutes). Continues to cry while he sits up. Frets and pulls at cord with both right and left hands. Tries to get his right thumb under the loop on his left wrist, but only half-heartedly and without attending to what he is doing. He seems to have pulled the loop very tight by waving and jerking his left hand (5 minutes). Failure.

Gua—Trial 8, November 28.
This trial is a failure. She walks aimlessly about crying. Then stops and pulls at the cord on her wrist with her teeth. Also pulls on the tail of the cord with her right hand. Cries ("oo-ooing") (1 minute). After a few frantic and random pulls she sits down suddenly and remains perfectly still (2 minutes). Gets up, goes as far from the point where cord is

fastened as it is possible to go, so that she has drawn cord taut, and walks in a circular direction through 180 degrees pulling on cord. Stops and pulls at knot with teeth. Has loop loose but walks away jerking it tight again. Cries (3 minutes). Walks away ignoring cord, and sprawls forward as it is jerked tight. Sits still. Then pulls against the cord, reaching and straining for near-by objects with her free hand as if to drag herself away (4 minutes). Lies perfectly still on her back (5 minutes). Failure. (This is the first time she has failed since trial 1. Think possibly she needed to urinate and was distracted because she could not get away to do so. She was discovered to have urinated, in fact, by the time the trial was over.)

Turning now to the successful responses.

Donald—Trial 22, December 16.
Solution time 24 seconds. Donald is so anxious to try the experiment that he hurries to the experimental board by himself and climbs upon it. He crawls into position, sits down himself, and puts his hand in the loop when I hold it before him. He immediately pulls *on the knot* with his right hand, at the same time trying to pull his left hand through the loop. His left hand is two-thirds out in 10 seconds or less, but the loop catches on his fingers as it is being removed and he has to loosen it a second time in order to free himself completely. Time 24 seconds.

Gua—Trial 20, December 11.
Solution time 35 seconds. Gua runs to board floor of her own accord and sits down. Is ready and waiting for me even before I approach the board. Extends her left hand and attempts to shove it through the loop before I have the loop opened sufficiently to admit it. She then pulls twice on the tail with her teeth but seems not to be able to make the knot "slip." Immediately she takes the tail with her right hand, loosens the loop by pulling on it, and thereupon withdraws her left hand. Time 35 seconds.

Their cooperation and apparent interest in mastering the problem began to show itself with Gua at about the eleventh trial and with Donald at about the fifteenth.

They would first extend their left arms so that the experimenter could slip the loop over the wrist. A little later they would place the hand in the loop themselves, and finally they would hurry towards and climb upon the experimental board as soon as it was placed in position, indicating by this act, it seemed to us, a pleasurable interest in the solution itself. It appeared, indeed, as if the chief motivation was not then as we had supposed, "escape from confinement," but rather something in the nature of "successful achievement" or "successful manipulation."

As far as the final results are concerned, there can be no doubt of Gua's considerable superiority. If we apply criteria of the type frequently used in learning experiments, we find that the ape achieved her first "four out of five solutions in less than one minute per solution," beginning with trial 9. Yet Donald achieved his first "four out of five solutions in less than one minute per solution" beginning with trial 20. Similarly Gua had 9 successes in 10 in less than one minute per success beginning also with trial 9, while the boy fulfilled this criterion beginning as before with trial 20. On the basis of these last two criteria Donald required about twice as many trials to "learn" the problem as Gua did. She was also superior, as we have already seen, in the smaller number of failures she made, although the initial successes of each were only one trial apart.

In the next, or *foot-in-loop* experiment, which is begun several days after the *hand-in-loop* tests are finished, the loop is placed upon the right ankle. Care is taken to pull it tight only when the tail-like end is upward and within easy reach of the subject. At the start the two are 13½ and 16 months old, respectively. Here is a test which, coming as it does after many successful solutions of one which is very similar, should permit the subject to *transfer* or carry over the knowledge acquired in the earlier situation and apply it to the present one.

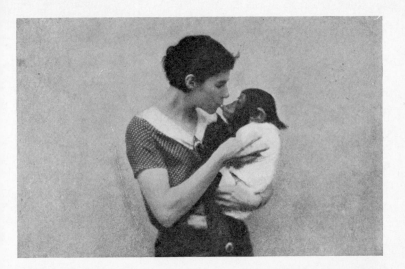

The kissing reaction seems to serve as a sign of forgiveness or relief after difficult or trying situations. It is used by Gua many times a day.

That the ape is not inherently afraid of water is suggested by her voluntarily entering sizable bodies of it.

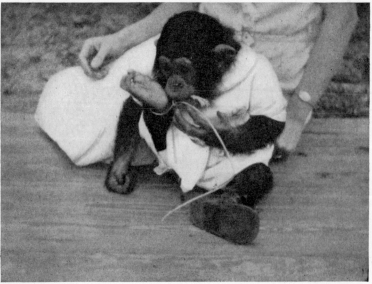

The upper picture shows the child removing the slip-knot in the *hand-in-loop test*.
Below: The ape attacks the loop in the *foot-in-loop experiment*.

Donald once more distinguishes himself by removing the loop on the very first trial within the short space of 35 seconds, in spite of the fact that he must get it over the protruding portions of his shoe in doing so. He looks up at us and smiles as he achieves this result. But on the second trial he fails to duplicate the performance. On the third, after a great struggle, the loop is finally removed in 3 minutes and 40 seconds. The fourth trial is again a failure, as is the sixth, while on the fifth the loop falls off over his heel when the boy gets himself in an unusual kneeling position. He seems as surprised as we are and makes pleasant sounds when he discovers himself freed in this manner.

Gua in her efforts fares worse than Donald and makes six consecutive failures on the first six attempts. Her behavior at times suggests that she is completely lost, for it deteriorates into an uncontrolled series of pullings and bitings which indicate little if any definite progress towards the goal. One gets the impression in some instances that she may be "aroused" or "excited." At other times she works more persistently, and often comes so close to a solution that it is painful to see her fail.

Each of the subjects appears to have two clear-cut tendencies that make it difficult for him to advance. The first of these is the reaction of moving the opened loop towards his own body and hence *up* the leg instead of *down* it. The second is to try and pull the foot out of the loop by bending the knee, rather than to lift the loop over the shoe with the hands. The test seems to be a very complex one for the subjects, since to solve it properly the loop must first be loosened and then pushed away while it is still held open. If they follow their primary inclinations of pulling the foot through the loop, the toe or heel of the shoe almost invariably catches on some part of it. In one or two cases we have seen Donald pick at the bow of his shoe laces, apparently confusing this with the slipknot of the cord, although the color and size of each are different.

Beginning with the seventh trial, in order to reduce the difficulty of the task, we remove the right shoe of each of the subjects. Immediately Gua makes 10 perfect solutions ranging in time from 4 to 32 seconds. Donald also performs successfully on the first two occasions but follows these with three errors, after which he is successful on every trial.

If we consider for the moment only those attempts in which the shoe was left on (namely, the first six) Donald has a distinct advantage, since he achieves three successes in six trials, while Gua makes nothing but failures. But if we choose to disregard the first six attempts or to place them in the category of a "training" or "habituating" series, it is Gua who has the advantage. For at once she satisfies all the criteria which we can apply immediately after the shoe is removed. She has no failures; her first success comes in trial 1; and the four-out-of-five and nine-out-of-ten criteria previously applied in the *hand-in-loop* experiment begin for Gua also with trial 1. Opposed to this, we see that Donald has three failures with the shoe removed; his first success is in trial 1; he makes 4 solutions in 5 under one minute each starting with trial 5, and 9 solutions in 10 under one minute each beginning with the same attempt.

Perhaps, as a result of such conflicting evidence, it would be well to divide the laurels in this experiment. This much can be said in support of Donald's failures when the shoe was removed: He undoubtedly had a more difficult task than Gua both because his heel protruded farther than hers and because his shorter toes would not allow him to fold or double the foot into as compact a bundle.

Which one of the subjects displayed the greater amount of "transfer" is difficult to say. Donald apparently adapted to the changed element in the situation somewhat more rapidly than Gua. The ape continued to run to the testing board and to offer her left hand, as if she were still doing the *hand-in-loop* test, up to and including the seventh trial of the new experiment. It was not until the ninth attempt that she advanced her foot. She then made another error in the tenth by offering her hand once more, even though her shoe had just been removed in preparation for the test. At times, when she was making consistent failures, she seemed reluctant to go through with another trial and had to be led to the board. Donald came to the board willingly for the first four trials, and began to show reluctance on the fifth. But he did not offer his hand during any of the *foot-in-loop* trials and first spontaneously extended his foot beginning with the ninth.

We next undertake what may be called the *suspended cookie test*. In this experiment there is hung from the ceiling of the room a cord at whose lower end is fastened a small metal clamp. The clamp can be made to hold a butter cookie of a kind which is liked by both infants. The cord is of such length that the cookie hangs well out of reach of either of the subjects. All other articles are removed from the room, excepting an ordinary straight-backed chair which is placed so that its nearest point is about a meter from where an imaginary prolongation of the cord would touch the floor. The solution of the problem, of course, is to push the chair beneath the cookie, climb upon it, and obtain the prize. Trials are not begun until Donald has reached the age of 17 months, so that there is no question about his ability to push the chair or climb.

Since each of the subjects has for many months been familiar with chairs of the kind used, one can legitimately raise a question regarding the degree to which the test will prove a measure of a new kind of behavior. Our records disclose that when as young as 10 months, Gua would pull Donald's walker beneath doorknobs, then climb upon the walker and swing from the knobs. About the same time she was also first seen to drag cardboard packing boxes from one room to another and sometimes to climb from them to chairs or tables. Donald, as well, when he became skillful at climbing, was seen on several occasions to pull boxes about and to clamber from them to chairs or tables. On the very day that the *suspended cookie test* is begun, in fact, he is observed to push a chair close to a small table, then to get upon the chair and so obtain several objects from the table. The important question in this regard: To what extent is such apparently constructive behavior deliberate and to what extent is it accidental?

In order to make sure that there will be no doubt about the function of the chair, the subjects are given four preliminary trials, *with the chair already properly placed beneath the cookie.* That is to say, they are admitted one at a time to the room after the chair has been adjusted, the cookie is pointed out to them, and they are allowed to climb up and obtain it.

But in spite of this preparation, and of the possible existence of ready-made responses which they may have picked up by themselves, Donald fails utterly on the first three trials of the test. Gua also fails in one of these and comes very near to failing in a second. A "failure" in this experiment consists of not getting the cookie within five minutes from the time the trial began. That their failures can by no means be taken as evidence of lack of effort is demonstrated by their repeatedly getting up and down again from the chair, and by their going beneath the cookie and reaching for it. They will even push the chair a few inches in one direction or another, thereafter climbing upon it and extending their arms toward the reward, regardless of the fact that the distance may be several times too far. Quite obviously there is a rudimentary understanding that the chair is somehow involved, but just how to get it in the right position is the insurmountable stumbling-block. In one instance Donald pushes the chair *away from the cookie* so persistently that he nearly has it in an adjacent room before he has finished. There is also a suggestion, particularly on the part of the child, that he is attempting to ask assistance from his elders. This suggestion arises from the numerous journeys he

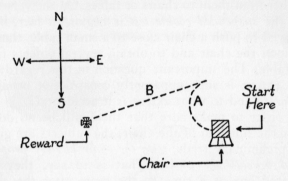

A = *The 180° pull*
B = *The straight push*

Fig. 11.—After a few trials in the *suspended cookie test* the child falls into the habit of pushing the chair in the same manner upon each trial, without apparent regard for the position of the reward. He first pulls the chair backward and to his right through an arc of 180 degrees, and then pushes it forward in a straight line. Although he seems to pay no attention to where he is pushing it—beyond following the formula of stereotyped movements—he is usually successful in getting it beneath the cookie provided the chair is always placed in the same position at the start of each trial.

makes to the cookie chair, which are followed in each case by his immediate toddling to the experimenter.

The final results show us that it is Gua who has triumphed again. She has only one failure in the first 20 attempts as compared to Donald's four failures in the same number of trials. Her first success comes in trial 1, while his first success is in trial number 4. Her first three successes in series begin in trial 3, while Donald's begin in trial 4. And if we resort once more to a time criterion by taking the first three trials in five whose time of solution is less than one minute each, we find that Gua reaches this goal beginning with trial 4, while Donald does not attain it till trial 13.

Throughout all these initial attempts the chair is invariably placed in the same position at the start, namely in a direction about one meter due east of the cookie. But we notice as the learning progresses that Donald seems to have fallen into the habit of pushing the chair under the cookie *in exactly the same manner upon every trial*. After a dozen or so successes he

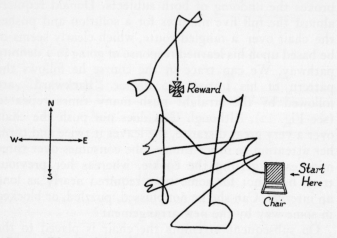

FIG. 12.—When the chair in the *suspended cookie test* is placed in a southeasterly direction from the reward instead of in its usual easterly position, the pathway traced by the child is like that diagrammed. The pattern of his original 180-degree backward pull followed by the straight push can be seen repeated many times in the tangled course he pursues.

apparently pays little attention to the position of the cookie. Instead he follows a more or less stereotyped series of movements which eventually put the chair in the correct place. His learning appears to be of a mechanical *motor* variety, rather than of a *perceptual* sort. Specifically the responses consist in his (1) going between the chair and the cookie, with his back to the cookie, (2) pulling the chair backward and to the right through an arc of 180 degrees until he has turned it around so it is between himself and the reward, and

(3) then pushing it in a straight line beneath the cookie (see Fig. 11). It is possible, of course, that Gua also has learned a series of movements, although her behavior varies so much from trial to trial that this does not appear to be the case.

To put the matter to a test, the chair upon a later trial is placed in a southeasterly direction from the reward instead of in its usual easterly position. We are surprised to find that this minor change very nearly proves the undoing of both subjects. Donald requires almost the full five minutes for a solution and pushes the chair over a tangled route, which clearly seems to be based upon his learned response of going in a definite pathway. We can trace in the course he follows the pattern of his initial 180 degree "backward" arc followed by the straight push many times repeated (see Fig. 12). Although Gua does not push the chair over a very great distance, she leaves it twice and turns her attention to other things. She consumes over three minutes in getting the cookie, whereas her previous trials have not for some time required nearly as long an interval. Can she be nonplussed, puzzled, or blocked in some way by the new arrangement?

On subsequent attempts the chair is placed to the west, south, and north, with the astonishing results of which samples are shown in Fig. 13. In most of these trials Donald proves a complete failure, while Gua obtains the cookie without delay. She does not react at all as she did the first time the chair was moved from its regular position, for she now seems to have no difficulty, regardless of its location. Indeed, the whole approach of the subjects to the problem is different. The boy almost never looks toward the prize, but starts to walk in a continuous series of turns and gyrations, often passing several times *directly beneath* the reward without stopping or even observing his position. The ape, on the other hand, can be seen to look upward both before and during successive pushes of the chair.

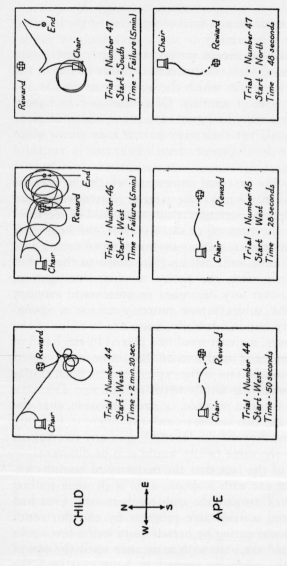

Dotted line = Reach   Break in line = Stop

FIG. 13.—Critical trials of the *suspended cookie test*, in which the chair is placed in other positions than its original easterly location with reference to the reward, give the results shown above. The child fails on many occasions to get the reward at all, and pursues such devious and winding pathways that at times he appears quite lost. Yet the ape usually solves the problem without delay.

218

As a result she seldom goes in the wrong direction and wastes little time in achieving the desired result.

We may examine as a final comparison of the learning of the two their ability to use simple tools or implements. This field should prove particularly interesting since the use of tools is often considered to be one of the chief departments in which the behavior of man is distinct from that of animals. Of course, our immature subjects can hardly be expected to prove highly efficient in this regard, yet their very *naiveté* may throw some light on the development of such behavior in youthful individuals.

Probably the first real implement which the average human baby learns to handle in order to attain a desired end is the spoon. Both of our subjects could be fed from a spoon at the time of, or shortly after, the beginning of the observations, so that the function of such a tool should not have remained long unknown to them. Yet in accordance with the policy of this investigation, there was never any organized or systematic attempt to teach the subjects how properly to use a spoon. Occasionally and incidentally, upon the impulse of the experimenters, a spoon would be placed in the hand of one or the other at mealtime, and would be manipulated for the subject by one of the experimenters. Such efforts were begun during Gua's tenth month and Donald's twelfth. It is quite possible, or even probable, that the training of the two in this regard was different, but only to the extent that the similar training of any two human children in the same family would also be different.

In spite of the fact that the majority of human children do not eat with a spoon, even with some spilling of food, until around the eighteenth month, Gua had demonstrated considerable progress by the thirteenth month and was eating by herself quite well a few weeks later. Donald ate only with assistance until the age of 17½ months when he seemed to have mastered the technique sufficiently well to manipulate this tool by himself. The ape, as a result, was considerably in advance of the child in the rate at which she acquired this behavior. It is interesting to note that the chief difficulty which Gua seemed to have with her spoon eating was in pushing the implement beneath the food. She was inclined to rest the bowl of the spoon flat upon the surface of the food and then push it to the side of the dish rather than to tilt the bowl sufficiently to entrap the food. While Donald had little trouble in this particular regard, his difficulty was in failing to keep the bowl of the spoon level as he transported it to his mouth. Often he would turn it upside down during this movement, thus losing the entire contents, a thing which Gua was almost never seen to do.

In the use of sticks or similar objects for poking or pushing there was no great difference apparent, although Gua was observed in such activity a larger number of times than Donald. At the age of 8½ months she took a spoon with which she had been playing and scraped the end of the handle vertically downward upon the wall. Since the wall in question was of roughened plaster, this made a very satisfactory grating and bumping noise, and was continued for perhaps half a dozen strokes. At 12 months she would push crumbs about upon the tray of her high chair with either end of a spoon, somewhat as she pointed to or poked at things with the end of her index finger. She was also observed to push at outdoor objects with small sticks and twigs, and to poke holes in the sand with them, while Donald would play similarly with clothespins.

In the attempt to investigate such tendencies more completely, a scheme to measure the learning ability of the subjects in the mastery of a simple tool is arranged. We may call this for convenience the *hoe experiment*. A wire screen of large mesh is fitted solidly into a doorway to a height of about 1.3 meters (4 feet 4 inches). Objects can be readily seen through the screen but the

Solutions of the *suspended-cookie test*.

The ape seldom spills her food in eating with a spoon, while the child is more inclined to turn the spoon over as he places it in his mouth, frequently losing much of the contents. Ages: Donald 18½ months, Gua 16 months.

only way they can be reached is by means of a small
space 9 centimeters (3½ inches) high which is left across
the entire width of the doorway between the bottom
of the screen and the floor. On the far side of the screen
is a rectangular box-like compartment like a drawer
with one of its ends removed. Into this receptacle,
whose width is the same as that of the doorway and
whose open end is facing the screen, various rewards
may be placed. The three vertical sides of the compartment prevent the prizes from being knocked or pushed
too far away from the screen (see Fig. 14).

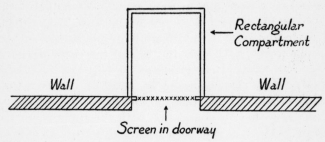

FIG. 14.—Ground plan of the *hoe experiment*. A screen of large mesh is fitted
solidly into a doorway. In the rectangular compartment behind the screen a
reward in the shape of a morsel of apple is placed. The only way the subject can get
the apple is to pull it out with a small hoe which will just fit through a slit between
the bottom of the screen and the floor.

A small wooden hoe of solid construction, with a blade
25 centimeters (10 inches) wide and a handle 66 centimeters (30 inches) in length, is provided with which
to drag out objects placed behind the screen. Since its
blade is only 5 centimeters (2 inches) in height it will
easily go through the space between the screen and the
floor, and so considerably extends the reach of the
subjects. A morsel of apple is placed (as in position 1,
Fig. 15) on the near side of the hoe blade, which is left
about 50 centimeters under the screen. The subjects
are introduced to the experiment at the respective ages
of 12½ and 15 months.

Much to our astonishment each of them when seated
before the projecting end of the hoe handle reaches for

it without any hesitation and pulls out the apple at once. This regardless of the fact that neither has had the slightest instruction or demonstration, or has even so much as seen the hoe before. A marked distinction appears in their behavior at this point, however, for it is very clear that it is the hoe in which Donald is interested. If permitted, he will push it back and forth upon the floor once he has obtained it, regarding it apparently as a fascinating new plaything. The apple he practically ignores, and often he will not touch it even if it is pointed out by the experimenter, unless the hoe is taken from him as soon as he has completed the response. On several occasions we must pick up the bit of apple and offer it to him while in one such instance, strange to say, he deliberately pushes our extended hand away and turns his attention to the hoe. We sometimes wonder if in the beginning he actually observes that he has pulled out the apple, or whether he is so absorbed in the hoe that its connection with the apple is not yet grasped. He has not been eating this fruit as long as Gua has, but he seems to be very fond of it when it is given to him under less distracting circumstances.

The ape behaves towards the hoe more as if it were a means to an end and not an object worth securing in itself. Upon her very first pull she drops the hoe as soon as the apple is within reach and walks away eating her prize. On later attempts she pays no special attention to the hoe unless for some reason or other she is not successful in getting the apple, when she may bite the hoe or pound it upon the floor. If we place the hoe under the screen *but without any apple* as an incentive, each will pull it out as usual. But Gua immediately peers through the screen in search of the missing reward, while Donald is not so obviously disturbed. His attention comes nevertheless to be gradually centered in the apple so that after a few trials he picks it up and eats it regularly.

Neither the child nor the ape has any special difficulty in solving the initial problem which has been set them.

From the first trial each has demonstrated that he can seize the hoe handle and remove the implement from beneath the screen. Of course, there is nothing else in the immediate environment which can be moved or manipulated, so that if the subjects do anything at all with the new features of their surroundings, there is not much else they can do except pull the hoe. At the same time their unhesitating and effective responses have proved somewhat more than we had expected.

We next place the apple slightly nearer to the screen than the hoe blade, and about 5 centimeters (2 inches) to the right of its extreme edge (as in position 2, Fig. 15). But surprising as it may seem, this change makes not an iota of difference in the reaction of either subject. Donald draws the hoe straight out with a single unbroken movement as before, while Gua also makes the same sort of response which she made originally. She even reaches beneath the screen for the apple following the pulling of the hoe, regardless of the fact that the reward is obviously far beyond her since it has not been touched by the hoe blade.

A long training series in which each subject is given 10 trials a day is then begun. Five of these trials come in the forenoon and 5 in the afternoon. The first and last trials of each series of 5 may be called *direct* trials, in which the apple is arranged in front of the hoe blade (as in position 1, Fig. 15), so that the subjects have no difficulty in obtaining it. The middle three trials of each series of five are trials in which the apple is placed at the side (as in position 2, Fig. 15). This plan of procedure is found necessary in order to guarantee that the subjects will receive some sort of prize for their efforts. To be sure, in spite of early failures, both by the sixth day are coming eagerly to the experimental equipment as soon as it is prepared for them. But since the position-2 trials at the beginning are invariably unsuccessful, the principals would soon lose interest and cease to pull the hoe at all if some such method were not employed for insuring them occasional rewards.

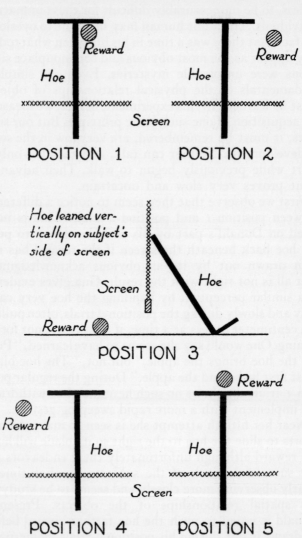

FIG. 15.—The various positions of the hoe and the reward in the *hoe experiment*. Getting the piece of apple from each of these positions constitutes at the start a special problem in itself for each of the subjects.

Here, then, is an elementary task which seems, nevertheless, to be immeasurably difficult for these immature individuals. The adult human may be prone to overlook the fact that there was a time in his life when what today may appear as the most obvious and commonplace situations were unsolvable mysteries. Even the simplest fundamentals of the physical relationships of objects must be learned. In this experiment, in fact, we measure the acquisition of one such basic principle. But our subjects, it must be remembered, are very low in the scale of development. Neither can talk, and each has only a short while previously begun to walk. Their advancement proves very slow and uncertain.

First we observe that they seem to notice a difference between position-1 and position-2 trials. This is indicated on Donald's part by his early tendency to push the hoe back beneath the screen if the reward has not been drawn out by it—an obvious acknowledgment that all is not right with the result. Gua gives evidence of a similar perception by handling the hoe very carefully and slowly during the position-2 trials, often pulling it a centimeter or less at a time, if the prize is not forthcoming. One would say she seems to have learned, "Pulling the hoe brings the apple," but not, "The hoe blade must first be behind the apple." During the regular position-1 trials she shows no such hesitancy but withdraws the implement with a more rapid sweeping gesture.

Near her fiftieth attempt she is seen to make definite efforts to slide the hoe to the right so its blade will hook the reward although unfortunately these endeavors are not successful. Each of the subjects by that time is clearly observing more closely and seems to be studying the spatial relationships of the objects. Presently Donald is noted to push the hoe farther inward before he draws it out during his position-2 trials. Sometimes, while these inward pushes are in progress he also moves the blade a little to the right so that it nearly catches the apple when he withdraws it.

Gua achieves her first success in the ninety-ninth attempt, while Donald is successful for the first time in the one hundred twentieth. Yet there is good reason to believe that both of these initial solutions are largely accidental. Soon Gua again appears to be making definite efforts to push the entire hoe sidewards to the right before she pulls it out. This method presently leads her to several subsequent solutions which are clearly *not* accidental.

But their progress altogether is so laborious and irregular that there is a real question whether either of the subjects is capable of mastering the problem completely. We wonder if Donald is backsliding when he falls, as was the case in the *suspended cookie experiment*, into the manner of making a mechanical series of movements upon each position-2 trial, without seeming to attend at all to the location of the apple. He pushes the hoe rapidly inward, jerks it out again far too speedily and inaccurately ever, except by the merest accident, to catch the reward. Gua for her part has to be encouraged to keep working, and sometimes when the apple is placed to the side she gets up and walks away without even touching the hoe. By the two-hundredth trial Donald has made only seven successes and Gua only nine.

We therefore introduce a change in procedure by undertaking actually to *assist* or *instruct* the subjects during every fifth trial. At the start of each series of 5 attempts, they still obtain the apple as before, since in the initial attempt the apple is always placed in position 1. Their next three efforts are regular position-2 trials without any assistance. Then, in the final attempt, their hands are placed properly on the hoe handle which *the experimenter moves for them* so as to obtain the reward. They are consequently taught or aided in one trial at every experimental sitting.

The ape in particular seems to respond rapidly to this instruction and makes 12 successes in the next 50

Toward the end of the research the ape can drink from a glass without difficulty.

(Facing p. 226.)

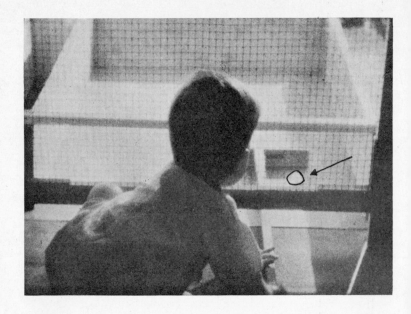

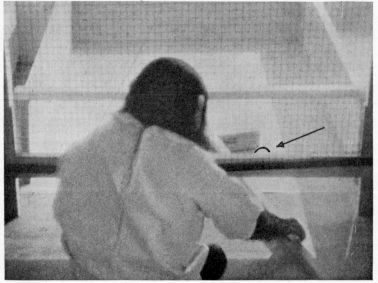

Showing the methods of getting the reward in the *hoe experiment*. In these trials the apple has been placed to the right of the hoe blade as in *position* 2 (see page 224).

trials. She also attains the criterion of four unassisted successes in five attempts, beginning with her two-hundred sixty-fifth trial. Donald, who has only four successes in the first 50 trials after the instruction is begun, does not reach the four-out-of-five criterion until his trial number 337.

There can be little doubt that Gua has proved herself the more apt pupil throughout this training. She has adhered more closely to the letter of the training than has the child, as the completed responses of the two demonstrate. She faces partly to her right, reaches to the right with both hands, and grasps the handle of the hoe in each. She then pushes the handle away from her, that is, to the right, often as she does so pivoting the handle about the blade rather than sliding the entire implement to the right. This usually places the blade at a precarious angle with reference to the reward so that there is a possibility it will not catch the apple when it is given a straight pull. But Gua seldom misses. Her entire method appears to be reproductive of that which the experimenter has demonstrated except that she does not push the hoe blade to the right and so get it behind the food quite as he did.

The procedure of the child bears more of an original stamp, and seems as well to be based on superior mechanical principles. He also places both hands on the hoe blade as Gua does, but at this point the similarity between their reactions largely disappears. For Donald usually pushes the hoe a little farther inward, simultaneously forcing the blade to the right behind the reward. In his movement of the hoe he may be said to be using the end of the handle which he holds largely as a pivot about which he pushes the blade. Whether the differences between the two should be interpreted to mean that the child has a better understanding of the relationships involved is probably questionable, although his method of solution, when analyzed, is more impressive than Gua's.

We proceed then to the third problem, by placing the hoe in position 3 (see Fig. 15) entirely on the subject's side of the screen, where it is stood or leaned against this partition. Although neither individual is from this point onward given any further assistance or instruction, in about 10 trials each is able on almost every attempt to slide the hoe beneath the screen and work it satisfactorily behind the reward.

The apple is next placed to the left of the hoe blade instead of to the right (position 4, Fig. 15). It is the very first time this has ever been done. Both subjects push the blade *to the right* on their initial two attempts, making the same reaction which they have been accustomed to making in the preceding position-2 trials. On his third trial, however, each gets the apple without difficulty and cannot thereafter be tricked into making the wrong reaction. By this time they have completed nearly 500 attempts of various kinds apiece, and inclusive of interruptions for sickness and other causes they have been working for three months on the experiment.

They are finally able to secure the reward under almost any conditions which we can arrange. For instance, if the apple is placed to the right of the hoe blade and on the following trial to the left, they are no longer fooled. The reward can be put practically anywhere behind the screen within the length of the hoe handle, while the hoe itself is retained on the subject's side of the screen. Still they will push the implement correctly beneath the screen and pull out the prize. When the hoe is left beneath the screen and the apple is concealed on the far side of its blade (as in position 5, Fig. 15), even this arrangement does not prove an unsolvable problem. For they will usually on such occasions pull the blade outward, move it to the side, and work it successfully behind the apple.

By the time the experiment is completed they are strikingly similar in their ability to obtain the reward without missing or making wrong responses. The child is perhaps more versatile in that he employs a somewhat greater variety of movements in his solutions; while Gua for the most part gets along with fewer reactions. If the apple is to the *left* of the hoe blade, it is likely (though not certain) that the ape will first withdraw the hoe and push it back on the opposite side, so that the apple is now to its *right*. She will then follow through with the well-learned right-hand reaction in getting the reward. Donald is more inclined to make both left and right responses, depending on the location of the apple, and does not seem to prefer one method any more than another. Yet despite such differences in the approach to the various arrangements, each subject can actually solve the problems which are set with about equal facility.

There is no gainsaying the fact that Gua has been more rapid in her progress as well as more responsive to the instruction which was given. Of course, the differences between the two are slight and in the later tasks, namely the position 3, 4, and 5 problems, one has learned about as quickly as the other. But where there are differences as in the position-2 trials, it is Gua who has arrived at the various criteria of learning sooner than the child. If we hold persistently to our original comparison in *rate of learning*, it is again the ape, we must admit, who has shown herself superior, even though her early advance is lost by the time Donald has mastered the position-2 solutions.

In spite of the fact that, when put to a direct comparison, the animal is found to learn many of the tasks which are given it in fewer trials than the human subject, there is one important aspect of learning in which the child is superior. This concerns the propensity for imitative or mimetic reactions, which was discussed in detail under the heading of play in Chapter VI. It is not necessary to undertake specific experiments in order to test this ability, for the difference is readily apparent from the spontaneous responses of the two.

As a distinct method by which the behavior of those in the immediate environment is accurately learned and reproduced, imitation is of tremendous importance. We are accustomed, in this connection, to regard the chimpanzee as a splendid imitator, so much so that the very name "ape" implies its capacities. Yet the child is a more versatile and continuous imitator than the animal, as we have already seen.

Chapter X

MEMORY AND RECOGNITION

ONE way to account for the chimpanzee's more rapid rate of learning as demonstrated by the learning experiments would be to say colloquially that she possessed a "better memory" than the child. On the basis of such an assumption it could then be argued that she *retained* and *reproduced* more of

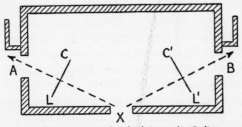

A , B = *Doors through which "incentive" disappeared*
X = *Starting doorway.* CL , C'L' = *Criterion lines*

FIG. 16.—Ground plan of the *delayed reaction experiment*. The subject is held at doorway X, while an incentive disappears from view through either doorway A or doorway B. After a suitable delay (during which in some cases he is occupied in other ways), the subject is released from doorway X and allowed to follow the incentive. If he shows that he "remembers" which way the incentive has gone by crossing the criterion line (CL or $C'L'$) in the direction of the correct doorway, the trial is considered a success. If he crosses the wrong line, the trial is considered a failure. If he crosses neither line within 45 seconds after his release, the trial is also recorded as a failure. The criterion lines are 1.6 meters from the starting point, X.

what she learned from one trial to the next than was the case with Donald. An early experiment in memory or retentivity was planned for the express purpose of testing the two in this regard. It was begun at the age of 8 months in Gua and 10½ in Donald and continued for about 8 weeks. We wished particularly to complete the trials by the time the child was approximately a year old, and so to obtain some record of the respective abilities of the subjects at the youngest possible ages.

The procedure in principle was that which was perfected in the hands of Hunter and called by him the *delayed reaction method*. The tests were made in one of the rooms of the house in which the subjects lived so that the general surroundings were familiar to them from the start. The room contained three doorways, one, which may be labeled X, located in about the middle of the south wall, and two others, A and B, located in the east and west walls respectively, about equidistant from X (see Fig. 16). The subject was forcibly detained beneath the lintel of doorway X while an incentive stimulus moved from X through either door A or door B and so disappeared from view. The incentive stimulus consisted of the preferred experimenter when Gua served as subject and of Gua herself carried by this observer when Donald was the subject. After the disappearance of the incentive a period of delay was allowed, at the end of which the subject was released. If he crossed the "criterion line" 1.6 meters from his starting point, in the direction which the incentive stimulus had previously taken, the trial was considered a success. If he crossed the criterion line in front of the wrong doorway, the trial was recorded as a failure. If he reached neither line within 45 seconds, the trial was also considered a failure. The intervals of delay were increased progressively to determine the maximum time within which the subjects could make successful reactions.

The experiment thus demanded the ability to differentiate between but two alternatives, the most distinguishing features of which were the rightness of one and the leftness of the other. But it may at once be objected that to measure merely how long the subjects could remember which of the doors was used is actually so very simple as to be beyond the necessity of testing.

Indeed, one might presume a full-grown human to be capable of reacting successfully in such a situation after a delay of years, possibly even over the span of a lifetime. It is known, on the other hand, that human ability in such experiments at least during childhood is related to age, so that it decreases rapidly with very youthful individuals; and many of the lower animals have been found to be unable to respond correctly in situations of this sort after delays greater than a few seconds. In view of these facts too much must not be expected of the infants whom we examine, even though in adult eyes the conditions may appear overly simple.

The human subject was able to take part in this experiment only by using his walker, since the trials were begun before he could get around by himself. When the delay was short he was allowed to remain seated in the walker under the doorway. The walker was held in place by means of cords running through pulleys and controlled by an assistant out of sight of the subject. At the termination of the interval the walker was released and at the same time it was given a slight forward pull by means of one of the cords (on a line midway between doors A and B). For the longer delays the child was removed from the walker and carried to an adjacent room where he was occupied till the end of the time period. In such cases a hood was slipped over his head and kept there during his transportation to the room in which he was detained for the interim. His return to the walker was accomplished in the same manner. While he actually remained seated in his walker at door X, therefore, he saw no one except at the start of the delay, when he observed only the experimenter carrying Gua away from him.

The ape in her turn was held in position during the shorter intervals by the non-incentive experimenter, and was similarly taken into the adjacent room for longer periods. Her transfer from the starting point and back again was also performed by means of the hood technique. Although she stayed in the same room with the second observer during these intervals her disturbance proved severe, particularly in the initial trials, and screaming accompanied by emotional evacuation would often result. It appeared at first to be something of a catastrophe for "the incentive" to walk away while Gua was forcibly prevented from following. Her vocalization and struggles to free herself were ample proof of the early effectiveness of this stimulation. Later, however, especially when the delays were lengthened, she became quieter and not infrequently she would fall asleep.

Preliminary attempts to restrain her by placing her inside a small box with a barred door which could be opened by means of a rope at the termination of the delay proved unsatisfactory. She was much upset by the confinement, would scream and bite at the bars, and threatened in some cases to injure herself. Her motivation in this situation may actually have been too strong since she was affected not only by the disappearance of the experimenter, but also by the confinement itself, which was received with great disturbance and was possibly taken as a sort of punishment.

The subjects were conducted rapidly through an early series of trials in which the delays ranged from 5 seconds to 2 minutes, without either making a single error. For the most part, Donald apparently took the shorter delays as a sort of play and seemed impatient to proceed in search of his companion. Yet, when the interval was increased, fretting and whimpering were of frequent occurrence except when he was removed from his walker during the waiting.

The greatest time which the child appeared able to bridge under these conditions was 5 minutes. He made 9 successful responses in 10 with this delay. Upon lengthening the time to 10 minutes, we found only about half of his trials were correct. The ape at first appeared to respond with such certainty that her interval was increased successively to 30 minutes, then to 1 hour, and finally to 3 hours. But the three-hour attempts were all failures and she was correct only 50 per cent of the time at 1 hour, so that it became necessary again to reduce the delay to 30 minutes. With this interval Gua responded correctly 7 times in 10. Five correct responses in 10 would have been expected on the basis of chance alone. Although her percentage of accuracy was not so high as it was for Donald's five-minute delay, it was still large enough we think to demonstrate the ability of the subject. It thus appears that under the special conditions of this test, the chimpanzee could span an interval several times that of the child, although the percentage of correct responses was not the same for both individuals.

It should be noted in this connection that the removal of the subjects from the room in which the response was later made had no effect upon the quality of their performance. It was not necessary for either of them to remain physically oriented with reference to the absent stimulus in order to react correctly. Yet such physical orientation in situations of this kind is the indispensable requirement of a correct response with many organisms lower in the biological scale.

To eliminate the possibility that Gua might be following a trail or a scent, a number of "controls" were employed. (1) The experimenter walked over both the right and wrong pathways during the period of delay. (2) The experimenter donned fresh clothing, even to shoes, and dragged the discarded garments over the wrong pathway. The original clothes were then left in the wrong place of concealment while Gua made her response. (3) The wrong pathway was retraced several times and *more recently* than the correct pathway, which was not gone over at all except when Gua first observed the experimenter disappear. This was made possible by the design of the house, in which one could take up his place of concealment after having previously left it without necessarily following the original pathways or even going again into the experimental room. All such tests showed conclusively that scent or odor was of no consequence.

Unfortunately, it was not feasible to give a large number of trials because of the rapidly changing ages of the subjects and the fact that, particularly with the longer intervals, only one trial a day could be undertaken. As it was, the child made in all 33 attempts and the ape 43, the greater number in her case arising from the one-hour and three-hour tests which she was given. It soon became necessary to discontinue the experiment altogether since Gua during her final attempts was obviously no longer motivated as she had been in the beginning. In spite of the early potency of the stimulation employed, she began to adapt to the whole technique so that her later responses were characteristically without interest or direction. Thus when she had reached the age of 10 months she was sometimes content even to remain out of sight of the favored observer, providing it was clear he was in the house with her. She was as a result not so prone to run after him when he went from one room to another, especially if the other experimenter was present. Her motivation, which was based alone on the tendency to follow a single individual, seemed no longer to be sufficiently effective.

Regardless of the fact that the chimpanzee in this test was able to respond correctly after a longer interval than the human, there were evidences of the common tendency to forget in each. No doubt the most unusual indication of the *forgetting* of a specific reaction was observed in Gua at the age of 10½ months. It shows the effect which shoes can have upon the manipulative ability of the toes. The observation, which is reported below, was made during the second administration of the *foot preference tests*.

October 4.

Footedness tests made today for the first time in over 2 months. During Gua's initial attempts at the present testing, she was quite incapable of seizing even a large morsel of orange with her toes. The best she could do was to touch the orange with her foot, usually with the sole. There was no grasping movement at all. This seems to show nicely the result of wearing shoes during the interval since the last footedness tests. The act of grasping with the feet has completely disappeared in this short time, although it was certainly present and reasonably proficient when the tests were originally given. Today, however, I had literally to teach her to hold objects all over again. This was accomplished by placing the piece of orange beneath her toes and closing the toes over it. I then assisted her to move the whole foot to her mouth while keeping the toes in a clenched position so the orange would not fall from them. It required at least a half-dozen trials with each foot before she could even hold the orange when it was placed under her toes. Her first attempts were awkward and consisted in some cases of extending the toes rather than flexing them. Usually the legs were stiffened also in such cases.

This deterioration in the toe-grasping reaction resulted, it is likely, from the enforced inability to exercise or use the parts involved. It occurred at such an immature age that the reaction to begin with was probably only insecurely established.

That each of the subjects forgot more complex reactions with considerable rapidity was also suggested from the learning tests. If on some unavoidable account it became necessary to omit the trials in the *hoe experiment* for a day or two, both Gua and Donald would return to the problem with an obvious diminution in skill. Frequently they would fail completely on many subsequent attempts. Their performance in this task, at least before they had completely mastered it, might be compared to the finely balanced training of an athlete in top form. A brief lapse, at any rate, would cause an immediate retrogression. Similar instances were noted from time to time in other experiments.

We are impelled to point out in this connection that it seemed occasionally as though the ape had forgotten responses to vocal commands when these responses would be retained throughout the same period by Donald. The words, "Get up on the bed," among other examples, which for many months had served as an effective stimulus, would cause Gua only to run aimlessly about at the age of 14 months as if she had quite lost their purport. Without spinning the interpretation out to too fine a thread, one may raise the question whether with more evidence it would be established that the child forgets words less readily than the animal, while the animal forgets movements less readily. This distinction can be phrased in the terminology of the older psychologists by saying that possibly the child possesses a better *auditory memory* than the ape and possibly the ape possesses a better muscular or *kinesthetic memory* than the child. Although the evidence is extremely sketchy and although one may object to the use of these terms, we are nevertheless inclined to suspect some such relationship.

It should be added at this point that there were a number of incidents in the daily lives of the subjects which suggested that each, *when not being tested*, was capable of reacting correctly after greater intervals than those employed in the *delayed reaction experiment*. The difference between their experimental and non-experimental performances may be due in part to the disturbing emotional factors of the former situation. It is quite likely, for instance, that crying or whimpering during the delay may in some cases have affected the ability to react after the interval of waiting. It is also possible—aside from the influence of emotional upset—that many of the non-experimental reactions were of lesser difficulty to perform than the experimental ones.

Often they were either acquired after a number of repetitions or else they were more in the nature of recognitions of familiar stimuli or situations. Some were typical examples of conditioning.

Among the instances of remembering which were observed after several repetitions of the stimulus situation falls Gua's searching for the strap of her high chair. This activity appeared at as young an age as 8 months. The strap proceeded vertically between the legs of the sitter and fastened the tray of the chair to the seat. When it was one day removed she reached for it during the very next meal, and then lay on her back upon the seat of the high chair and looked upward for it. She had not previously touched this plaything for fully six hours. This is a case of memory for an object in a specific *place.*

When 9 months old, the little animal discovered a paper label or address tag pasted upon the bottom of a rug which remained for some time rolled up at the side of one of the rooms. It became her habit to go to this label and gnaw upon it, pulling off with her teeth such paper scraps as she could get. The label so attached was on the surface of the rolled rug nearest the wall and was consequently not perceptible to Gua until she looked over the top of the roll. In order to discourage this biting behavior, we turned the rug through 90 degrees so that the label was then resting against the floor upon the bottom of the roll. Twenty-four hours after her last previous attack upon the label she approached the rug at the approximate point where the label had been, and peered over the top of the roll for it. On a second occasion somewhat later she returned to the rug in the same place and looked several inches to the right and the left of the position on the roll where the label had been.

Further evidence of memory for places after delays of two or three days was often afforded by the ape's tendency to make her way to outdoor hose connections in search of a drink. There were more than half a dozen of these which she regularly visited, many of them entirely concealed by shrubbery. If she had not been out for several days because of inclement weather, or if for other reasons she had been kept away from the faucets, her return to them, often by devious pathways and quite regardless of their complete concealment in bushes or foliage, would be made on the first opportunity without apparent difficulty.

Belonging more precisely under the heading of *recognition* comes the fact that at 9 months of age, Gua at once seemed to miss the chosen observer from social groups of which she was a member. It made no difference whether she was reasonably well acquainted with the remaining members of the group. It made no difference if the experimenter disappeared stealthily while her back was turned. His absence, soon detected, would lead to frantic searching behind shrubbery and tree trunks, accompanied by crying or screaming and other evidence of emotional upset. The disappearance of the second experimenter from similar groups in which the first was not included would produce analogous behavior.

Shortly after the *hoe experiment* had been started, both Gua and Donald would go to the screen where the apple was to be obtained as soon as the experimenter appeared carrying a saucer containing the reward. This reaction, which suggests a recognition of the saucer and its function, was first noted 5 days after the beginning of the trials. Upon the occasion of its initial appearance 30 hours had elapsed since the last previous trial of the experiment.

Probably the most striking incident of such a nature occurred three months after the completion of the experimental observations and hence applies to the child alone. At 22 months he was presented with the watch used in the *watch manipulation tests* (see Chapter VI). This had not previously been offered him since the last application of the test, four months before. As far as is known he had had no other watch in his hands during this period nor had he been close enough to one to react to it at all. Yet his response was immediately to place the experimental object to his ear as soon as he had grasped it. He thereby showed that he identified the watch as "a thing to be put to one's ear" and that he had not lost this seldom employed reaction even after so considerable an interval.

One may well ask concerning recognition whether Gua took the chimpanzees which she encountered at the Experiment Station as members of her own kind. This is a query which, like many others, we cannot definitely answer. But there can be no doubt that she reacted to the apes differently and apparently more intimately than she did to strange humans or to other animals. Their cages seemed to serve as a source of attraction for her and she would touch their hands if permitted. When she passed individuals several times her size in the halls or passageways she would often go towards them, sometimes to the great disturbance of the larger animals who seemed not entirely to make out this hybrid creature. A small hand mirror held before her face at the age of 8 months caused her to reach behind this at first with caution and hesitancy, then in a continuous series of groping hand movements.

That Donald, on the other hand, did not place unknown chimpanzees in quite the same category with Gua was apparent at the age of 12½ months, when he had recently learned to say "bow-wow" upon sighting a dog. Taken near the caged apes his first reaction was again "bow-wow." Certainly he had never previously employed this word where Gua was concerned, and probably he never would have done so under any ordinary circumstances. For Gua he seemed to accept in all respects as a fellow human.

There was one striking feature of the ape's recognition of her human friends, particularly within the first few weeks, which should throw some light on the manner in which she recognized. This consisted of the fact that their change in visual appearance produced by donning new garments apparently destroyed, for Gua, all semblance of familiarity. A person whom she knew well when attired in a white shirt and duck trousers was not at all the same individual if he presented himself in a gray suit and straw hat. Even after she had become attached to the experimenters, she would bark and shun them if they were dressed in unfamiliar costumes. Pursuing her under such cirumstances would often lead to emotional outbreaks and she would scurry away exactly as she ran from a total stranger. But once she was in the arms, where she could make the characteristic identification through smell, her anxiety would be largely dissipated.

One infers from such behavior that the mysterious transformations of her human associates were quite beyond her infantile comprehension. Of course, throughout the brief 7½ months of Gua's cage life, none of her intimates had ever before been able on a moment's notice to alter their appearance as could her later friends. She was consequently unprepared from earlier experience for such complete metamorphoses. It was obvious from the reactions which she made that her early recognitions were in no case based upon the appearance of the face nor on the bodily size or proportions of the individual.

The following statements will illustrate some of her responses in this regard:

July 23.
Gua sees my brown khaki coveralls hanging over the handle of the baby carriage. Her back is towards me and she rushes for the coveralls with arms outstretched, saying, "Oo-oo."
August 10.
Today I removed some white trousers I had been wearing in the presence of Gua, and placed them over the back of a chair. I then put on a pair of trousers which she had never

seen before. As soon as the new trousers were donned she immediately left me, climbed onto the seat of the chair, and placed her left hand (affectionately?) upon the old trousers. If Gua has become used to holding to and following a pair of trousers of a certain kind and something comes out of those trousers, is that any reason for leaving them?

December 18.

She was aroused from sleep last night and taken to the nursery chair. She seemed wide awake as we returned towards her bed. When we passed Mrs. Kellogg attired in a brown winter coat and hat which were new to Gua, she bristled and began giving the aggressive bark. We therefore carried her close to Mrs. Kellogg, whom she slapped. She also barked and wriggled to get away, giving every evidence of complete lack of recognition if not of fear.

It was some time before Gua seemed to have solved the mystery of this chameleon-like skin changing. She would then almost always recognize us, regardless of garb. But to what extent this advancement was a question of her acquaintance with our existing wardrobes, and to what extent she had learned to base her visual recognition on the exposed parts of the body, our observations cannot disclose. It is quite possible that the former is the correct explanation, since occasionally, even after many months, new garments still seemed to upset her. Her tendency to identify the individual in terms of his costume may also account for her preference for certain particular garments and her attachment to them when their owners were absent.

Chapter XI

INTELLIGENT BEHAVIOR

IN an empirical record of this sort it is hard to differentiate clearly and completely between intellectual and learning behavior, and any distinction which we do make must of necessity be somewhat arbitrary. There are some psychologists who consider the two to be practically synonymous and who would even define intelligence as "the speed or rate of learning." If we accept this view without reservation we may turn again to Chapter IX, where learning has already been discussed. Our learning experiments then become "intelligence tests" and the question needs little further consideration.

Other psychologists profess to see evidence of intelligence while the learning of a special problem is in progress, and to some extent independently of that learning. If the subject at any given stage of advancement solves the problem on which he is working *in an instant*, such an achievement is considered distinctly intellectual. But he must suddenly *see into* the solution and thereby make an entirely new response which has not previously been attempted. It is this characteristic of sudden insight or of "seeing into" the manner of the solution accompanied by a change in attack upon the problem which is the intelligent feature. The more gradual mastery of a task involving the step-by-step accumulation of skill is more commonly regarded as learning *per se*. The difference between the two depends not only upon the time of solution but also to a considerable extent upon the difficulty of the problem. Obviously one could not learn to operate a typewriter "in an instant" or "in a single step" although he might complete the solution of a puzzle at least after a little study in this manner. During his mastery of typing, on the other hand, one might discover certain short cuts or new methods which would considerably accelerate his progress. These rapid advances under some circumstances would likewise be regarded as intelligent in character.

The subject's attack upon many problems it may now appear can be viewed from either of two angles. If one is interested primarily in the *initial solution* or in abrupt advancements involving new kinds of reactions, these sudden spurts toward the goal he may regard as intelligent. But if one is interested in the more gradual perfection of already existing responses, he may choose to call this slower development improvement through repetition—or learning. The experiments already cited to compare Donald and Gua with respect to their learning ability could consequently have been employed as devices for the measurement of intelligent behavior had we confined ourselves only to special parts of them. But the prolonged and persistent nature of the training, together with the large number of repetitions, is more typical of a study of learning.

In the present chapter we shall pass over these earlier results and review instead certain previously undiscussed items which appear to possess more directly the quality of "suddenly seeing into" the solution of a new problem. But we shall also follow the orthodox practice of the educators by actually comparing the performance of the two subjects in a standard infant's intelligence test.

One of the earliest examples of Gua's application of abrupt and new responses toward the solution of problems which confronted her occurred about a month after she had come to us. Her left shoe had become loosened and apparently for some reason was uncomfortable upon the foot. At the time she was standing upon all fours and directing her attention to a play object a short distance away. She then began in an apparently preoccupied manner (that is, without turning towards the shoe or changing her general bodily attitude) to scrape the left foot upon the floor. The scraping movement, which was repeated five times, was always made in a forward-to-rear direction, the foot being lifted towards the front as in walking. Since the shoe did not come off as a result of these efforts, she abruptly ceased her play and turned towards the offending member. She then grasped the heel of the shoe in her left hand, but with the foot still remaining on the floor, and gave several vigorous pulls. This failing, she raised the heel and scraped it against the left arm in the region of the biceps. By this time the shoe was almost removed, so that a few subsequent scraping movements upon its return to the floor caused it to fall from the foot. There are good grounds for considering the pulling of the heel with the left hand and its scraping against the arm as well-directed attempts to remove it, even though neither was successful in itself. These were new responses in a new situation, which one would find it difficult to explain, it seems to us, as "random activity." Altogether the entire series of reactions in getting the shoe off seemed to suggest a comprehension, at least of a rudimentary sort, of the general mechanism of its removal.

A further difficulty which Gua sometimes had with her clothing she solved very neatly at the age of about a year. The trouble in this case arose from the fact that her continual activity often made it next to impossible to keep the children's romper suits she wore satisfactorily buttoned. These garments customarily fastened by two or three buttons between the legs. When they became loose the front of the dress would sometimes hang like an annoying apron or skirt, often almost concealing Gua's short members and frequently causing her to stumble. She abruptly overcame this difficulty by picking up the dangling edge of the unbuttoned rompers in her mouth, and so ran about quite freed from its entangling train.

Once at 14½ months she was discovered mouthing a tiny brass disc like the head of a nail. For fear that she might swallow it the experimenter immediately said to her, "Give it to me." As she attempted to do so it slipped from her lips to the floor, whereupon she made numerous unsuccessful attempts to retrieve it with her fingers. Her characteristic response to this vocal command was to pick up the object indicated in her hand and offer it to us. This she had already well learned. But try as she would, she could not seize the minute disc (because of its small size and the awkwardness of her own fingers) with sufficiently accurate prehension to lift it from the floor. Instead of "giving up" when faced with this situation she suddenly made a new combination of old reactions which solved her difficulty at once. This she accomplished by leaning forward and picking up the object with her lips. She then transferred the object from her mouth to her right hand, which she extended toward the experimenter as she walked toward him in completion of the task.

Without a doubt the most striking single example of such sudden problem solving occurred about two weeks previous to the incident just reported. The experimenter had placed Gua upon a small four-legged stool, and commanded her to "sit there" or "stay there" while he worked at a temporary task a short distance away. But for some unknown reason she seemed very anxious to be taken by him and screamed and cried when she was unable to have her way. Possibly this impulse was prompted in part by the fact that she had shortly before received her daily bath, although she was by then quite dry and should have been sufficiently warm. Her crying was so persistent that we seated our-

selves a little more than a meter from her stool to observe and await developments. The ape would whimper
for a few moments and then start to climb down from
the stool. Upon each such occasion she was again cautioned to "stay there," with the result that she would
at once withdraw the feet she had slid stealthily from
the top of the stool. Each thwarted attempt would be
followed by a torrent of cries and screams. Once or
twice she rolled on her back upon the seat of the stool
and tumbled to the floor although, immediately upon
striking, she would get up in haste and dutifully scramble back upon the seat.

At length she abruptly solved the problem in an
astonishing and original manner. Her solution was such
that she did not disobey the experimenter and yet she
had her own way. It seemed to serve as a sort of compromise between the two requirements. To accomplish it,
she got down upon the floor, quickly pushed the stool
across the space which separated her from the observer,
and at once climbed up again. After this change in
location, she was still "staying there" as she had previously been instructed, but the position, "there," was
now so close that she could reach out and touch the
experimenter.

There can be little question that this behavior was
distinctly intelligent, although several factors should
be considered in its interpretation. First, she was
thoroughly familiar with movable pieces of furniture,
and, although she had as yet no experience in the *suspended cookie test*, she had previously been observed
to push boxes and chairs. She had of course never
handled this particular stool in such a manner, but she
had nevertheless been acquainted with it at the time
of her solution for no less than six months. Second, it is
probable that the initial push of the stool towards the
experimenter was accidental. This no doubt occurred
during one of her falls, when she may have pushed it
inadvertently for a little distance. Aside from these

conditions, the behavior it seems to us offers clear evidence of a definite plan of action with a goal in view. It would be quite inadequate to account for Gua's getting to the floor, standing upright while she placed her hands on the edge of the stool, pushing it for a full meter in our direction, and getting onto it again, entirely or even primarily as the result of "chance," "accident," "instinct," or "random movements." It was clearly a sudden solution involving a new response in a situation in which this response had never previously been employed.

But if by means of such incidents we present Gua at her best, we must also for the sake of accuracy and completeness present her at her worst, namely when she displayed a stupid lack of insight in what often appeared to us to be elementary situations. An early example of such unintelligent behavior occurred repeatedly at about the age of 8 months. If one simply folded her hands, a manipulation to which she would readily submit, she seemed at that youthful stage to be almost unable to separate them. This was partly because of the crook or bend towards the ends of the fingers, which caused them to act to some extent like hooks. Her difficulty was furthered in all probability by her tendency to exert muscular tension towards closing the fists at the same time that she strained with her arms to pull them apart.

More than once on subsequent occasions she entrapped herself by the awkwardness of her own hands. On one such instance she was hanging by one arm from a door knob, when in order to free the first hand, she placed the second also upon the knob but over the first. Immediately thereafter transferring her weight to the second hand, she found it impossible to extricate the first from beneath it, because of the pressure exerted by gravity. She hung in this way crying for help and pulling continuously to free the captured member until someone released her. On another occasion she placed one of her hands over the upper edge of a folding table which was leaning against the wall. She could not thereafter remove the hand because her own weight as she climbed upon the leaning surface of the table top put greater pressure upon her fingers, which

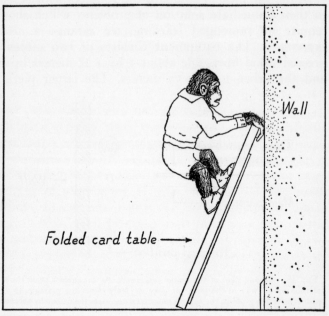

FIG. 17.—An unusual example of "stupid" behavior in the ape consists of her catching her hands beneath the edge of a folded card table, and then climbing upon it so that her own weight makes their release difficult.

were pinched between the table edge and the wall (see Fig. 17).

The physical position of parts of his own body or of objects which he handled, if sufficiently complicated by the force of gravity, occasionally led Donald as well into several "stupid" difficulties. When the human subject was using his walker, for example, he would often fret because he could not pick up things from the floor upon which the wheels of the walker were at that moment resting. And even at the relatively mature age of 15 months he once caught his right hand beneath his left foot, upon which he was partly leaning to maintain a sitting posture. He cried continuously for help in this situation apparently being unable to release his own fingers.

In the attempt to compare the subjects with respect to their immediate solution of problems which should require no prolonged learning, we arrange a *detour experiment*. The equipment consists of two pieces of pressed wood fiber, one about 1 by 1.25 meters in size and the other 1 by 0.55 meters. The larger piece is

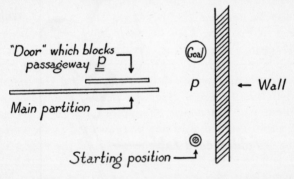

FIG. 18.—Ground plan of the *detour experiment*. As the subject nears the main partition on his way to the goal, the door suddenly closes the passageway *P*. In order to solve the problem the subject must then negotiate the detour by proceeding around the partition.

leaned against a heavy stool so that it remains in an upright position, perpendicular to one of the walls of the room and with its nearest edge about 0.5 meter from it. The second piece will then fit into the space between the larger piece and the wall so as to make a small doorway. When the "door" is closed, the combined surface of the two pieces gives an area nearly two meters wide and a meter in height (about 6 by 3 feet). The experimenter can easily stoop or squat on the side of the partition where the stool is located, and can manipulate the door by sliding it back and forth into and out of the opening (see Fig. 18). The subjects are introduced to this arrangement at the respective ages of 8½ and 11 months.

As in the *delayed reaction tests*, it is Gua who serves as the "incentive" for Donald, and the preferred observer who serves as the "incentive" for Gua. The test proceeds with the experimenter coaxing and beckoning the subject who makes his way through the doorway. This we may call a *direct* trial. It is undertaken to familiarize the subject with the new arrangement and to encourage him to go through the doorway to the incentive stimulus. On the *obstruction* or *detour* trials, the subject is enticed in the same manner, except that the instant he reaches the partition the door is abruptly closed in his face. Can he then solve the problem by satisfactorily negotiating the detour around the end of the screen? He is continually called by the experimenter, even after the door is closed and the incentive is visually obscured. Because this is a simple puzzle-problem and not a test of memory, there is no reason why the subject should not be reminded of the presence of the incentive during the progress of the trials.

It is Donald who is tested first. He is seated in his walker about two meters in front of the testing board, while the observer, holding Gua in his arms, stoops on the other side of the narrow doorway. The child responds to the first *direct* trial immediately, and pushes his walker through the narrow aperture without difficulty.

But in his second attempt, which was also to have been a *direct trial*, he goes toward Gua and the experimenter *by proceeding around the detour*. Such a reaction is totally unexpected since no effort whatever has yet been made to block the shorter pathway by closing the door. He has consequently solved the problem even before it has been set him. His behavior in this instance is no doubt to be related to his exploratory tendencies.

On subsequent detour trials when the door is suddenly shut before him, he sometimes bumps his walker against it or slaps it with his hands. But after a few seconds' delay, he turns and goes without further hesitation around the obstruction. Since he makes five successful responses in series there can be no doubt about his mastery of the problem. A fortnight later, to be sure, when we arrange the experiment in entirely different surroundings for the purpose of photographing it, he fails four times in succession, and cries when the door is shut before him. This is easily explained, however, by the unfamiliar environment and the presence of several strange adults who no doubt disturb him.

When the ape is given her initial *direct* trials, she rushes through the opening and climbs into the arms of the experimenter. Upon our sudden closing of the obstruction door, she immediately stops moving as if puzzled by our disappearance and reverses direction until she has returned almost to the starting point. There she sits down for a moment, then starts off as if going around the partition, but sits down again before she has moved a meter. She remains rooted in this position, curiously enough without uttering a sound, and no amount of coaxing from behind the screen will budge her. She therefore fails to solve the problem.

On the second *detour* trial her behavior is much the same. She backs away and sits down as if nonplussed. As in the initial attempt she will make no further move even though the "incentive" raises his head above the partition so he is visible to her.

On the third attempt she ultimately finds her way around the obstruction, but only after Donald and the other experimenter have previously disappeared from view in the same direction. When she is thus left entirely alone she proceeds in a wide circle as if she is afraid, by hugging the most distant walls of the room. She does not approach within two meters of the obstruction screen. On subsequent tests, although she makes more conventional responses, she will often retreat and sit down when the door is shut, waiting as long as a minute before she successfully completes the detour.

Considering for the moment only the initial performances of the two, we find Donald clearly superior in solving this problem. And yet Gua has some advantages which he does not possess. Among these may be mentioned her superiority in unassisted locomotion, and the possibility, judging from her behavior in other experiments, that she is the more strongly motivated of the two. Sliding doors of the type used in this test are, moreover, entirely foreign to Donald, while Gua during her cage life has at least been near a heavy iron partition which closes in a similar manner.

Like the child, the ape also makes a few failures during later attempts, although these are not numerous. Her failures are without exception accompanied by emotional outbursts. On such occasions she will run away from the detour partition the minute the door is closed, in a typical fear or temper tantrum, giving no attention apparently to where she is going. In one instance, when the equipment is arranged so that the doorway does not close perpendicularly to a wall, but instead against a vertical screen of wire mesh, she performs an original solution of climbing over the top of the closed door by hanging from the wire.

A striking feature of their behavior which bears directly upon the theory of learning is the fact that each of the subjects, after a few successful detours, begins to "short-circuit" exactly as Donald originally did in his second *direct* trial. The ultimate response made by each, *whether the door is left open or closed*, is therefore to go around the obstruction board and not towards the doorway, as shown in Fig. 19, step 3. This reaction is clearly not the one which has been *most frequently* practiced; instead it involves at least in part an entirely new pathway and it is suddenly introduced at some point in the trials when it has never hitherto been made. Aside from the direct course permitted when the door is

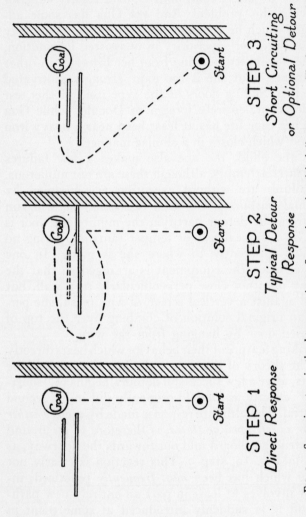

FIG. 19.—Successive steps in the *detour experiment*. Step 1 shows the original direct response. The first successful detours are made after the manner of Step 2. Ultimately, each of the subjects follows the pathway of Step 3, even though the door in front of the goal is left open throughout the entire trial.

255

open, it is the shortest route which the subjects can take.

Such responses may well be called *optional* as opposed to *enforced* detours. The first optional detour appears in Donald's behavior (ignoring his performance on the second *direct* trial) in trial 11. The first optional detour for Gua comes in trial 7. That the subjects are each able to make this new response in the same situation and so solve it completely and satisfactorily, regardless of the position of the door, may be regarded, we think, as additional evidence of insight.

Both Donald and Gua seem also to be capable of reactions which, *if noted in adult human beings*, might be regarded as suggestive of the mental process of "making a decision" or a choice. This becomes clear from certain observations of their behavior when they have reached the respective ages of 15 and 17½ months. The particular responses in question are elicited in connection with a hitherto undescribed test which may be called the *names experiment*. Although this will be reviewed in more detail in Chapter XII, it will suffice here to say that it consists in general of selecting, upon command, one among three articles placed on the floor in front of the subject. Following a specific auditory stimulus from the experimenter, the subject picks up first one and then another of the articles, identifying them as far as possible by name. The experiment is, in fact, no more than a controlled series of trials in the mastery and comprehension of the names themselves.

After some 20 attempts at this task, Gua begins on many trials to manifest a sort of hesitancy or indecision. When asked for one of the objects she will reach forward, withdraw her hand, reach toward a second one, but withdraw again before she has touched it; after looking from one to the other of the two she has selected in this manner she will "make a decision" and falteringly pick up one. Her delay in such instances may amount to as much as 5 or 10 seconds. It is noteworthy

A regular child's nursery chair, with a few minor alterations to make it small enough for Gua, is used throughout her evacuation training.

The child solves the problem in the *detour experiment* by proceeding around the detour even though the direct pathway to the goal is open.

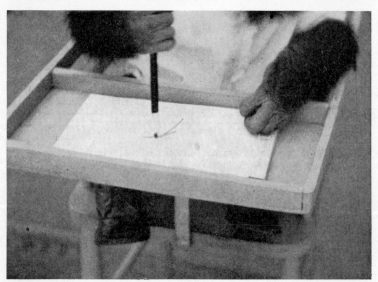

The "writing" test of the Gesell series brings forth satisfactory responses from both subjects. Their ages when the test is first passed are: child 14½ months, ape 12 months.

that the hesitation always seems to show itself in a choice between two of the objects instead of between all three which are employed in the experiment.

Although Donald has to his credit at this time about as many correct selections as Gua, he shows a similar indecision much less frequently, but usually reaches without delay for one of the objects even though it may be the wrong one. Perhaps it would be going too far to say that such activity indicates a psychological state of deciding, choosing, or "thinking," although some persons might so interpret the reactions of the subjects. We make no implications one way or the other in this regard, but report only what is objectively observed in each individual. There are many possible explanations which may range between astonishing extremes.

The final and most exhaustive measure of their higher abilities consists in the monthly application of the Gesell Tests for Pre-School Children. These comprise a series of nearly 150 simple devices and observations which have been carefully standardized. That is to say, the most frequent responses of a large number of normal, superior, and inferior children in the situations employed are on record and can be used to check the reactions of later testees. It is known in this way that the majority of healthy four-month-old babies will hold their heads erect with little wobbling. It is also known that normal nine-month infants will usually reach for a spoon held before them. If a specific subject shows no such interest in a stimulus of this sort there is cause for examining him further. In one of the more advanced tests the problem is to obtain a tiny sugar pill or pellet which is dropped into an open glass bottle in front of the child. If at the age of 1½ years he makes no effort to retrieve the pellet by thrusting his finger into the neck of the bottle, by picking up and shaking or examining the bottle, by turning or knocking it over or attacking it in other similar ways, it is possible that he is retarded in some important structural or psychological aspect.

About ninety of the tests of the Gesell series are applicable at one time or another to Donald and Gua. The specific scores of the subjects in these tests are details which need not concern us here. We shall confine ourselves rather to the general progress of the testees from month to month and particularly to *differences in test performance* between them. The items in which we have a special interest are consequently those in which the child surpasses the ape and those in which the ape is in advance of the child.

It should be noted in this connection that (exclusive of such minor variations as are bound to appear in individual cases) the performance of the human infant is in the main about average for his age. For purposes of comparison, therefore, the test results of Donald may serve as a sample "normal" record for a child of his age in the particular human environment in which he has been reared. If the chimpanzee is better, equal to, or worse than the human "control" in some particular phase of behavior, we may say broadly speaking that she is correspondingly better, equal to, or worse than the average child who is 2½ months her senior.

The development of language responses, which form an important part of the Gesell Tests, we leave to a separate consideration in Chapter XII.

I

When the subjects are first examined in this way Gua is 8 and Donald 10½ months of age. At that time they prove to be so similar in all but seven of the tests and observations recorded, that their abilities in these departments may be regarded as equivalent. Of the seven, four are tests in which the ape clearly surpasses the child and three are tests in which the child has the upper hand. Among the boy's superior achievements are (1) his playful reactions during his bath, which are of a distinctly higher type than those displayed by the ape. He is similarly more advanced (2) in his ability to pick up a small pill or pellet with a fine thumb-and-finger pincer reaction, while (3) his manipulation surpasses Gua's when he plays with objects, as in exploiting a piece of paper, etc.

At this early date we can find little evidence of the influence of the human environment upon the activity of the chimpanzee. But she comes off with flying colors (1) in a comparison of "creeping" or "crawling," provided we choose to classify her all-four locomotion in such category, since this has never been one of the child's accomplishments. She is (2) able to walk upright with assistance while the child is not, and (3) she can "climb for an object" about as well as a two-year-old human. To our surprise (4) she seems to display a more active interest in her own reflection in a mirror than the boy.

The score for the first testing, therefore, in terms of the number of items in which one subject is superior to the other, gives the chimpanzee the advantage in four tests and the human the advantage in three.

II

When the measurements are made a month later both ape and child show considerable development. This is indicated in Donald by the fact that he passes nine new tests in which he was unable to score the month before. In two of the nine he succeeds in overtaking Gua. He is able at this time to walk upright with assistance, as she did during the first examination, and his reactions to the mirror image are about like those of the chimpanzee. Four of the new tests which Donald passes are tasks in which the animal similarly scores, so that neither gains an advantage in these items. Thus they both receive credit for standing upright without assistance; for responding to the expression "no, no" if they start to touch a forbidden object; for holding three small red cubes in their hands; and for progress in bowel control.

The child has definitely forged ahead of the ape in three entirely new performances which Gua has been unable to duplicate. These consist (1) in his superior inhibiting of the hand-to-mouth reaction, so that he no longer chews or bites as many inedible objects as the animal. He also (2) succeeds in placing a small red cube in a tin cup when commanded and shown how to do so, and he likewise (3) removes the cup when it is inverted over the cube.

Although these three achievements are not yet equalled by Gua, she nevertheless passes seven tests during the second series of measurements which she did not pass during the first. Four of these it will be remembered Donald also passed at the same time. Two are beyond him, and in one she has come up from behind the child to equal his earlier performance. The animal is actually graded higher (1) in upright walking, for the human subject at 11½ months can walk only with assistance, while the chimpanzee, at 9, can take four of five steps entirely by herself. At this age also she (2) displays affectionate behavior which is comparable in general to that of many children 1½ to 2 years old. And she has overtaken Donald in the development of playful reactions during the bath.

The total scores up to this point in terms of the tests passed exclusively by one subject and not by the other, are then as follows. For the first month, Donald, 3; Gua, 4. For the second month, Donald, 3; Gua, 2. Total for the first 2 months, Donald, 6; Gua, 6.

III

In the third examination the subjects progress by an even greater margin than they did in the second. The child, then 12½ months old, advances in ten additional tests which he was previously unable to pass, and the ape, 10 months old, advances in eight. Six of the new tests of each are passed in common by the other subject, so that their competitive record is unaffected by these particular advances. Perhaps the most important developments recorded in the six new tests in which the scoring is equal consist in the acquisition of such playful childlike tricks as playing peek-a-boo, and in the ability to imitate simple acts performed by the tester. Each will now rattle a spoon in a tin cup when encouraged and shown how to do so, and each will also ring a small bell by waving it back and forth. Donald is able, furthermore, to match Gua's earlier performance of walking without help, and receives the same rating which she got in this behavior during the last testing. But although the scores are the same, since each "walks upright without assistance," the ape is really superior with respect to the distance which she can walk and the agility which she displays. Gua, for her part, overtakes Donald in the task of placing the cube in the tin cup, a test in which he was successful the month before, and she also equals his performance of playing with or exploiting a sheet of paper at which he was superior two months earlier.

With regard to the number of *new* tests passed by one subject *but not by the other*, the human here takes a commanding lead, for he has the advantage of three further tests while Gua bests him in not a single additional performance. One of the child's superior acts is (1) in unwrapping a cube from a small bundle of paper which has been crumpled around it before his eyes. In another (2) he succeeds in securing the pellet after it is dropped through the neck of the glass bottle. His final and most advanced problem consists (3) in inserting a round block in the circular hole of a three-hole "form board." The two remaining holes of this simple puzzle are in the shape of a square and a triangle respectively. The infant at first observes the examiner perform this trick; but he must do it correctly himself immediately afterward and not attempt to place the round block into either the triangular or the square hole.

Although the ape maintains her earlier superiority in climbing and in affectionate behavior, she has no additional developments in which the child has not also advanced at the same time.

Since Donald now has to his credit three further tests which Gua has not solved, the total cumulative scores become: for the child, 9; for the ape, 6.

IV

Their ages at the fourth testing are 13½ and 11 months respectively. The human subject on this occasion advances in five additional tests, while the animal succeeds in seven. Three of the new performances of each are also accomplished for the first time by the other subject. These consist in tossing a rubber ball into a box upon command of the examiner, of pounding or squeezing a rubber doll so as to produce a whistling sound, and of building a small "tower" of blocks by placing one block upon another.

The child advances beyond the ape (1) through saying "ba, ba" for "bye, bye" when someone waves at him. Although at first glance this may appear to be a matter of language, Gua could also have scored on this test even without uttering a sound, had she learned to *wave* "bye, bye" in the same situation. Donald is likewise superior (2) in bowel control in that he is beginning to "tell" the observers before impending evacuations.

The ape on the other hand equals two of the human's earlier performances by unwrapping the cube from the paper bundle and by securing it from beneath the inverted cup. The latter problem was originally solved by Donald two months previously. She definitely surpasses him (1) in her early progress of eating with a spoon and (2) in "asking" for special dishes at the table by reaching towards them (pointing?) and by giving an appreciative grunt when she observes them.

Since Donald advances in two performances which Gua has not duplicated, while Gua also betters the child in two, the scores up to this time stand: Donald, 11; Gua, 8.

v

At the fifth administration of the tests, the ages of the subjects are 14½ and 12 months. Donald advances beyond his immediately preceding record in three additional respects and Gua improves in two.

Although one of the advancements of each subject is in the same test in which the other also progresses, Donald clearly makes a higher score than Gua in this particular task. The test consists (1) in scribbling with a pencil or crayon upon a piece of paper. Gua does this excellently after a brief demonstration by the examiner, but Donald does it for the first time *spontaneously*, that is, without any demonstration whatever. In spite of such splendid reactions on the part of the chimpanzee, we must according to our system of scoring give Donald complete credit for a superior response. He also advances in two further performances which Gua seems unable to duplicate. One of these is (2) building with blocks in which he now succeeds in adding two blocks to the examiner's demonstration tower. The other (3) involves his behavior during the form-board test, in which he is at present able to place the circle into its proper hole without any assistance at all. It is to be noted that Gua also succeeds in solving the form-board problem at this testing, but only after careful and repeated demonstrations. At the same time, therefore, that she equals the performance which the child first showed two months earlier, the boy surpasses his own previous mark in the same test. As a result he receives additional credit for it in the scoring for the current month.

Since there have been, then, three further departments in which the child has shown himself superior, and no *new* aspects in which the ape has surpassed the child, the cumulative month-by-month scoring becomes: for Donald, 14 tests; and for Gua, 8.

VI

During the sixth testing, when the subjects are 15½ and 13 months of age, respectively, the child increases his advantage by an even greater extent. This in spite of the fact that he succeeds altogether in only three new tests while Gua succeeds in four. But he already possesses the advantage in so many directions that it is possible for the ape to make considerable progress in those performances in which she has previously been behind the boy without surpassing him in any entirely new accomplishments.

As a matter of fact, this is about what happens during the present series of measurements, for three of Gua's four new tests have already been passed by the human subject. Thus she now achieves the performances of scribbling spontaneously and of adding two blocks to the examiner's tower. Each of these tests the human subject first accomplished a month before. She also succeeds in getting the pellet out of the glass bottle, a task which was first solved by Donald three months earlier. The method by which she accomplishes this is to tilt the bottle against her lips as if it were a drinking glass, and so to receive the pellet in her mouth. The remaining new test in which she scores involves the matter of eating with a spoon. As we have already seen, Gua registered her first progress in this activity two months before. By the time of the current testing she has advanced considerably over her previous score and has consequently left the human subject that much further behind. She now (1) eats by herself "without much spilling," a performance which compares favorably to that of a year-and-a-half- or two-year-old child, and she is therefore given a high rating for this progress in development.

Donald, for his part, overtakes Gua in the single respect that he can now climb about as well as she did five months earlier. He is given two superior scores, however, because of the fact that he is judged to be slightly better (1) in bladder training and because (2) he "tries to turn door knobs" even though he cannot open the doors to which they are attached. The ape, at her present age, does not similarly direct her attention to the knobs.

Since the boy now has the advantage in turning door knobs and in bladder training, while Gua is superior in the rapid development of her spoon eating, the cumulative scores, including the present testing, become: for Donald, 16; for Gua, 9.

VII

The seventh examination brings out striking progress in new performances but no appreciable change in the general relationships which already exist. Each subject on this occasion masters six new tests, two of which are also passed by the other subject. Of the remaining four, each overtakes the other in two and surpasses him in two. The child, at 16½ months, begins to demonstrate affectionate behavior like that which Gua first showed five months earlier; and he has learned to "climb for an object" as she did at the first testing. Gua, at 14 months, scores in bladder training, as Donald did in the sixth testing. She also makes her first *fine prehension* of the small pellet by picking it up with the thumb and index finger. This compares with Donald's similar achievement six months earlier when the task was first set him.

One respect in which the child excels the ape concerns what Professor Gesell has called (1) "dramatic play." He has, for example, made imitative reproductions of the experimenter's walk, while the ape has not been seen to indulge in such subtle forms of activity. The child will also (2) point to a part of the body (the nose) when told to do so, while Gua has not yet acquired this response. The chimpanzee, on the other hand, advances beyond Donald in that now she can (1) *actually open doors* by turning the knobs. This is an accomplishment which many children two or even three years old find difficult. In addition, she shows a more marked interest (2) in looking at pictures than the child does and so is rated higher in such perceptual behavior.

Since each subject advances beyond the other in two respects, the total scores now stand: Donald, 18; Gua, 11.

VIII

At the eighth application of the measurements, Donald has reached the age of 17½ months and Gua 15 months. The child at this time succeeds in six new performances, while the chimpanzee is not far behind with five. Oddly enough there are no duplications whatever in their separate advancements and each subject surpasses the other in four new tests. The remaining two developments for Donald consist in his overtaking Gua in the early use of the spoon, his present behavior in this regard comparing, therefore, with hers four months previously. He is also beginning to point to special dishes at the table, an item of behavior in which Gua has also scored for the past four months. The ape in her turn matches the boy's activity of the last previous testing by pointing to her nose when told to do so. It might be mentioned in passing that the diminutive size of the chimpanzee nose should render this accomplishment a relatively more difficult one for the subhuman than for the human subject.

The four new tasks in which Donald proves superior are (1) in drawing a straight line in imitation of the examiner, instead of simply scribbling; (2) in placing both the circular and the triangular blocks in their proper holes in the form board; (3) in correctly locating the circular block even after the entire form board has been "reversed" by rotating it through an arc of 180 degrees in the attempt to confuse the subjects; and (4) in adding as many as three blocks to the examiner's demonstration tower. He therefore makes a further advancement in block building in which he previously (at the fifth testing) received credit for a performance which was at that time better than Gua's. The grading of this task in some of the other testings has been the same for each subject, although there has always been a marked difference in manipulative facility which the test scoring does not take into full account. A certain clumsiness or awkwardness seems to make it difficult for Gua to release the blocks which she places upon the towers she constructs. As a result it is hard for her to build without upsetting the product of her efforts.

The superiority of the ape may be seen to display itself during the present month (1) in the inhibition of forbidden acts. She obviously seems to know in some cases what is taboo, and refrains without command if one of the experimenters is observing her. She also receives a higher score because of (2) the behavior of "greeting people." She will now grunt her salutation to old acquaintances in a manner analogous to Donald's saying of "ba, ba" for "bye, bye" four months before. The human subject has since suffered a regression in this behavior, so that it seems only fair to give the ape full credit for her present advantage. Finally, she is better in both (3) bladder and (4) bowel training, since she now very often "asks" to go to the toilet. The child, to be sure, scored four months previously (that is, at the fourth testing) in announcing his needs with regard to the bowels. But like the case of the salutations, this behavior did not persist, so that the ape at present is clearly his superior in this respect.

Each subject, therefore, adds four new credits to his previous score, which brings the respective totals to 22 for Donald and 15 for Gua.

IX

The ninth and last testing is made when Donald has reached the age of 18½ months and Gua is 16. The human subject succeeds at this time in four tasks which he has never done previously, while the ape succeeds in only three. In one of the tests about which there may be considerable question the scores show the two to be the same. This grading comes again in the uncertain task of block building, where structural differences in the hands of the subjects play such an important part. For Gua achieves the astonishing result of building a tower of six blocks, *providing we steady her arm* when she releases successive blocks, so that the tower will not collapse. But if the arm is not in some way supported, she has difficulty on some attempts in building even a tower of two blocks without destroying it as the second block is released. Although Donald, on the other hand, builds only to a height of three blocks, he does so in imitation of the examiner's model, without further assistance of any kind. In a quandary over these differences the examiner finally gives each subject the same score.

The child overtakes the animal in the matter of inhibiting forbidden acts and in his interest in pictures, which has noticeably increased. He also reaches the level of the ape in bowel control, since he is now beginning again to tell of his needs as he originally did at the fourth testing. But he is not at this time credited with passing a new test in the restoration of this accomplishment, for such credit was allowed four months before.

The ape, in her turn, reproduces the child's earlier results with the form board. In fact she not only accomplishes the surprising task of placing both the circle and the triangle in their proper holes without any assistance, but she adapts to the reversed form board as well. The only respect in which either advances beyond the other consists in Donald's performance of (1) pointing separately to his nose and to his ears upon verbal direction. Gua is still able to indicate only one part of her body (the nose). The child by this means raises his previous monthly score by one point.

The final results in terms of the number of tests in which each subject is superior to the other, carried forward from month to month, are consequently: for Donald, 23; for Gua, 15.

Shall we conclude from these figures that the ape is about two-thirds "as intelligent" as a human child 2½ months her senior? A conservative reply to this question is that such a statement considerably oversimplifies the case. It serves too much as a general catchall and fails to take account of many essential details.

The system of scoring, by which we have made our comparison is, on the face of it, but a crude sort of indicator. This can be readily shown if, instead of selecting the tests each month which are passed by one subject *but not by the other*, we consider the new accomplishments of each without regard to whether the other passes or fails in the same tests. By such a rating we find that Donald improves from the second to the ninth testing, inclusive, in a total of 46 new tests, while Gua passes 42 new ones. The comparative month-by-month advances in the number of new Gesell tests passed suggests a difference no greater than that to be expected between two children of about the same age. The results are given graphically in the growth curves in Fig. 20.

Of course such striking similarity in the respective records may be attributed to some extent to practice on the part of the subjects throughout the nine separate testings and to their growing familiarity with the test materials. The technique of the testers, which was uniformly the same for each individual, may also have played some part in regularizing the two performances. To the extent that these influences affected the subjects, their behavior may be said to show the effect of the common environment.

It must not be forgotten in this connection that there are a number of learned tasks in which the ape has shown herself to be actually above the average human

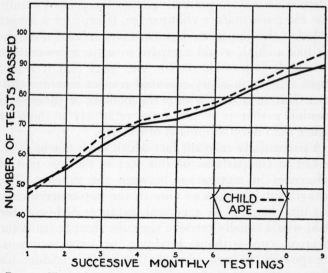

FIG. 20.—The total number of *Gesell tests* passed during successive months is shown in the growth curves above. Although the child has a slight advantage, the striking similarity in the curves is evidence of the remarkable progress of the chimpanzee (see text).

as old or even older than herself. Examples of superior behavior of this sort consist of her "telling" the experimenters in bladder and bowel training, her unusual progress at eating with a spoon, and her striking advancement in opening doors. There are other quite obvious respects in which Gua is inferior to normal humans of her own age. Instances of this are her retardation in picking up the pellet with the thumb-and-finger reaction of the child, her apparent inability to make any progress towards inhibiting the hand-to-mouth reaction, and her lack of speech development, which has been omitted entirely from the present discussion.

Certainly variations in structure and in the rate of maturation can account for many of the differences in the test behavior of the two. But Gua's early cage life of $7\frac{1}{2}$ months may also have influenced her performance in a number of significant and yet unknown aspects. There is no way of predicting from the present results how the more mature chimpanzee, if kept for a longer period in the human environment and treated throughout like a child, would compare with the more mature human. It is possible on the one hand that it would prove inferior in every essential respect to older children. But it is also within the bounds of theoretical possibility that it would score relatively as high or higher than normal humans of like age.

A particularly relevant fact which must not be overlooked in comparisons of this sort is the question of differences in motivation between the subjects. The behavior of Donald and Gua in the cup-covered-cube test may be cited as a typical instance. Although the child would usually retrieve the cube from beneath the inverted cup without prodding or encouragement, the ape could be induced to get it only after considerable effort on the part of the examiner. As a result one might at first glance have believed Gua incapable of performing this act without more outside assistance than the child needed. Yet she could duplicate the performance of the boy with equal accuracy and even greater speed, as was readily shown if we placed a bit of apple or orange beneath the cup. She thereby demonstrated that she knew well enough how to proceed but that the cube or "manipulative interest in the response itself" was not effective in urging her to action. In instances of this sort it is clearly the incentive which materially influences the behavior of the subject. Differences in motivation, in addition to the more obvious structural and

271

maturational factors, may therefore account to a large extent for differences in performance.

The same knotty problem is a vitally important feature, not only of the intelligence tests, but of the learning experiments and comparative tasks of every sort with which our two subjects have been confronted. Since it is extremely difficult to control the degree of motivation even by the most careful laboratory procedures, it should be obvious from the more homelike atmosphere in which these studies were conducted that no exact measure of it could be undertaken. This would have been a problem of no small proportions with two organisms of the same kind. But with Donald and Gua, whose emotional backgrounds were at the start so divergent, it proved a matter about which little could be done.

It was impossible to motivate the subjects according to the common practice in experiments upon animals by withholding food or water until they were in need of it, and then permitting them to work for such a reward. This method would not only have threatened the health of each of our charges, but it would have militated against the prescribed conditions of the research as well. Even in those specific tests in which food was used as an incentive, it is doubtful if either subject ever became very hungry. We have witnessed each of them work diligently to secure a nibble of apple or a bit of cookie, only to ignore the reward entirely once he had obtained it. In no case, we think, can their appetites be said to have formed particularly effective motives for experimentation.

It became evident, however, from the early behavior of the subjects that actual success in the solution of a problem was a powerful stimulus for further work. "Nothing succeeds like success" is an axiom which seemed to be demonstrably effective with these small individuals. If they had made a number of poor trials on any particular test, there was a real danger that they might thereafter lie down on the job altogether and not even attempt to work.

A similar tendency to cease working was noticeable when a task had been so well learned that it became automatic, or, in other words, when it had been considerably "overlearned." In such cases the interest in the thing seemed to be lost to the subjects, who would often trifle over a simple problem for minutes when they had previously demonstrated many times that they could solve it in a few seconds. This peculiar inhibition seemed to assert itself more especially near the end of a relatively long solution, but when that solution was imminent, than on other occasions. Oddly enough it was Gua who appeared to be subject to it to a greater extent than Donald, possibly because she learned in general at a faster rate and so in the same number of trials would "overlearn" to a greater degree.

Both were remarkably susceptible to praise as a motivating factor—much more so than they were to punishment or blame. In fact, it is our candid opinion that one of the most effective types of motivation which could be employed for simple learning experiments in the case of each of the subjects was verbal commendation of this sort. The praise usually consisted in saying, "That's fine. That's a good boy (or girl). Now you know how to do it, don't you?" The effect of such stimuli was more directly observable upon Donald than it was upon Gua, in that he would frequently respond by looking up at the experimenter and smiling. But in spite of the lack of an overt reaction of this sort in the ape, praise proved for her to be quite as satisfactory a motivating device as for the child. One entire experiment (the *names experiment*, see Chapter XII) in which each of them worked splendidly had no motivation except verbal commendation or rebuke administered by the experimenter after appropriately successful or unsuccessful trials.

273

Without a doubt it was the separation from the experimenter in the *delayed reaction tests* which served to produce the most serious emotional upheaval on the part of Gua. Although Donald in similar tests was occasionally disturbed, there is no denying the fact that the ape seemed in general to be much more affected than he was. It is reasonable to suppose, therefore, that her motivation was greater throughout the earlier trials in this particular experiment than the child's, and this may account in part for her superior "memory" as measured by them. Probably it would be going too far to say that one of the characteristic differences between the subjects consisted in Gua's greater susceptibility to motivating influences. Yet surely her emotional activity and the violence and severity of her impulses, as judged from her behavior, would suggest that with less subtle incentives this was likely to be the case.

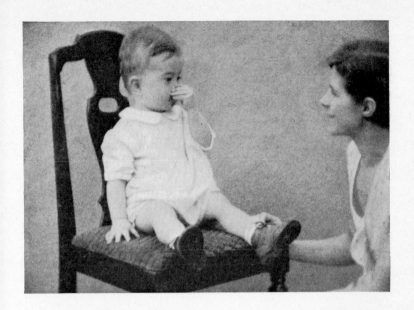

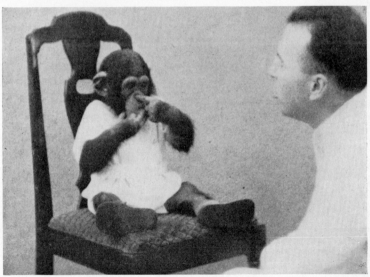

They are here responding to the command, "Show me your nose." The child seizes his nose between his thumb and fingers, while Gua points to hers with her index finger.

Walking together serves at different times as evidence of a common "understanding" of the command, "Take Gua's hand." This remark, addressed to Donald, is at first responded to more successfully by the ape than by the child. In a number of other instances Donald likewise demonstrates that he comprehends commands originally reserved for Gua, by suddenly responding to them before she is able to do so.

Chapter XII

COMMUNICATION AND LANGUAGE

ALMOST from the beginning of her human training Gua seemed to possess a rudimentary,
non-vocal form of communication by means of
which her impending actions could be predicted by
those who knew her well. This was not so much a language of gesture as it was a language of action. Any
performance which was about to be undertaken, or for
which apparently she possessed some unsatisfied impulse, would often be indicated by incipient or intro-
ductory reactions to the performance itself. We do not
mean to suggest that this was necessarily a "conscious"
procedure by means of which she "tried" to make herself understood. It consisted rather in preparatory
behavior the significance of which the observers themselves, because of their intimacy with Gua, came to
know. And yet it frequently served as an effective means
of communicating her needs. If hungry, for instance,
she would bite or chew at the clothing of the experimenter or at his fingers, or she would suck at objects
she placed in her mouth. Sometimes if her high chair
happened to be very close to us she would start to climb
into it. When she was properly seated for a meal and a
cup of milk was held before her she would either protrude her lips and lean towards the cup if she wanted
more, or she would reach out and pull the cup towards
her mouth by hooking her fingers over its brim. Occasionally she pushed the cup away when she had had
enough, although her customary reaction in such cases
was to turn her head away or turn her back. Similarly,
when she had finished her meal she would usually rise

275

to her feet in the high chair and start to climb out of it herself.

Once, when she was 9½ months old, one of the observers attempted without ceremony to feed her in the kitchen of the house. But she refused to open her mouth when the cup of milk was offered. On a neighboring table was a bowl of apples which had been peeled and sliced preparatory to making apple sauce. The report of her subsequent activity appears in our notes as follows: "Then she scrambled from my lap, went to the table where the apples were, chinned herself on its edge, and extended her lips towards the apples. She might as well have said in so many words, 'I don't want any of that milk. Give me some apple.'"

In the beginning it seemed as though she responded more readily to gestures or to "tactual communication" on our part than she did to vocalization. Merely touching a finger to her lips proved during the first few weeks to be an efficient way of stopping her biting of furniture. This method became effective, of course, because we first forcibly pushed her mouth from the object bitten. Similarly, a slight touch on her side or back would immediately cause her to turn and give attention in that direction. The latter stimulus was commonly employed by the observer as a means of securing her attention throughout the entire period of the research.

With her further development, the "language of action" became somewhat more complex. Thus during Gua's tenth month she would indicate sleepiness by suddenly throwing herself prone upon the floor in the very midst of some activity. Although she usually remained there for only a few seconds, the abruptness of this behavior and its repeatedness left little doubt as to the interpretation. If prepared for a nap immediately after a response of this kind, she would usually fall asleep at once. Thirst she showed when in the house by repeated trips to the five-gallon water bottle, by licking it, biting the cork, or tipping it. Her strong attraction for water faucets, both indoors and out, may be recalled in this connection.

She began at an early age to remove her bib without assistance as soon as she had eaten all she wanted. This she accomplished by pulling it off over her head. By the time she was a year old she would also aid us in putting it on by bending her head forward; or if the strings of the bib were already tied, as was sometimes the case, she would help pull the loop downward over her head. On such occasions she invariably ate a good meal. At certain other times she failed entirely to offer any assistance when we fastened the bib upon her; instead she pulled it off as soon as this operation had been completed and before she could be offered food. In these instances she usually ate nothing at all.

When she had become 15 months old she would similarly indicate in a non-vocal manner certain play impulses, particularly that of being swung or whirled by adult friends. Her method was to reach upward, seize one or, if possible, both hands of the playmate selected, who was always standing when she made such advances. She would subsequently walk three or four steps to the side, and hang from the appendage she had taken so that her own weight would start her swinging. This maneuver was interpreted by the humans upon whom she practiced it as an invitation to swing, spin, or be held so that she could do acrobatics.

The communication of her bowel and bladder needs, which was frequently of a non-vocal nature, formed toward the end one of the most important and regular features of this elementary language. Her signals in such cases were sometimes accompanied by sound, but there were many instances in which anticipatory actions of other sorts were employed alone.

Without a doubt the most impressive example of Gua's non-vocal communication occurred at the age of about 13 months in a learning problem which neither of the subjects ever completely mastered. The task was to drink orange juice from a small-necked half-pint bottle 25 centimeters (10 inches) in height. After a number of trials Gua had progressed to the point where she could hold the bottle in the correctly tilted position as she poured the orange juice into her mouth. But curiously enough, in spite of this progress, she seemed quite unable to get the bottle safely from the floor to her mouth unless someone placed her hands properly upon its sides and assisted her to lift it without spilling the contents. Once the initial movements had been made, however, she would follow through by holding the bottle without difficulty as she consumed the liquid. Her helplessness at the start of each drink was often a spectacle for the arousal of pity. Orange juice was probably her favorite drink, and yet with such an incentive so near at hand she knew not how to obtain it. She would bite and suck the neck of the bottle, point to the reward in the bottom, put her finger in the neck of the bottle, and look (imploringly?) at the experimenter.

Ultimately, she evolved an entirely new solution of the difficulty, which was accomplished in the following manner. She reached with her right hand towards the attendant observer, whose left hand at the time was about 15 centimeters away from her. She then took the fingers of the observer's hand in her own and *pulled his hand to the base of the bottle*. We were so astonished at this original turn of events that for a moment we did not realize its full purport. No other interpretation seems possible except that Gua was "asking" us to start her successfully in the procedure of manipulating the bottle. That the ape's behavior could hardly have been accidental is shown by the fact that during the further course of the tests it appeared no less than seven times. Its second occurrence came two weeks after the first. Its third, fourth, and fifth, two days after the second. And the last two in a final trial two days after the fifth attempt.

In the matter of *vocal communication*, on the other hand, the difference between the subjects was favorable to the child, who was obviously superior to Gua even at the younger ages. Yet the ape herself made remarkable progress in the use to which she put some of the vocal reactions she possessed.

It seemed for a time as if the human subject employed voice inflection or intonation, *without articulation*, largely as an emotional reaction. Often his vocalization would be made with closed lips. The pitch would frequently vary over a wide range, even within a single vocalization. The length of the sound also seemed important, as was the intensity. If he encountered a new and attractive plaything he would be likely to vocalize in a relatively high-pitched rising intonation which may be diagrammed like this, "⟋." If he had some apparently unpleasant experience, such as picking up an object which upon physical contact was discovered to be wet and sticky, his vocalization would proceed in a downward pitch. It would also start several notes lower than the "pleasant" type of vocalization. One might represent it in diagram like this, "⟍."

By the time the child had attained the age of 17 months it seemed to us that one could with some justification regard these two types of sound as roughly equivalent in articulate language to the words "yes" and "no," respectively. He greatly extended their use by combining them with a crude sort of pointing which consisted in extending the arm towards the object indicated, with the fingers spread in fan shape and the wrist bent backward. Sometimes he would hold or touch the object in question. By means of such gestures and the "yes" vocalization he seemed to be able to "ask" for many of the things he wanted. He would point to the crack between the front door and its frame and make the questioning "yes" sound to go out; he would touch the high chair and vocalize in the same way to be put

up into it; or when he wished some immediately un-
attainable object he would stretch his arms towards
it and make the same sound. Once, when we presumed
he was very hungry, he pulled himself up on the lower
rung of his high chair, got his bib, and toddled to the
kitchen holding it out to one of the experimenters. His
desires were audibly affirmed during this maneuver,
as in the previous instances.

If he was forbidden from certain behavior or required
to do something he seemed not to like, the opposite or
"no" type of intonation would be produced. Crying,
of course, was resorted to in extreme cases for both
positive and negative wants. But definitely understand-
able cues or gestures on the child's part *without vocal
accompaniment* were almost entirely absent, so that there
was little which compared specifically to Gua's "action
language."

It is quite possible in this connection that the environment in which the subjects lived was not particularly
conducive to the early development of articulate language responses. One might reasonably make such an
inference, at any rate, since Donald, as measured by
the language tests in the Gesell series proved before
very long to be considerably retarded for his age. At
11½ months he had at his command three words, in
addition to the customary babble sounds of "da-da,"
"ma-ma," etc. These were "Gya" for Gua, "din-din"
for food or dinner, and "daddy." His initial use of
words was consequently about that of the average year-
old infant. Yet for some strange cause, the child did
not progress beyond this level until after the termination of the nine-months period of observation. There
were three other "words" which he said at later periods,
namely "ba" for boo, "da" for down, and "bow-wow"
for dog. It so happened, however, that in spite of this
total of six he never seemed to possess more than three
during any month. The new acquisitions oddly enough
were accompanied by the loss of the old, so that the

number of words in his entire vocabulary remained unchanged. In regard to the use of words he was therefore less in advance of Gua than he might have been. Indeed it can be safely said that neither subject really learned to talk during the interval of the research.

No doubt the necessity of spending so much time with tests of various sorts was to some extent responsible for this retardation. In addition the opportunity of associating with other children, an advantage possessed by most infants, was in view of the confining nature of the work of comparatively infrequent occurrence. The important fact with reference to this question is that despite the child's lack of progress in the acquisition of human language responses, it was precisely in the development of *articulate* sounds in which he significantly outshone the ape. There was no attempt on Gua's part to use her lips, tongue, teeth, and mouth cavity in the production of new utterances; while in the case of the human subject a continuous vocalized play was apparent from the earliest months. It was as if the child, like other normal humans of similar age, was *practicing* the formation of new vowels and consonants. In this manner the earlier cooing, singing, or humming of the young baby was transformed into a continual "la-la-la," "ngah-ngah," "gee-gee," etc., which constituted his later babble. Although Gua in her turn could form several vowels and although she seemed to be able to manipulate her lips and tongue with perhaps greater facility than the boy, no additional sounds were ever observed beyond those which she already possessed when we first made her acquaintance. There were no "random" noises to compare with the baby's prattle or to the apparently spontaneous chatter of many birds. On the whole, it may be said that she never vocalized without some definite provocation, that is, without a clearly discernible external stimulus or cause. And in most cases this stimulus was obviously of an emotional character.

The superiority of the child in *vocal imitation* stands also as a striking difference between the two subjects. His specific reproduction of certain noises made by the ape we have already considered (see Chapter VI). In view of the human's rapid adoption of such barks or grunts, and his subsequent employment of them in new and original situations, one can easily realize the full possibility of the so-called wild children taking over completely the growls and noises of the animal associates with which they are reported to have been found.

The vocalizations which Gua possessed, and which she made use of in such later language responses as she developed, can be generally classified, it seems to us, into four main groups.

1. *The Bark*. This is a guttural grunt resembling the bark of a small dog. It may vary in pitch and intensity although it never reverts to anything in the nature of a growl. Growling, in fact, is not one of the chimpanzee's accomplishments. Usually Gua's bark occurs within a baritone pitch range and is given in a series of two or more short syllables such as a dog might emit. It seems to signify aggression and is often accompanied by attack, threat of attack, or slapping. In some cases it appears to suggest anger or warning. The general behavior which goes with it would be likely to occur in the adult human along with such words as, "Get away from me," or "Let me alone." The bark is commonly elicited by the presence of strangers, especially if they make unwelcome advances toward Gua. The onlooker is likely to interpret it as a sound of *unpleasant* character.

2. *The Food-bark*. This is so closely related to the first sound that there is some question whether it should be separately classified. But it is usually softer—occasionally so soft as to be entirely unvocalized. It then resembles what might be called a "whispered bark." Whether vocalized or unvocalized the sound is initiated by a sudden release of air by the soft palate. If vocalized,

it is low in pitch with a vowel like the *u* in the word
"but," sometimes changing to the *oo* as in "look" (see
earlier description in Chapter VI). On some occasions,
when Gua is very hungry and suddenly sees food, the
sound may rise in pitch and intensity until it is indis-
tinguishable from bark number one. Yet the situations
in which it occurs are to be sharply differentiated from
those in which the first sound is made. The food-bark as
judged by human standards seems clearly to be a *pleasant* sort of utterance, frequently one of anticipation.

3. *The Screech or Scream.* This is a shrill cry often
very loud and piercing in the soprano pitch range. It is
frequently accompanied by a palate trill. From a distance such vocalizations somewhat resemble the yelps
of an injured dog, or the call of a parrot or of some wild
bird. (The screams of Gua were occasionally mistaken
for parrot sounds by the uninitiated.) They are distinctly
sounds of *unpleasant* character, given mostly in fear,
we think, and rarely perhaps in pain.

4. *The "Oo-oo" Cry.* By far the commonest sound,
this can be compared, if one wishes a subhuman analogy, to the whining of a dog. Or, to stretch a point, one
might say it is like the fretting or mild crying of a human
infant. Gua utters it with the lips protruded in a pout
so as distinctly to form the vowel *oo* as in the words
"choose" or "loose." It can occur in all pitches from a
soft low contralto to a loud high note which merges into
the scream. At other times it can be so faint as to be
quite unvocalized. In such instances it resembles the
"whispered bark" of the food sound. Apparently it is
unpleasant in connotation, but not necessarily so violently unpleasant as the scream. It sometimes possesses
a whimpering, pleading, or imploring quality. Again
it seems to serve as a sound of alarm, trouble, uncertainty, or fear. Gua "oo-oo's" in this manner when she
is scolded, when left alone, when she soils her clothing,
or when she hears a strange noise which causes her to
run to one of the experimenters for protection.

These comprise the principal vocalizations in the repertory of the animal subject. Of course she was capable in addition of human-like sneezes and coughs, while her laughter as we have seen was strikingly human in many respects. Her vocalizations were sometimes combined by one merging into the other so as to produce sound patterns of considerable complexity. It is to be noted, however, that the chimpanzee was never observed to emit any prolonged single utterance. All her sounds were in the nature of short syllables which occurred in rapid succession, the independent units of even the scream continuing for only a second or two. A curious fact in this respect is that her hiccoughing, which was a common enough reaction, proved to be a procedure of complete silence. For although her whole frame would shake with the severity of the upheaval, she emitted not the slightest sound.

As was the case with Donald's rising and declining voice inflections which came to be employed to some extent as affirmative and negative signals, so Gua herself after a few months appeared similarly to differentiate between certain of her vocalizations. The food-bark, which has been characterized as the anticipatory sound suggestive of pleasure, was in many cases employed, so it seemed to us, as a human might use the word "yes." The "oo-oo" cry, conversely, came to serve as a rough equivalent for "no," typifying in this respect a negative, withdrawing, or avoiding reaction. The most important development with reference to these sounds probably consisted in the extension of the use of the food-bark to situations where no food was present.

At first this extension was no doubt aided by the experimenters, who, noticing Gua's almost universal tendency to grunt at the sight of an orange, sought to condition her to make the same sound upon hearing the spoken word "orange." Twice each day before she was given her regular ration of fruit juice, the experi-

menter would say, "Do you want some *orange* juice?"
or "Do you want some *orange*?" The emphasis in these
cases was always upon the word "orange." At the start
she would respond with the appropriate grunt only
when some of the actual fruit was in sight, when she
witnessed the orange juice in preparation, or when she
observed it in her cup. But after about 30 repetitions
she began to bark, "Uh, uh," as soon as we pronounced
the word, the "conditioned response" by that time
having been fully developed. This training was completed before the age of 11 months.

Within the next three months she continued to extend
her use of the sound entirely beyond its original connection with food, although no further conditioning or
other assistance was given. Anything desirable which
was momentarily out of reach came to be grunted for
in this manner. Sometimes she would bark repeatedly
when the experimenters could not at once discover the
object of her vocalizations. But eventually in most such
cases something was found in the immediate vicinity
which seemed to serve as the stimulus for the sounds.
The food-bark in some situations seemed to be used
also in the capacity of an exclamation of delight, as
when she saw familiar friends after a short absence, or
when she encountered by surprise some particularly
choice plaything. If the ape suddenly came upon some
of Donald's breakable toys, which were often kept from
her because of her roughness, she at once pounced upon
them with affirmative exclamations. And during the
later months, whenever she observed us uncover the
typewriter and prepare it for operation, her barking
exclamations were suggestive of the young child who
says, "Oh, goodie!" For the typewriter and particularly
its cover had by then become delectable playthings.

Answers to questions were also quite commonly made
by means of the affirmative bark. She would consequently reply in this way not only to "Do you want
some orange?" but also to similar queries ending with

the words "milk," "din-din," and "apple sauce." There were even certain non-food questions which sometimes drew forth the same vocal reply. This was especially the case with, "Do you want to go bye-bye?" and "Do you want to go for a ride?"

In the use of "oo-oo" on the other hand, there was a less obvious extension to broader fields than occurred with the food-bark, since this whining, pleading cry fitted naturally into many negative situations. Almost from the beginning there were but few instances in which it was employed where a humanly articulated "no" would not have served as well. At the early age of 8 months for example, she would object in this manner if required to hand us any special plaything in which she seemed to be interested. Her crying at a later date when she soiled herself might be interpreted in human terms to mean "No, no. Don't punish me." Or when she was left at home while Donald went for a ride in the perambulator, "No, no. Don't leave me." It was her common method towards the last, when she was unable to make a successful evacuation response, to "oo-oo" gently and put her arms about the experimenter.

We must confess at this point to a special training which was undertaken daily with Gua for several months in the endeavor to induce her to say the word "papa." She was laid face upward upon the experimenter's lap while he slowly and distinctly uttered the syllables "pa-pa." From the very start of these attempts she showed a lively interest in the facial movements, and was content to observe what went on without climbing from our lap. There seemed to be no difficulty at all in making her *look* fixedly at the mouth of the experimenter, although any imitative attempts to reproduce the reactions were quite lacking. To encourage her further, we began therefore, to manipulate her lips in time with our utterance of the word, so as, if possible, to aid in making some connection between the sound and the movements.

After a month or two of such efforts we were greatly encouraged to notice occasional lip reactions on the part of the animal, although whether these resulted from the training or from some other cause it would be difficult to say. At any rate such movements as she made were never movements of separating or opening the lips such as one would make to produce the consonant *p*. Rather were they what one might call undirected or incidental movements, often in the nature of a twitch. The lips as a whole would move outward (in a pout) or downward or sideward, and in some cases the tongue would be stuck out between them. At times also when we said "Papa" Gua would advance her index finger slowly towards our mouth and insert it between our lips. Rarely after such a performance she has put the same finger slowly upon her own lips and into her own mouth. But beyond such slight and occasional suggestions the results were never successful.

The question may be raised, as a result of these observations, whether an organism of this sort could ever progress very far in the actual articulation of human sounds. It seems reasonable to suppose that if such a thing is at all possible it would be most likely to occur under some such propitious circumstances as those afforded by the present investigation. That our own meager results were not positive should by no means argue against its future accomplishment, for within the same time period, as we have seen, the progress of the child was also extremely slow. The chimpanzee has long been known to possess vocal and mouth parts which should from a structural point of view permit the utterance of words. We quote from no less an authority than Professor Yerkes ("The great apes") who himself quotes other writers on this question.

It seemingly is well established that the motor mechanism of voice in this ape is adequate not only to the production of a considerable variety of sounds, but also to definite articulations similar to those of man.

Other animals lower in the phyletic scale, as for example the crow and the parrot, have for generations been trained to pronounce recognizable human syllables. There are, moreover, published scientific records concerning individual specimens of anthropoid ape which report that these animals have succeeded in saying several genuine words. It is to such facts that some of us owe our optimism about the possibilities.

Two important objections to this question remain to be considered. The first, a neurological objection, regards the accomplishment as unlikely because of the ape's deficiency in a certain brain region known as Broca's area. This section in the brain of man seems to be indispensable for the development and maintenance of articulate language. The other, a psychological objection, which has arisen out of the present observations, lies in the clearly inadequate preparation for speech in the chimpanzee as compared with the child. For months before a single comprehensible word is pronounced one sees the human subject continually exercising its voice, making new sounds, and manipulating the various organs in original ways. It seems probable that such activity is an indispensable requirement for what is to come later. Yet the chimpanzee makes not even a start in this direction.

We are still not entirely convinced, despite these serious difficulties, that speech in the ape might not ultimately be produced to the extent of a few rudimentary utterances. Of course, if such an achievement is at all possible, it could come about only as a result of laborious and painstaking work upon every lip and tongue movement. And even assuming success in such initial steps, it is still probable that many months of special training would be necessary to get the animal to utter one simple syllable. Although the possibility may still remain, we feel safe in predicting, as a result of our intimate association with Gua, that it is unlikely any anthropoid ape will ever be taught to say more than half a dozen words, if indeed it should accomplish this remarkable feat.

Let us consider finally the ability of the subjects in the *comprehension of language*. We are here faced, as in many earlier instances, with the problem of inner mental processes, for we cannot tell in a strict usage of the term whether the subjects introspectively *comprehend* what is said to them or not. All we can do is to observe whether they are able to react distinctively and individually to separate words and phrases. This, then, must serve as our criterion of "comprehension" which is employed in these pages only in this more objective sense.

Surprising as it may seem, it was very clear during the first few months that the ape was considerably superior to the child in responding to human words. She began to react distinctively to separate vocal stimuli within a few weeks after she had entered the human environment. Yet it seemed to us before she had reached this stage as if she responded to such sounds, chiefly *in terms of their intensity*. Thus the chorus of screaming apes at the Experiment Station would cause her to bark or scream likewise. She would similarly jump at a shout from the experimenter, but would react less noticeably if he spoke in a quiet tone. Soon no doubt she began to recognize the voices of individuals, and thereafter probably the articulation of simple words. "No, no" was the first command to which she began to respond, and "Kiss, kiss" the second. It would be hard to find two simple words whose sounds, when they are spoken, differ by greater amounts.

Characteristic reactions to these two stimuli were acquired by Gua even before the first month was over. At this time the child had no consistent responses to specific words whatsoever. By the second month the ape had a total of 7 distinctive responses to vocal stimuli while Donald had but 2. Her superiority continued throughout the third and the fourth months, at the end of which she was capable of 14 such reactions, to the boy's 8. Even in the fifth month she was still ahead with a total of 21 as against 20 for Donald, although the human subject was then rapidly overtaking her.

If one wishes to justify the early inferiority of the child in responding to vocal commands there are good reasons upon which he can fall back. To some extent Gua's capacity to comprehend can be related to her greater activity. It is quite obvious that Donald could not react to such a sentence as "Get up on the chair" before he was able to climb. Again, her progress may have been in part a matter of obedience or tractability. If one of the subjects did not respond to a vocal stimulus, it was often difficult if not impossible to say whether he failed because the command was not understood or whether he was simply uncooperative. Since we have already had occasion to note Gua's superior obedience in similar connections, this might be used to account in some such manner for her superior responsiveness as well. But even with full allowance for such considerations, the chimpanzee possessed a clear advantage throughout the first half of the research.

The use of gesture, demonstration, and of actually "putting the subject through the act" was often a necessary feature of the training in the comprehension of new phrases. In teaching the child the response to "Take it out of your mouth," the mouthed article was always removed by one of the experimenters if Donald did not make the proper reaction. Similarly, before he acquired the responses to "How big are you?" and to "Pat-a-cake" and among others, the hand-waving reaction to "Bye-bye," the subject's arms were for a considerable period appropriately manipulated. This method, we think, is commonly employed by parents everywhere in teaching infant offspring.

Following are significant instances in which the ape was similarly instructed:

July 21.

She was standing holding my trousers near the five-gallon bottle of distilled water around whose cork before insertion had been wrapped a strip of oiled paper. About 15 centimeters (6 inches) of this strip protruded from the neck of the bottle. (1) Gua tore off a piece of the paper with her teeth and was promptly reprimanded with the command, "No, no." At the same time the paper was forcibly taken from her. Although she made avoiding movements and refused at first to give it up, we pressed her cheeks inward on either side and so induced her to open her mouth. (2) A few moments later she tore off a second piece of the paper. Procedure repeated, except that she released the paper more easily. (3) It was repeated a third time after a short interval. On this occasion Gua opened her mouth of her own accord and permitted us to take the paper. (4) For the fourth time she started towards the bottle. "No, no" was said sternly. She stopped before she touched the remnant of paper, turned away, and said, "Oo-oo-oo."

In learning to "close the door" her progress was of the same nature. Although Gua could successfully *open* small doors in cupboards, as well as full-sized doors, the concept, "close," seemed to be most difficult for her to grasp. During the initial stages of her progress she would sometimes go to a door, put her hands upon it, and push, without regard to whether she was actually pushing it closed or farther open. Frequently in such cases she pushed against whichever side of it she happened to be at the moment. In the attempt to overcome this difficulty we first demonstrated "closing" as the command was given by taking her hands and pushing the door shut with them. A little later pointing and arm gestures were the only assistance which was necessary. Finally, after a month or more had elapsed, the words could be said alone and she would make the correct reaction.

As the subjects advanced in the acquisition of any particular response, therefore, such "extra stimuli" as may originally have been indispensable could in many cases be entirely omitted. Complex reactions which were made at the start only with elaborate gesticulations from the speaker were ultimately called out by the voice alone when the speaker was screened from the subject. But there were some commands in which gesture was always necessary—particularly those in which some specific place among many, or some specific object among several, was indicated. Hence, a special chair was often pointed to for "Get up on the chair." Similarly, the object was indicated in "Go and get *it* and bring it to me," and the place where the object was to be put, in "Put it back." Whether other phrases or sentences could be reacted to without gesture or other assistance depended principally, it seemed, on how well they had been learned at the time.

Towards the middle of the nine-months period, the sudden development of the child, typified no doubt in his locomotion, enabled him to equal and surpass the animal subject in respect to the number of words and phrases which he then comprehended. By the end of the sixth month of the comparison he possessed 32 distinctive responses to vocal stimuli, while Gua had only 28. This lead he slightly increased till at the time the ape was returned to the cages, their respective abilities measured 68 for Donald and 58 for Gua.

Throughout the later months, in fact, the progress of the child became so rapid that it is quite possible our data do not do him full justice. If errors of such a nature exist they are in part assignable to the method of recording the comprehension of new phrases. One could never be sure when a new response was first noted, whether this was actually elicited by the appropriate vocal stimulus, or whether it was traceable to some other incidental cause. As a result, it often became necessary to wait several days or even weeks before a sufficient number of similar situations arose to insure the advisability of recording the reaction. In this way neither subject received full credit for his current "comprehensions" at any given time, and the one who was advancing more rapidly was naturally handicapped to a greater degree.

In addition to this fact there was no method of testing the subjects for the comprehension of previously untried phrases which the investigators had no suspicion the subjects might know. It was consequently only by the merest accident that many of the later expressions reacted to, particularly by the child, were discovered. We would find repeatedly, much to our surprise, that he made a complete and adequate response to some new command which had never previously been given him. He ultimately responded in this way to many of the statements originally directed to Gua. If the chimpanzee was told to "Kiss Donald," the boy himself would offer Gua his cheek. It was similarly ascertained that he knew the response to "Get up on the chair," and to other commands, when he abruptly complied before the ape could do so. There were one or two similar instances in which Gua suddenly made new responses to commands previously reserved for the child. But a larger proportion of her reactions seemed to develop more gradually, in a slow and laborious manner characteristic of trial-by-trial learning.

It may be noted at this point that all the questions which Gua answered vocally were identical except for the final word or two. They were all of the general type, "Do you want ———?" That the ape may therefore have failed to differentiate clearly between them seems likely. And yet it was obvious that the responses to the separate queries did not all appear at the same time in Gua's development. Moreover, the food-bark or "yes" bark was made not only to questions of this special form, but also to the words "orange," "din-din," "applesauce," "milk," and "bye-bye" when these words were used entirely by themselves. In some cases, notably in connection with "bye-bye," the vocal reaction was accompanied by running to the perambulator and climbing into it, while "oo-ooing" was common in reply to statements or commands which at the same time produced distinctive reactions of other sorts. These facts suggest that differentiation was present to some degree.

It seems reasonable to suppose, nevertheless, that the more complex statements to which the subjects responded were not grasped by either individual except as hazy total concepts. They were probably perceived as general sound patterns or as *Gestalten*, in which the separate elements or words had no special connotation at all. To take a specific illustration, suppose we consider the sentence, "Take it out of your mouth." It is quite likely in this case that neither subject at any time during the nine months could have reacted distinctively to the words "out" or "mouth." This particular command as a matter of fact "meant" more to Gua than its words actually signified, for she would always deposit the object removed upon the floor or else cast it vehemently from her. Concerning also such expressions as "No, no," "Stop," and "Don't bite," there may be further question. Since the responses to each of these items were much the same and since the intonation of the speaker was similar for them all, there is small reason to suppose that they were carefully differentiated by the reactors.

With certain other words suitable "controls" could be employed for finding the exact stimulus to which the subject was responding. To discover whether Gua's "yes" bark to "Orange?" or to "Do you want some orange?" is elicited by the articulate sounds, by the questioning intonation of the voice, or by the situation in which oranges can be seen, smelled, or suspected, we proceed as follows. We say "Orange?" when her back is turned to us, and when our back is turned to her, or again, when she is in one room and we are in another. In each of these cases we find that the response is the same as if she is observing us. When we change the nature of the questioning intonation from "Orange?"

(⌣) to a gruff "Orange!" (⌐) or to "Orange" (——), the response is also the same. But if we say "Grapefruit?" (⌣) there is no affirmative grunt from Gua. The ape will similarly make the appropriate response to the word "Kiss" or "Kiss, kiss" if her head is turned away from the observer when the word is spoken; or even if the word is inserted at random in a long sentence, like "Does the little girl think she would like to kiss me?" Both subjects will respond in addition to whispered as well as to vocalized language, suggesting that intonation is not of major importance in this connection.

In the endeavor to obtain an objective measure of their capacities to react to new words we introduce them to the *names experiment*. Their ages at the time are 14½ and 17 months respectively. Three articles known to be entirely new in the experience of each individual are given arbitrary nonsense names, which must therefore be new as well to the subjects. The articles are never seen by either Donald or Gua except during the tests, their everyday names are not spoken at all, and their experimental names are heard only as the trials are in progress. One of the objects is a piece of red garden hose, 46 centimeters long by 2.5 centimeters in diameter (18 inches by 1 inch). To this we assign the arbitrary name of "reet." The second object is a piece of chain 33 centimeters (13 inches) long, composed of 5 large links. This is called for the purpose of the experiment, the "meub." The third is a piece of woven canvas belting, 2.5 centimeters wide by nearly 2 meters in length (1 inch by 6 feet). The name given it is "doax." These three items are arranged in front of the subject, and equidistant from him, while the observer is behind the subject, entirely out of sight. He then commands, "Give me the reet" (or "doax" or "meub," as the case may be). If the subject picks up the correct article, he is praised. If he hands the wrong one, he is censured in a stern voice, the correct object is pointed out to him, and he is made to hand it.

Although both Donald and Gua are given nearly 100 tests apiece with each of the three articles, the number of correct reactions which they make is little more than would be expected from chance. Yet each is obviously affected by the praise, and the child occasionally whimpers when he makes a wrong selection. The difference between the subjects, small though it is, is slightly favorable to the chimpanzee. In view of the opposing differences in comprehension already noted during the later months, such results from this problem are a surprise. Most remarkable is the fact that neither subject appears able really to learn the arbitrary name of any of the articles after so many repetitions.

In opposition to such negative findings are the results of one of the Gesell comprehension tests. In this test the subject is shown a small white card on which are printed crude ink drawings of a cup, a dog, a house, and a shoe. At the age of 17½ months, Donald responds to the command "Show me the bow-wow" by correctly pointing to the picture of the dog, although he cannot pick out the shoe or any of the other objects. But Gua, at 15 months, successfully indicates both the "bow-wow" and the shoe, in this respect again demonstrating an advantage over the child. It is quite possible her success in this situation may in part be due to a superior ability to perceive printed pictures.

The responses which the subjects made to language stimuli throughout the entire nine months are given in the following list. These are all well-established reactions about which there can be little uncertainty. If the separate words of the various statements are tabulated, Donald is found to have a "comprehension vocabulary" of 107 while Gua's is 95. But since, as we have seen, the words in the longer phrases are probably not reacted to as individual units, such an analysis has little value except for its comparative interest.

WORDS AND PHRASES COMPREHENDED
DONALD

Num-ber	Date recorded	Word or phrase spoken	Response
	Age 11 months		
1	8/4	Come here. Come on.	Comes.
	Age 11½ months		
2	8/23	How big are you?	Puts hands over head.
	Age 12½ months		
3	9/16	No, no.	Stops activity in progress.
4	9/16	Chair-chair.	Urinates or defecates. Sometimes utters vocalized grunts.
	Age 13½ months		
5	10/18	Bye-bye? Do you want to go bye-bye?	Runs to speaker to be placed in baby carriage. Later (11/15) runs to carriage and tries to climb in.
6	10/18	Din-din? Do you want din-din?	Runs towards speaker. Usually holds out arms.
7	10/18	Donald!	Looks at caller. Inhibits activity. When "No, no, Donald" is said, he responds very differently than he does to "No, no, Gua."
8	10/25	Down.	(Said by adults when object falls on floor or as he throws something on floor.) Responds by saying "Da" for down. 11/16—says "Da" when he loses balance and suddenly sits down.
	Age 14 months		
9	11/2	Peek-a-boo.	Peeks from behind chair or other object.
10	11/4	Shake hands.	Shakes hands.
11	11/4	Stop.	Stops.
12	11/4	Don't bite.	Stops.
13	11/7	Don't touch it.	Withdraws hand from forbidden object.
	Age 14½ months		
14	11/15	Want to go for a ride?	Runs to wagon and tries to climb in. Distinguishes between this and "Bye-bye" or "Do you want to go bye-bye?" (item no. 5).

WORDS AND PHRASES COMPREHENDED.—(*Continued*)
DONALD

Number	Date recorded	Word or phrase spoken	Response
15	11/16	Where's Daddy?	Looks toward Mr. K.
16	11/16	Where's Gua?	Looks toward Gua.
17	11/16	Do you want some { orange? milk?	Imitates Gua's food bark by saying "Uha, uha." Does it more promptly and more consistently than she does.
18	11/16	Sit down.	(When he starts to stand up in his high chair.) He sits—usually.
19	11/22	Now give me your other hand.	(Used by Mrs. K. when holding Donald and washing his hands.) Donald responds by reaching with the other hand, even when he must disengage it from around neck of Mrs. K.
20	11/30	Close the door.	Pushes it shut.
	Age 15 months		
21	12/2	Pat-a-cake.	Smiles and claps hands.
22	12/2	Not in your mouth.	Refrains from placing object in mouth.
23	12/2	Give it to me.	Gives object to speaker.
24	12/12	Bye-bye.	(Accompanied by hand waving and sight of person walking away from him. Intonation different from item no. 5.) Donald responds by waving in return.
25	12/12	Put on your shoe.	Picks up shoe and tries to put it on.
26	12/12	Give me the shoe.	Picks up shoe and holds it out.
27	12/12	Now give me the other one.	Gives that also.
	Age 15½ months		
28	12/15	Who wants to go in the carriage?	Runs to perambulator and tries to get in. (Apparently understands "carriage.")
29	12/16	Stand up.	(When on hands and knees.) Stands up.

WORDS AND PHRASES COMPREHENDED.—(*Continued*)
DONALD

Number	Date recorded	Word or phrase spoken	Response
30	12/20	Hand Mother your bib.	Reaches behind himself to back of high chair and gets bib, which hangs over back of chair, handing it to Mrs. K.
31	12/29	Go to {Mother, Gua, Daddy, Melissa.	Responds correctly to these names.
32	12/29	Take it to {Mother, Gua, Daddy, Melissa.	Takes object to person named.
	Age 16 months		
33	1/1	Bring it to me.	Brings object indicated.
34	1/1	Bring me your bib.	Brings bib.
35	1/1	Where is your shoe?	Puts hand on shoe.
36	1/1	Bad boy. You are a bad boy.	Frets or cries.
37	1/1	Are you finished?	(Asked when on nursery chair.) Gets up.
38	1/6	Kiss Donald.	(Said to Gua.) Donald responds by turning towards Gua and offering his cheek for a kiss.
39	1/8	Wave your hand.	Moves both hands up and down from shoulders.
	Age 16½ months		
40	1/15	Where is your nose? Show me your nose.	Seizes nose and smiles.
41	1/16	Get up on the chair.	Climbs up.
42	1/19	Kiss Mother, Donald.	Leans forward and offers cheek.
43	1/20	Put that back.	(When he has just taken some forbidden object.) Puts it back. (The place to put it is usually indicated by gesture.)
44	1/23	Take Gua's hand.	Takes it and holds it when walking.
	Age 17 months		
45	2/1	Open the door.	Seems to be able to distinguish this command from "Close the door."

WORDS AND PHRASES COMPREHENDED.—(*Continued*)
DONALD

Num-ber	Date recorded	Word or phrase spoken	Response
46	2/2	There's a bow-wow.	Peers from windows of car or house. Sometimes says "Bow-wow."
47	2/2	Supper's ready.	Runs to high chair and hangs on it, trying to climb in.
48	2/2	Take Daddy the paper.	(As he is handed paper.) Takes newspaper to Mr. K.
49	2/3	Open your mouth.	Opens it—usually.
50	2/3	Take it out of your mouth.	Removes object. (Similar to "Not in your mouth"—item no. 22.)
51	2/6	Hug Donald.	(Remark addressed to Gua.) Donald responds by hugging Gua.
52	2/12	Let's get the wagon.	Runs to closed door of room where it is kept.
53	2/12	Go over and play with the wagon.	Goes across room to wagon.
Age 17½ months			
54	2/15	Show me the bow-wow.	(Said during Gesell test as small white card containing ink drawings of a dog, a shoe, a house and a cup, is held before subject.) Points to picture of dog.
55	2/15	Now, roll it to { Gua me.	(Direction given when subject is playing ball with Gua or with one of the observers.) Holds out both hands and drops ball.
56	2/22	Light the light.	Climbs upon chair and operates electric switch.
57	2/22	Go in the kitchen and light the light.	Goes in kitchen and does so.
58	2/23	Show me your ear.	Holds ear. Distinguishes now between this statement and "Show me your nose" (item no. 40).
59	2/23	Go get the cookie.	(Said in *suspended cookie experiment*. Subject is sitting on a chair at side of room waiting till experimenter is ready.) Climbs down and goes after cookie.

WORDS AND PHRASES COMPREHENDED.—*(Continued)*
DONALD

Number	Date recorded	Word or phrase spoken	Response
60	2/23	Stay there.	Stays.
61	2/26	Put it down.	Puts down object he has picked up.
	Age 18 months		
62	3/6	Blow the horn.	(When in the automobile.) Presses horn button.
63	3/7	Car.	This word used indiscriminately in a sentence seems to put Donald on the alert and cause him to follow the speaker about, as if to be close at hand for a ride.
64	3/8	Close the drawer.	Pushes drawer closed. Response similar to that made to "Close the door" (item no. 20).
65	3/8	Are your hands dirty! What dirty hands you have!	Raises palms of hands, extends fingers and looks at hands.
66	3/12	Push Gua around.	(When Gua is seated in walker.) Does so.
67	3/12	Go away from there. Get away from there.	Does so.
	Age 18½ months		
68	3/23	Let's change your suit, Donald.	Looks down at suit and pulls at button.

WORDS AND PHRASES COMPREHENDED
GUA

Num-ber	Date recorded	Word or phrase spoken	Response
	Age 7½ months		
1	7/11	No, no.	Stops activity in progress.
	Age 8 months		
2	7/21	Kiss, kiss.	Kisses.
	Age 9 months		
3	8/15	Come here. Come on.	Comes.
4	8/15	Gua!	Looks at caller. Inhibits activity.
5	8/15	Chair-chair.	Urinates or defecates. Sometimes utters unvocalized grunts.
6	8/15	Shake hands.	Extends right hand.
7	8/15	Get up in the chair.	Gets up.
	Age 11 months		
8	10/16	Bad girl. You are a bad girl.	Cries or "oo-oo's."
9	10/16	Don't bite.	Responds by stopping.
10	10/16	Orange? Do you want some orange?	Responds by giving food-bark, like "Yes, yes."
11	10/16	Din-din? Do you want some din-din?	Same. (Response to "orange" acquired about 2 weeks earlier than to "din-din.")
12	10/18	Stay there.	Remains seated in chair or in corner.
13	10/18	Don't do that.	Response same as for "No, no" (item no. 1).
14	10/24	Bye-bye. Do you want to go bye-bye?	Runs to perambulator and climbs in. Later (1/9) gives "yes" bark as she runs to perambulator.
	Age 11½ months		
15	11/2	Get down.	(Command given when she starts to climb on table, sink or other forbidden places.) Responds at once by getting down.
16	11/2	Stop.	Stops activity in progress.
	Age 12 months		
17	11/15	Do you want some $\begin{cases} \text{milk?} \\ \text{apple sauce?} \end{cases}$	Grunts "Yes, yes," that is, gives food-bark.

302

WORDS AND PHRASES COMPREHENDED.—(*Continued*)

GUA

Number	Date recorded	Word or phrase spoken	Response
18	11/15	Sit down.	(When starts to stand up in high chair.) Sits.
19	11/15	Give it to me.	Holds object out towards speaker.
20	11/15	Not in your mouth.	(When an object she has is moved towards her mouth preparatory to insertion.) Closes her mouth and moves object away from it.
21	11/28	Kiss Donald.	Kisses him.
	Age 12½ months		
22	12/5	Open your mouth.	Opens it.
23	12/9	Be still.	(When experimenter is holding her or trying to put her to sleep.) Is quiet at once.
24	12/9	Take it out of your mouth.	Will take out with her hand whatever she may have in her mouth, and cast object away from her or let it drop from her hand.
	Age 13 months		
25	12/15	Who wants to go in the carriage?	Runs to perambulator and climbs in.
26	12/17	Close the door.	Pushes it shut.
27	12/20	Give me your other hand.	(Accompanied by gesture on part of experimenter who holds out his hand as, for example, in washing her hands.) Offers other hand.
28	12/20	Hand me your bib.	(When bib is placed on high-chair tray before a meal. Gua is seated in high chair.) Picks up bib and offers it to experimenter.
	Age 13½ months		
29	1/1	Are you finished?	(Asked when on toilet or nursery chair.) Gets up.
30	1/1	Come out from under the bed.	Comes.
31	1/1	Get up on the bed.	Gets up. (Cannot, however, distinguish this from "Get up on the chair" and if chair is placed close to bed, she may get on either at either command.)

WORDS AND PHRASES COMPREHENDED.—*(Continued)*
GUA

Number	Date recorded	Word or phrase spoken	Response
32	1/9	Do you want to go for a ride?	Gives "yes" bark. Does this also at present when asked "Do you want to go bye-bye?" (See response no. 14.)
33	1/9	Go get it and bring it to me.	(When object on floor is pointed to.) She gets object and brings it to speaker.
34	1/10	Give it to Donald.	(Object is an obvious one and Donald is pointed to.) Gives it.
35	1/14	Lie down.	Lies down. (Apparently distinguishes this from "Sit down"—item no. 18).
	Age 14 months		
36	1/19	Go to { Mamma, Donald, Papa.	Goes. (Seems to be able to distinguish these names by now. But she knows Donald's name best.)
37	1/22	Take Gua's hand.	Originally said to Donald, to get him to hold her hand when they were walking together. We found to our surprise, however, that Gua at once knew perfectly what it meant and offered her hand to Donald. In fact, on later repetitions she would take Donald's hand and hold it, better than he would hold hers.
38	1/25	Show me your nose. Where is your nose?	Points to nose with index finger.
39	1/25	Put that back.	Returns to shelf or table object she has removed. (The place to put it is usually indicated by gesture.)
	Age 14½ months		
40	2/2	Don't touch.	Refrains from touching object.

WORDS AND PHRASES COMPREHENDED.—(*Continued*)
GUA

Number	Date recorded	Word or phrase spoken	Response
41	2/2	There's a bow-wow.	(Usually said while riding in car.) Stands up and peers out of window.
42	2/6	Hug Donald.	Puts arms about him.
43	2/12	Go to your mother.	Goes to Mrs. K.
44	2/12	Wait a minute.	(When ready to eat, ready to get up from toilet or about to make other response.) Waits.
45	2/13	Take it to { Mamma Donald (or with gestures— to any other person not a total stranger.)	Does so.
46	*Age 15 months* 2/15	Show me the bow-wow.	(Said during Gesell test as small white card containing ink drawings of a dog, a shoe, a house and a cup, is held before subject.) Points to picture of dog.
47	2/15	Show me the shoe.	(Same card held before subject.) Points to picture of shoe.
48	2/15	Now, roll it to { Donald me.	(Direction given when subject is playing ball either with Donald or with one of the observers.) Pushes ball away from herself with both hands.
49	2/17	Put it down.	Puts object down at once.
50	2/17	Let that alone.	Withdraws from object.
51	2/17	Don't put that in your mouth.	(An extension of "Not in your mouth"—see item no. 20). Removes object.
52	2/23	Go get the cookie.	(Said in *suspended cookie experiment*. She is sitting on a chair at side of room waiting till experimenter is ready.) Gets down and goes after cookie.

WORDS AND PHRASES COMPREHENDED.—(*Continued*)
GUA

Number	Date recorded	Word or phrase spoken	Response
53	2/25	Stay with your mother.	(Said when Mr. K. is about to leave house.) Usually runs to Mrs. K. and clings to legs, oftentimes looking back at Mr. K. and "oo-ooing" at the same time.
54	2/27	See the cow. There's a cow. Look at the cow.	(When riding in auto.) Stands up and peers out of window.
55	*Age 15½ months* 3/6	Blow the horn.	(When in car.) Presses horn button.
56	3/7	Good-bye.	(Said by Mr. K. as Gua is going away from him or as Mr. K. walks from her.) Stops, cries "Oo-oo" and rushes after Mr. K.
57	3/8	Close the drawer.	Does it at once. (Meaning and response (also sound) of words very similar to "Close the door" which she has known for sometime—see item no. 26.)
58	*Age 16 months* 3/17	Go away from there. Get away from there.	Withdraws.

Chapter XIII

CONCLUSION

WE HAVE now compared the subjects in a considerable variety of ways. These have included not only the activity or behavior of the two, but also, in a less exhaustive manner, their growth and bodily dimensions. Obviously, however, our greatest interest lies in their reactions—especially those which can be said to show the effect of the environment in which they lived. To what extent did the civilized surroundings of the ape influence or fail to influence her ultimate behavior? We should like to be able at this point to analyze the responses of the chimpanzee and to classify them one by one as either dependent upon the human environment or as probably independent of it. It shall be part of our task in this chapter to make a classification of this nature even at the risk of possible scientific criticism.

Such an endeavor need not necessarily drag us too deeply into the confusing by-paths of the heredity-environment controversy. After all, if we are interested chiefly in the influence of the human environment, we should have no serious trouble in selecting from a list of Gua's responses those reactions which could not have occurred without certain indispensable features of the civilized surroundings. There would be no necessary error in saying that the African aboriginal who is raised in the United States becomes civilized as a result of his removal to the civilized environment; or to account for the distinctive language accents of different geographical groups as an outgrowth of their immediate surroundings. In the same way we can say that the urban child learns the games of the streets because the opportunity to acquire them is presented in the city, while the offspring of the frontiersman picks up knowledge of the woods because he lives there. Neither could develop **as** he does in these special ways were it not for the definite effect of the stimuli which are thrust upon him as he grows.

But even though these statements are true, they do not mean at all that we can ignore the part played by the genes, for, strictly speaking, the influence of both heredity and environment can be shown to exist in any behavior whatsoever. Consider the fact that Gua sometimes skipped while Donald did not. This, one would say, is a learned or acquired attribute on the part of the ape, since Gua picked up her skipping by holding the trousers of the experimenter. Hence this is an ability which depends upon the environment to bring it into being. But heredity is also important here as in all other cases. For if through some inherited deformity or peculiarity the feet or legs of the chimpanzee had been so affected that she could not skip then the reaction would never have appeared even though the outside stimuli to skip were present.

To employ an analogy of Professor Jennings' we may say the materials ("heredity") of which an automobile is made are quite as necessary for its performance as is the method ("environment") by which the automobile is built. That environment is important in all behavior should appear from the fact that stimulation of some sort (usually from the external surroundings) must elicit every reaction, unlearned as well as learned. And that heredity is equally important should appear from the obvious fact that, without it, there would be no organism to respond. The very best methods of manufacture in themselves could never produce performance in an automobile without the materials upon which these methods could be used.

The same arguments are applicable to any response of either of the subjects which can be pointed out. Heredity and environment work together in determining the character of each individual act. The living organism as a whole is a product of both of these factors and never under any circumstances of only one of them. Yet we can, in a general way, determine the relative extent of their influence in the behavior of different individuals, especially when either heredity or environment is approximately the same from one individual to the next. If identical twins—whose heredities are certainly as near alike as it is possible for two heredities to be—develop in the same way *when reared in different environments*, their likenesses are said to demonstrate the regulating function of their common hereditary background. Of course these likenesses may also be traceable, at least in part, to the early influence of the common environment which may have got in its work before the twins were separated. But if the separation is made at a young enough age, the validity of the original conclusion need not be seriously endangered. Again, take two subjects like our own, whose heredities are known to be different. If these subjects grow differently *when reared in like environments*, their difference in development is attributable to their difference in heredity. Yet here, as in the preceding instance, one must take account of the possible effect of the early environment. For it is conceivable that distinctive outside influences may have produced divergent tendencies before the two were brought together.

More important for the present research are two further inferences which can be drawn, it seems to us, without entangling qualifications. They refer to the fact that the child and the ape (when reared in the same environment) acquire a great deal of new behavior which is the same. To account for such like characteristics on the part of the subjects, we can say:

1. That the heredities of the two are similar enough in these particular respects to permit similar reactions to the same stimuli.

And we can also draw a final conclusion, namely,

2. That the environment is the activating factor in bringing out the potentialities of the subjects for similar development.

What shall be our criterion in the separation of those responses of the ape which show the particular effect of the human environment from those which seem not to do so? As a test upon each act we shall ask the following question: *Could the chimpanzee possibly have developed this behavior had she been reared without the pertinent stimuli of the civilized surroundings?* If the answer is "Yes" or "Doubtful," we shall classify the response as probably independent of the special influence of the human situation. If the answer is "No," then we shall feel justified in classifying the act as dependent upon the civilized environment.

Armed with this measuring device we may proceed in the analysis of Gua's behavior. But first, a recapitulation to orient us in this task: It appears that an individual with a regular or normal heredity may develop in certain special ways as a result of distinctive external factors. Each subject in this investigation has been favored with a normal or regular heredity, although the environment of one has been radically changed to determine how much this will make it like the other. Nevertheless, in spite of the fact that the respective heredities are apparently quite "normal," these heredities are also markedly different one from the other. At the same time, they are *similar enough* to permit the possibility of the two organisms being similarly affected by the same environment. How, then, do the subjects compare when the same external forces are directed against them? Of course the effect of their different "hereditary traits" is apparent in nearly everything we do to them. Yet the things in which we are specifically interested are the effects of the common environment. Exactly how much alike does this environment make the subjects in spite of their known variation in heredity?

I. DIFFERENCES FAVORABLE TO THE CHILD

In the attempt to answer this question we begin with its negative aspects. For we turn first to some important differences between the two individuals and consider the performances in which Gua remains upon another level from the boy. A difference "favorable" to Donald is not necessarily one in which he shows any special aptitude, nor is it one in which Gua is necessarily deficient or inferior. Only as the ape does not duplicate the performance of a human being is the resulting difference considered under this category. The items listed here represent therefore the principal ways in which the chimpanzee deviates in one way or another from human norms or standards.

Within this larger class of differences we may then make a secondary grouping according to our predetermined plan, into (1) those responses which would probably have developed as they did even though Gua had been kept in a thoroughly non-human environment, (2) those which seem to us to be more directly dependent upon the specific nature of the civilized surroundings, and (3) those which are doubtful. But even though we make such a division to the best of our ability, it is too much to expect that all who read this passage will agree with the writers in the placing of every item. An endeavor such as this leaves room for individual opinion. Still, the results of our efforts should not conflict by too wide a margin with the judgment of others who might undertake the same task.

1. *Non-environmental Differences.* The first clear-cut differences in behavior to be noted as we skim over the early findings consist of Gua's higher blood pressure and her lower pulse rate. In this grouping also should

come her greater consumption of water, which is due no doubt to her probably possessing fewer sweat glands than the child. That Gua's mouth is more mobile as an organ of prehension is likewise independent of the civilized environment. It is the same with her more consistent avoidance of bright lights, her (apparently) keener hearing, and her many distinctive emotional reactions. Similarly we should place her greater propensity to bite and chew, her inability to pick up small objects with the fingers, and her deficiency in articulation in this category. Her further deficiencies in exploration and manipulation, her attention to stimuli for only a relatively short time, and her inferiority in imitation seem also to us to belong under this heading.

These characteristics we think are independent of the specific humanizing features of the environment in which Gua lived. Certainly this need not mean that the influence of some sort of environment cannot be proven in every one of them. But it does mean that they would probably have developed much as they are in almost any environment which permits healthy and regular growth. They are qualities which for the most part are traceable to bony development, the chemistry of the muscles, the character of the nerve centers including the brain, and the shape and form into which the parts of the organism naturally arrange themselves unless fundamentally altered by violent, irregular, or abnormal outside factors. They are ways of behaving which to our way of thinking would not be strongly affected by training or education.

2. *Environmental Differences.* There are other differences in behavior between the subjects; but there are none *involving the ape's deviation from human standards* in which the particular influence of the civilized surroundings can be shown to play an indispensable part. We therefore find ourselves unable to list any reactions under this heading.

3. *Unclassified Items.* Can it be said that the reason Gua possessed a greater tendency than the child to avoid strange humans was because she in some way had learned from her associates to behave in this way? Although there are grounds for considering this characteristic an environmental one, it is possible, we must admit, to build up a case for the opposing view. This is consequently a difference between the subjects which comes in the doubtful grouping. Their particular food preferences and aversions may similarly be traceable to the human surroundings, yet here also we are less sure of such a statement. In the matters of the greater psychological dependency of the ape and her stronger attachment to one person, there is even greater uncertainty.

The important point in this connection: The majority of the differences in behavior thus far listed show the chimpanzee to be unaffected in any special or dominant way by the particular civilized aspects of her surroundings.

II. LIKENESSES BETWEEN THE TWO

When we take up the aspects in which Gua was like Donald, we find a shift in emphasis, for in this category a large proportion of the reactions of the chimpanzee seem to be explainable as a result of humanizing influences. Within this second major grouping there may again be some question about many of the responses classified, concerning both their influence by the civilized environment and also the degree of their similarity from one subject to the other. It is to be pointed out in this connection that the reactions given are not necessarily *exclusively* human, but they are nevertheless respects in which Gua resembled the child.

1. *Non-environmental Likenesses.* Of the similar features of behavior which seem to be relatively independent of the human situation, the reflexes of the two are important. So also are their common drowsy reactions of nodding and of rubbing the eyes. Probably the

313

perception of motion, as in motion pictures, should be placed here, as well as the susceptibility of both subjects to the illusion of reversed sound localization. Their like responsiveness to tickling is no doubt chiefly a matter of similar sense organs and nerve connections, while the sleeping postures of the ape probably resembled those of the child because of the shape and proportions of her body. Perhaps, in addition, we should classify Gua's tendency to forget and her manlike laughter under this heading, although there is a serious question about the latter.

2. *Environmental Likenesses.* The upright walking of the subjects, which in many respects was similar, would probably have failed to develop as it did without the humanizing influences. We should therefore consider it an environmental likeness. Here also may be put many of the common play reactions of the two, such as playing with shoes, playing with human faces, playing ball and tag, and playing with the telephone and typewriter. Their like reactions to sizable bodies of water we should classify in this category along with the conditioning to vocal commands and to other specific stimuli, since all these were of necessity controlled or elicited by particular outside influences. Similarly many other definite tasks in which the ape came close to the child's performance, such as pointing to the nose, work with the form board, and scribbling.

3. *Unclassified Items.* Concerning playing in the sand, the affectionate behavior of one subject for the other, and the avoiding reactions of each to animals, the classification is less clear. Of course these responses could hardly have appeared as they did except for immediate environmental influences. And yet, the particular human phases of the environment can hardly be considered indispensable; for it is conceivable that similar behavior might well have developed in quite different surroundings. The hand preferences of both individuals, which shifted as a result of outside stimula-

tion, might similarly have changed much as they did under vastly different environmental conditions.

III. DIFFERENCES FAVORABLE TO THE APE

There remains a third major class of characteristics in which Gua was neither like Donald nor peculiarly like an animal. These are respects in which the chimpanzee was different from the child, yet in which she went beyond him and so behaved like a human older and more mature than he. Her progress in this regard may be ascribed largely to her more rapid rate of development.

1. *Non-environmental Differences.* Among the human-like advances of the ape which were probably not outgrowths of the civilized environment belong her superior muscular coordination and more rapid rate of involuntary movement. Her demonstrations of greater strength, accuracy in auditory localization, the compensatory movements during rotation, and her superiority in remembering may also be considered independent of any necessary human effects.

2. *Environmental Differences.* In this, the most important group, is shown the capacity of the chimpanzee to acquire responses peculiar to the civilized surroundings which are more complex or more proficient than those of the child himself. Since the performance of Donald was about average for his age, the respects in which the ape surpassed him are respects in which she was generally more advanced than the average human approximately as old as herself. They cast no necessary reflection upon the child, but are rather points of special credit for the ape. She may thus be said to have become "more humanized" than the human subject in the acquisition of behavior of which the child was still incapable.

Here should be placed Gua's skipping. Here also we should put her greater cooperation and obedience, which is a feature of the behavior of well-trained older children. And here belongs her tendency to kiss for forgiveness and her skillful opening of doors. Her more frequent sly behavior suggests the mischievousness of a lively boy, while her superior anticipation of the bladder and bowel reactions may be cited as a more obvious mark of progress. Finally, under this heading should be placed her striking ability to eat with a spoon and drink from a glass, which compare favorably to the corresponding abilities of children considerably older than the ape. These items in our opinion are traceable to the influence of special factors in the human environment which were favorable to their acquisition.

In most of the behavior in which Gua has shown herself to be typically *un*like a child, we can say with reasonable certainty that human influences have been of slight significance. Differences in bodily dimensions and in the design and operation of the parts of the organism have usually asserted themselves, while the stimuli peculiar to the household situation seem to have altered or affected her responses to but a minor degree. In the behavior in which Gua was like humans of her own age or older, on the other hand, the features of the civilized surroundings have proven in many cases to be the dominating or activating influence. It must not be forgotten that results of this sort show also that the heredity of the ape is enough like that of the human to permit this similar development in the same environment. Yet, without the necessary stimulation from without many of her childlike reactions would never have appeared. Such a finding, it seems to us, should point to the immense importance of the surroundings and treatment in the upbringing of the infant organism, whether animal or human.

The particular ways in which the external situation affected the development of the ape are necessarily complex. The physical features of the surroundings can be considered only secondary, since they formed but a small part of the stimulation which influenced her reactions. Simply keeping Gua in the household in which she lived for nine months would by no means have produced the behavior which she ultimately acquired. It is doubtful, in fact, if under these circumstances she would have turned out very differently from the usual caged or captive infant chimpanzee. Even had she lived in a house with the benefit of intimate human contacts, but without those contacts specifically directing her in the pathways of the typical human infant, the results would surely have been greatly different from what they were. The cases of anthropoid apes reared as household pets furnish good indications of the probable nature of the final reactions.

More precisely, it is what may be called the *psychological environment* which was the significant factor in Gua's advancement. This comprised, besides the external situation, all the minute and often unconsidered "environmental conditions." One might define it as the sum total of everything which could cause any kind of a response in the living organism. Of unquestioned significance in this respect was the care, treatment, and leadership offered the ape by the humans with whom she was connected. The praise of her associates and their continual verbal explanations probably formed a particularly important asset. It was special civilizing stimuli of this sort—furnished Gua by the *reactions* of her friends—which served above all else, we think, as directing influences. The ape's own reactions to such stimuli, much more than to the inanimate features of the human household, led her onward as the young child is led in performance of new and more complex tasks.

There was no time during the nine-months period when the human environmental standards were relaxed. Gua was never treated like a helpless incompetent or like a pet, nor was she ever confined or chained as the experimenters might wish recreation or freedom from their task. The features of her surroundings, on the other hand, were not forced upon the ape in any laborious or systematic manner. Nor was she driven into particular ways of reacting by special or unusual methods of reward or punishment.

Perhaps the psychological environment, as we have conceived it, should include the temporal sequence in which the successive stimuli were presented. The upbringing of the chimpanzee was certainly to some degree a matter of building upon existing reactions elicited by former stimuli, new reactions elicited by other stimuli to which she could not originally have made adequate responses. In this way it involved a gradual, step-by-step procedure of gentle persistence. Conditions favorable to such development served themselves as a powerful molding factor without the necessary introduction of physical punishment, which played but a minor role in the training of the ape. They afforded the same coaxing and encouraging features which are a part of the environment of most civilized children today.

In placing this emphasis upon the stimulation which Gua received we are not unmindful of her greater rate of maturation, which gave her a striking advantage in almost every phase of activity. This is but another way of saying that her more rapid development permitted her, during the ages of comparison, to adjust more readily to the same outside stimuli than the child did. It is obviously, therefore, to the differences in maturation to which one must point to account for many of the differences in behavior between the chimpanzee and the boy. The ape, being equivalent in growth and general development to a child of at least twice her own age, displayed at the same time behavior which was equivalent in many instances to that of a human of near her own physiological status.

Still, the concept of "maturation" cannot completely explain the achievements of the chimpanzee. We must not permit its apparent inclusiveness to divert us from the main issue. For we cannot ignore the fact that Gua's advancement in rate of growth would never have led to her notable progress unless the very special opportunities for that progress had been presented by way of the environment. We had known and expected beforehand that the ape's faster growth would place her ahead of the human subject in such respects as strength and agility, the capacity to climb, and muscular coordination. Yet who can say that maturation alone, or maturation and heredity together, could ever by themselves account for door opening and eating with a spoon? One must add to "maturation" the concept of "environmental opportunities." The characteristics of the organism are combined with and influenced by the external situation in the building up of responses. Gua's development, in fact, may be said to have grown out of the interaction between herself (the organism) and the environment (all the stimuli) which she received. Her reactions to the situations in which she found herself produced changes in those very situations; and the modified surroundings correspondingly elicited new or altered responses from the ape. The combined, unified, or interlocking effect of these two elements was responsible in Gua's, as in every other case, for the ultimate nature of the resulting behavior. In the present investigation it is the particular influence of the environment, and the part it plays in such a combination, which is demonstrated.

But there is still another factor of great importance in explaining the ape's accomplishments. This consists of her *faster rate of learning*. What enabled the chimpanzee to eat with a spoon, drink from a glass, skip, and announce her bladder and bowel needs better than the average child of her own age was unquestionably the fact that she *learned* this behavior more rapidly. It should be clear, therefore, that, as far as Gua is concerned, an increased rate of maturation parallels to a considerable extent an increased rate of learning.

This is a phenomenon with which we are not entirely unacquainted among humans, for it is a common observation that girls of young school age are better pupils than boys of the same age, owing no doubt, to the fact that they are more mature than the boys. To find, however, that such a relationship would also exist for organisms of related but nevertheless of entirely different biological families is something of a surprise. If rate of maturation paralleled rate of learning throughout the entire phyletic scale, then we should expect that dogs, who mature five or six times as rapidly as humans, could also perform human-like tasks at a correspondingly earlier age even than apes. Mere rate of maturation does not necessarily imply "rate of acquiring human-like behavior."

Surely no one would say that the speed or facility with which one learns is entirely independent of native or hereditary influences. Its relationship in Gua to the rate of maturation points to the common dependency of each upon something within the organism. The retarded learning ability of mentally deficient humans who in many cases are congenitally afflicted is probably the best evidence of the influence of the genes upon learning. In fact according to the view of many psychologists, intelligence itself is chiefly inherent. We are nevertheless beginning to believe that performance upon an intelligence test can be markedly influenced by the social and environmental background of the individual taking the test. It has recently been shown in this connection that the inferiority of rural school children, when compared in intelligence tests with city school children, is in part a matter of the different environments in which the two live and have been reared.*

Perhaps the general ability to learn is also to some extent a matter of environment. This without reference

* H. E. Jones, H. S. Conrad and M. B. Blanchard, "Environmental handicap in mental test performance," *University of California Publications in Psychology,* 1932, Vol. 5, No. 3, pp. 63–99.

at all to the fact that such ability is measured only by the specific acts which are learned—and these being traceable to outside stimuli, are necessarily environmental acquisitions. Of course it would have been impossible by any other means except those here employed to subject the ape to the continuous and persistent repetition of stimuli necessary for learning specific human tasks. But the reason these acts were learned lies not alone in the continued occurrence of the necessary stimuli. It depends also on the attitude of the subject. It demands, in other words, that the *motivation* be propitious for the forming of responses which the stimuli favor. Would it be going too far in such reasoning to suggest that the intimate, friendly, and homelike surroundings in which Gua lived were probably more conducive to her learning the tasks set her than are the surroundings of caged or laboratory animals? This, again, is a question of motivation. But it is not so much a question of the blind strength of the driving force as it is a question of the building up of an unafraid and cooperative attitude. Obviously the establishment of such an attitude must depend to a great extent upon the environmental situation.

We soon discovered in this connection, from many hours of intimate contact with Gua, that she was astonishingly sensitive even to the very weakest of stimuli. Faint noises, the sound of a raindrop, a distant automobile, a muffled footstep would cause immediate changes in blood pressure, pulse, and breathing rates. Adaptive movements which enabled her to see or hear more of the stimulus would also result. There seems, therefore, to be some reason to suppose that the chimpanzee and probably dogs, cats and other higher animals as well, are quite as sensitive to unusual, irregular, and incidental outside influences as are human beings. If this is at all a correct inference, then how responsive must these animals be to the extreme forms of punishment and deprivation employed in many of the ordinary types of experiments performed upon them? It seems likely that the physiological reactions produced in certain of these artificial and confining laboratory situations must be very violent. Yet the possibility of such disturbing conditions and their effect upon the results are often given little weight in tests upon the behavior of subhuman subjects. Who, indeed, has thoroughly considered the point of view of the animal? Professor Köhler and his followers have come closest to it, but it is doubtful if even this group of great leaders has stated the case forcibly enough. We have learned in clinical psychology to lead the child gently and gradually in the administration of various children's tests, while in many cases our animal investigators seem to be trained only in the stern mechanics of formal precision.

It is clearly in defense of the capacities of the animal that the results of the present research are most significant. They strongly suggest that, if given sufficient opportunity, the animal subject may considerably outdo himself, particularly if he belongs at a high level in the biological scale. They stand, we think, as a concrete demonstration of the effects of the general environment upon performance in a variety of specific situations. In our opinion they show beyond a doubt that what one tests in any given experiment is never a virgin specimen influenced only by its immediate surroundings. What one tests rather is an individual which at the start already possesses a well-developed equipment of reactions many of which have been learned as a result of earlier influences. It is in part these reactions acquired in the past which influence the present activities of the testee. We can never with perfect fairness compare two different species or even two members of the same species unless we are sure that their early environments have been reasonably similar.

To test a captive anthropoid seized by force in the jungle, kept later in a cage, and motivated by hunger in some particular experiment is one thing. To test a human child who is kindly and gently talked to and who is never under any circumstances caged or starved is certainly a very different thing. We treat one organism in ways we should never think of treating the other and, in so doing, we often tacitly assume that this treatment—sometimes years of it—has little or no effect upon any particular segment of behavior which we may later choose to measure. Even providing all the details of the experimental situations are the same for subjects of different kinds (which is often not the case), the *total situations*, including the divergent past learning of the individuals, can never be the same. Yet there are specialists in the separate fields of animal and child study who seem prone to ignore the fundamental variations which ordinarily inhere in the two fields. The continual direct comparison of results from one field to the other is proof of this error. Surely if the enormous difference in the backgrounds of the subjects, as well as in the methods of investigation, were always considered, the findings from the two fields would be less frequently compared. Or comparisons, if made, would be more uniformly accompanied by suitable reservations.

Perhaps at this point, while we are in an appropriately critical attitude, we should turn for a moment upon our own work and consider some significant deficiencies in this investigation itself. For since we have now completed our survey of the abilities of the subjects, we can readily see ways in which the research could have been improved. Without doubt the most important factor in this regard involves the ages of the subjects at the start of the project. In fact, if such a task were to be undertaken a second time, there are two inflexible requirements we would demand. First, the ape should be obtained, in accordance with the original plans, at the age of a month or younger. This would eliminate the unknown influence of an earlier wild or captive environment and would permit more comprehensive conclusions upon the genesis of various types of behavior.

Second, the ape should be reared not in a family with one child, but in a family of several children, the youngest of which is at the start at least a year older than the animal subject. There are advantages both to the anthropoid and to the humans which should accrue from these conditions. The ape would have as continual associates children who were its equal or superior in maturation and agility. Its companions would thus be constantly able to serve as leaders in the development of new behavior. The children, on the other hand, should be correspondingly less inclined to follow or imitate the animal.

Third, in a repetition of the same research it would also be desirable to continue over a longer period of time, although this can hardly be classed as an inflexible requirement. There is always the tendency to say, "Yes, of course. But even though the ape was superior in some respects she would not have remained so if the comparison had covered a long enough interval." Such an outcome without question presents a possibility of great importance. It is also quite possible, nevertheless, that the matter of time would prove less significant than at first it may appear. For example, had the experiment continued for twice as long and the results remained much as they are, the same objection could be raised. Had it lasted three or four times as long with similar findings, one could always say the same thing. Indeed, if we are entirely open-minded on the subject, we can hardly overlook the logical possibility that the ape might continue to demonstrate a superiority in many outstanding ways. Such a contingency from an unprejudiced viewpoint should be placed on a parity with the possibility that the child would eventually triumph in those respects in which he was found to be less proficient than the ape. It is rather, therefore, to determine in which way the further development would lead, whether for "better" or for "worse," that it would be advisable to keep on for a longer interval.

We note, finally, by way of criticism, that there is a strong tendency in an investigation of this type to commit the error of anthropomorphism, that is, to ascribe to the animal and to the young child adult- and manlike attributes which they do not actually possess. Of course no one can ever tell except by the somewhat doubtful methods of inference or analogy whether animals or even human infants are capable at all of such complex mental experiences as of *feeling* or *thinking*. And yet, if one sees them behave in peculiar or unusual ways, he may be sorely tempted to interpret that behavior as it appears to him. In such cases one runs the risk of giving the objective actions a mental quality based upon his own experience. Hence, if a tiny baby, immediately after spilling some milk, begins to cry, the incautious onlooker may say, "He is angry or disappointed." In all strictness, however, the elements of "anger" or "disappointment" are added by the observer. All that is objectively known is that (1) the milk is spilled and (2) the baby cries. It is possible, to be sure, that the observer is correct in his appraisal, but, unless the baby in some way can tell him, the correctness of his inference must forever remain unknown.

This inclination to see in all other organisms the same feelings, emotions, thoughts, and impulses which man himself experiences has met with such severe treatment at the hands of many contemporary scientists that some have tended, so it seems, to lean in the opposite direction. As a result, elaborate precautions are often taken in scientific discussion to avoid the use of words which by the remotest suggestion possess an introspective or anthropomorphic savor.

But note that in the present research we set out at the start to discover just how manlike an animal could be. We deliberately attempted, in other words, to make

the non-human subject *as anthropomorphic as possible.*
All the conditions of the study were directed towards
this very end. How, then, can we recount manlike
activity without ascribing to the subject the manlike
qualities which this activity implies? The question of
anthropomorphism in this particular instance seems to
present an unusual difficulty. Probably the most obvious answer to this question is to confine oneself rigidly
to the discussion of behavior, and this in the main is
what we have endeavored to do. We have therefore tried
to avoid such expressions as, "The ape was afraid," and
have usually substituted instead, "She acted *as if* she
was afraid," or "She *seemed* to be afraid." Yet to a large
extent even statements of this sort, which cover broad
general phases of behavior, are colored by the impressions of the onlooker. We have taken the view that
such impressions, if carefully evaluated, were better
recorded than left out, since their omission often fails
to give the picture completeness. The description cannot
be composed entirely of details. There must perforce
be some generalities. If included, on the contrary, they
may do violence to the actual events.

It is impossible to escape such arguments. The reader
of a written report must accept his facts as somewhat
tarnished or affected by the hands through which they
have already passed. He is committed to form his own
conclusions through the intermediate eyes of the observers. The personal element can seldom if ever be
eradicated from observations of this sort. But to the
extent that the observer, like a field glass or a telescope,
presents a distorted or foggy view, he may be accused
of misrepresentation.

We sincerely hope to avoid any such accusation. It
has been our wish to give an accurate and non-partisan
account of the development of the subjects without on
the one hand sensationally glorifying the capacities of
the chimpanzee or on the other hand attacking or
belittling them. We have tried to remain on the side-

lines as careful but unbiased observers. If we have failed, we are genuinely sorry. If, in addition, we have in any way offended the sensitive or critical reader, we beg his indulgence for the unknown influence of personal attitudes, which it seems no one can ever quite escape.

REFERENCES FOR FURTHER READING

The following books and articles may serve as a guide for additional reading in the fields indicated. They represent in no sense a comprehensive or detailed list. Effort has been made to confine those mentioned to publications likely to be of general interest. For this reason the citation of original papers in the scientific journals has been made only when less technical sources seemed inadequate.

CHAPTER I

An Experiment Outlined

On the topic of the wild children the reader may turn to J. G. M. Itard, "The wild boy of Aveyron" (trans. by G. and M. Humphrey), New York, Century, 1932; A. F. Tredgold, "Mental deficiency," New York, William Wood, 1915, p. 301; P. C. Squires, "'Wolf children' of India," *American Journal of Psychology*, 1927, 38: 313–315; and W. N. Kellogg, "More about the 'wolf children' of India," *American Journal of Psychology*, 1931, 45: 508–509.

An excellent brief review of the heredity-environment discussion with additional references will be found in R. S. Woodworth, "Psychology, revised," New York, Holt, 1929, Chapter V. A more detailed account is given by H. S. Jennings, "The biological basis of human nature," New York, Norton, 1930.

For a specialized proposal of the ape-rearing experiment, see W. N. Kellogg, "Humanizing the ape," in the *Psychological Review*, 1931, 38: 160–176.

CHAPTER II

Some Basic Similarities and Differences

The method of making anthropometric measurements is described by A. H. Schultz, "The technique of measuring the outer body of human fetuses and of primates in general," *Contributions to Embryology*, 1929, Vol. 20, *Carnegie Institute of Washington Publication* No. 394: 213–257.

For observations on the strength of the chimpanzee see R. M. and A. W. Yerkes, "The great apes," New Haven, Yale University Press, 1929.

Appropriate lists of the commoner reflexes are given by H. C. Warren and L. Carmichæl, "Elements of human psychology," Boston, Houghton Mifflin, 1930, while a more thorough study of reflexes and reflex behavior will be found in F. Fearing, "Reflex action," Baltimore, Williams & Wilkins, 1930.

The relation of physical to mental growth is reviewed with accompanying references by B. L. Wellman, "Physical growth and motor development and their relation to mental development in children" (Chapter VIII in "A handbook of child psychology," edited by C. Murchison), Worcester, Mass., Clark University Press, 1931. The growth of a young chimpanzee with special emphasis upon its physical and physiological aspects has recently been reviewed in detail by Carlyle F. and Marion M. Jacobsen and Joseph G. Yoshioka, "Development of an infant chimpanzee during her first year," *Comparative Psychology Monographs*, 1932, Vol. 9, Serial No. 41.

CHAPTER III

Health, Eating, and Sleeping

By far the most excellent compendium of information upon the chimpanzee and other apes is "The great apes" (New Haven, Yale University Press, 1929), by R. M. and A. W. Yerkes. In this will be found splendid discussions of the health, eating habits, and sleeping postures of wild and captive specimens. A recent monograph by H. W. Nissen, "A field study of the chimpanzee," *Comparative Psychology Monographs*, 1931, Vol. 8, Serial No. 36, contains interesting naturalistic observations upon the foods of wild chimpanzees and upon nest building.

An article by H. T. Woolley on "Eating, sleeping, and elimination" (Chapter II in "A handbook of child psychology," edited by C. Murchison), Worcester, Mass., Clark University Press, 1931, may also be referred to for information about the child and for a bibliography covering the topics in question.

CHAPTER IV

Dexterity, Arm Movements, and Walking

On the development of muscular coordination and walking in the young baby, see M. W. Shinn, "Biography of a baby," Boston, Houghton Mifflin, 1900, and "Notes on the development of a child," *University of California Publications*, 1899, Vol. 1. "The mind of the child," Part I, "The senses and the will" (trans. by H. W. Brown, New York, Appleton, 1890), by W. T. Preyer, contains further observations upon a single infant, while M. Curti, "Child psychology,"

New York, Longmans, Green, 1930, may be consulted for a more generalized treatment.

In A. Hrdlička, "Children who run on all fours," New York, McGraw-Hill, 1931, are numerous instances of human infants who developed early habits of locomotion like those of animals. The report of H. W. Nissen, "A field study of the chimpanzee," *Comparative Psychology Monographs*, 1931, Vol. 8, Serial No. 36, takes up walking in the wild chimpanzee while R. M. and A. W. Yerkes, "The great apes," New Haven, Yale University Press, 1929, contains additional information under this heading.

CHAPTER V

The Senses

For a general discussion of the topic of sensation and the special sensory capacities of man see R. S. Woodworth, "Psychology, revised," New York, Holt, 1929, Chapter VIII. A more technical and detailed analysis of the subject will be found in L. T. Troland, "The principles of psychophysiology," Vol. II, "Sensation," New York, Van Nostrand, 1930.

Excellent studies of the sensitivity of the very young infant, with many additional references, are given in "The behavior of the newborn infant" (*Ohio State University Contributions in Psychology*, 1930, No. 10), by K. C. Pratt, A. K. Nelson, and K. H. Sun. Special observations of the development of the sensory capacities of children have also been made by W. T. Preyer, "The senses and the will" (Part I of "The mind of the child," trans. by H. W. Brown), New York, Appleton, 1888, and M. W. Shinn, "Notes on the development of a child," II, "The development of the senses in the first three years of childhood," *University of California Publications in Education*, 1908, Vol. 4.

What is generally known of the sensitivity of the chimpanzee is summarized in R. M. and A. W. Yerkes, "The great apes," New Haven, Yale University Press, 1929.

CHAPTER VI

Play

The play of chimpanzees is reviewed by R. M. and A. W. Yerkes, "The great apes," New Haven, Yale University Press, 1929. W. Köhler in "The mentality of apes," New York, Harcourt, Brace, 1924, gives many special instances of such play.

For a discussion of play and imitative activities in children, with a survey of some of the chief theories of play, see M. Curti, "Child psychology," New York, Longmans, Green, 1930. The play of older children is also briefly reviewed by H. Marshall, "Children's games" (Chapter XV in "A handbook of child psychology," edited by C. Murchison), Worcester, Mass., Clark University Press, 1931.

CHAPTER VII

Social and Affectionate Behavior

The social behavior of chimpanzees is described by S. Zuckerman, "The social life of monkeys and apes," New York, Harcourt, Brace, 1932. W. Köhler, "The mentality of apes," New York, Harcourt, Brace, 1924, also contains many interesting observations on the social life of a small captive group.

For a general review of social behavior in humans see any recent *social psychology* as for example, F. H. Allport, "Social psychology," Boston, Houghton Mifflin, 1924, or J. R. Kantor, "An outline of social psychology," Chicago, Follett, 1929.

Social activities in the child are specially treated by C. Bühler in "The social behavior of the child" (Chapter XII in "A handbook of child psychology," edited by C. Murchison), Worcester, Mass., Clark University Press, 1931.

CHAPTER VIII

Emotional Behavior

A brief but adequate discussion of the problem of emotion is given by R. S. Woodworth, "Psychology, revised," New York, Holt, 1929, Chapter VII. More controversial points will be found in M. L. Reymert, "International symposium on feelings and emotions," Worcester, Mass., Clark University Press, 1928. Special books upon this topic, as F. H. Lund, "Emotions of men," New York, McGraw-Hill, 1930, and W. M. Marston, "Emotions of normal people," New York, Harcourt, Brace, 1928, may also prove of interest.

For emotional behavior in chimpanzees, with some excellent photographs, see R. M. and A. W. Yerkes, "The great apes," New Haven, Yale University Press, 1929.

M. C. Jones in "The conditioning of children's emotions" (Chapter III in "A handbook of child psychology," edited by C. Murchison), Worcester, Mass., Clark University Press, 1931, deals especially with the development of emotional reactions in young humans.

CHAPTER IX

Learning

The solution of more comprehensive problems of the same general type as those reviewed in this chapter has been skillfully studied in older chimpanzees by W. Köhler, "The mentality of apes," New York, Harcourt, Brace, 1924. Many of the same tests were subsequently repeated on children by A. Alpert, "The solving of problem-situations by preschool children; an analysis," *Teachers College, Columbia University, Contributions to Education*, 1928, No. 323.

For a critical discussion of the process of learning in the developing individual see K. Koffka, "The growth of the mind," New York, Harcourt, Brace, 1927. Special consideration of learning in children will also be found in J. Peterson, "Learning in children" and H. T. Woolley, "Eating, sleeping, and elimination" (Chapters X and II in "A handbook of child psychology," edited by C. Murchison), Worcester, Mass., Clark University Press, 1931.

A more generalized treatise on learning may be found in textbooks on the psychology of learning or educational psychology, as, for example, P. Sandiford, "Educational psychology," New York, Longmans, Green, 1930; W. F. Book, "Economy and technique of learning," Boston, Heath, 1932; or H. L. Hollingworth, "Educational psychology," New York, Appleton, 1933.

CHAPTER X

Memory and Recognition

Experimental studies of the delayed reaction in animals and children have been published by W. S. Hunter, "The delayed reaction," *Behavior Monographs*, 1913, Vol. 2, Serial No. 6; O. L. Tinklepaugh, "An experimental study of representative factors in monkeys," *Journal of Comparative Psychology*, 1928, 8: 197–236; R. M. and D. N. Yerkes, "Concerning memory in the chimpanzee," *Journal of Comparative Psychology*, 1928, 8: 237–271.

The entire topic of memory and recognition is briefly surveyed in such books as R. S. Woodworth's "Psychology, revised," New York, Holt, 1929.

CHAPTER XI

Intelligent Behavior

One may turn with profit to "The mentality of apes" (New York, Harcourt, Brace, 1924), by W. Köhler, for probably the best evidence of the solving of the "insight" type of problems by chimpanzees. A. Alpert, "The solving of problem-situations by preschool children; an analysis," *Teachers College, Columbia University, Contributions to Education*, 1928, No. 323, may be consulted for typical children's performances in the same situations.

A comprehensive survey of the Gesell Tests, and a discussion of the responses of children of various ages and abilities are given in A.

Gesell, "The mental growth of the pre-school child," New York, Macmillan, 1930. Records of Gesell test performance in a baby chimpanzee reared during its first year of life in a mixture of half pet-like, half captive environment may be found in "The development of an infant chimpanzee during her first year" (*Comparative Psychology Monographs*, 1932, Vol. 9, Serial No. 41), by Carlyle F. and Marion M. Jacobsen and Joseph G. Yoshioka.

CHAPTER XII

Communication and Language

Concerning the development of language in the child see D. A. McCarthy, "The language development of the preschool child," Minneapolis, University of Minnesota Press, 1930. J. Piaget, "The language and thought of the child" (trans. by M. Warden), New York, Harcourt, Brace, 1926, also contains excellent discussions of the language capacity of children somewhat older than the present subjects. Such books as W. T. Preyer, "The mind of the child," Part II, "The development of the intellect" (trans. by H. W. Brown), New York, Appleton, 1889, may also be examined for specialized studies of individual subjects.

Scientific reports of "talking" anthropoid apes have been made by L. Witmer, "A monkey with a mind," *Psychological Clinic*, Philadelphia, 1909, 3: 179–205 and W. H. Furness, "Observations on the mentality of chimpanzees and orang-utans," *Proceedings of the American Philosophical Society*, Philadelphia, 1916, 55: 281–290.

TESTS AND EXPERIMENTS

DATES OF TRIALS OF PRINCIPAL TESTS AND EXPERIMENTS

Observations upon the two subjects were begun on June 26, 1931, and ended March 28, 1932. The various trial dates of the more important measurements are given below

Test or measure	Trial date	Page
1. Anthropometric measurements..	7/30, 8/31, 9/30, 10/31, 11/30, 12/30–31, 1/31, 3/3	21– 23
2. Physiological measurements.....	Weekly 7/5 to 3/20	26– 27
3. Speed of involuntary movement (the startle test to a sound stimulus).	7/15, 8/22, 9/16, 10/29, 3/19*	28
4. Tests of special reflexes.........	7/12, 7/22, 10/28, 1/29	34– 37
5. Hand-preference tests..........	Weekly 7/2 to 10/2; thereafter as follows: 10/29, 11/20, 12/28, 1/18, 2/17, 3/17	54– 57
6. Foot-preference tests...........	7/17, 7/24, 10/4, 11/6, 12/10, 1/18, 2/18, 3/22	57– 58
7. Grasping or prehension tests....	9/30, 12/2, 3/7	61– 63
8. The cap-on-head test..........	8/17, 9/17, 11/21, 12/18, 1/17, 2/21, 3/24	64– 65
9. Other tests of coordinated arm movements.................	7/22, 8/23, 9/23, 12/5, 3/9	65– 66
10. Perception of motion pictures...	10/20, 1/7	91– 92
11. Perception of printed forms and pictures.	10/16, 11/20, 12/18, 2/21, 3/19	93– 95
12. The sound-localization experiment.	Daily (with exceptions) 1/6 to 2/3	99–101
13. Tests of the sense of equilibrium	9/4, 11/5, 11/20	102–104
14. Taste tests....................	8/24 to 9/15	105–109
15. Tests of the sense of smell......	9/10, 11/10, 1/11, 3/12	109–111
16. Accuracy of touch localization..	9/12, 11/12, 1/17, 3/21	111–113
17. Tickle tests................	7/25, 8/26, 9/11, 11/12, 1/17, 3/21	114–115
18. The watch-manipulation test....	12/9, 1/11, 2/10, 3/12	136–137
19. Bladder and bowel training.....	Continuous 7/1 to 3/28	194–206
20. The hand-in-loop experiment....	Daily 11/9 to 12/27	207–210
21. The foot-in-loop experiment.....	Daily 1/4 to 1/28	210–213
22. The suspended-cookie test......	Daily and twice daily 2/8 to 3/14	213–219
23. The hoe experiment...........	Daily and twice daily 12/5 to 3/10	220–229
24. The delayed-reaction experiment	7/16 to 9/23	231–236
25. The detour experiment........	8/3, 8/20, 9/12	251–256

THE APE AND THE CHILD

DATES OF TRIALS OF PRINCIPAL TESTS AND EXPERIMENTS.—(*Continued*)

Test or measure	Trial date	Page
26. Gesell ("Intelligence") tests (see Chap. XII and Index for individual tests in Gesell series).	7/15, 8/15, 9/15, 10/15, 11/15, 12/15, 1/15, 2/15, 3/15	257–272
27. The juice-in-bottle test.........	9/22 to 9/26, 11/19 to 12/18, 2/10 to 2/13	278
28. The names experiment.........	Twice daily 2/6 to 3/22	295–296

* Italicized figures are dates when motion-picture tests cited in text (page 28) were made. The observations on the other dates were without the picture-recording technique.

Index

A

Abreu colony of apes, 16
Adaptation, to environment, 189; to nursery chair, 197–198
Affectionate behavior, 148–151, 159–162, 260, 265, 314; fluctuation of, 160; preference for one person, 159–162
Allport, F. H., 332
Alpert, A., 333
Angry behavior, 182–184
Anthropometric measurements, 21–23
Anthropomorphism, 168–169, 325–326
Anxious behavior, 181
Appearance of ape, 20–21
Arm movement tests, 64–66
Articulation, 281, 287–289, 312
Attention, 133–134, 276, 312

B

Barking of ape, 282
Bashfulness, 153, 185
Biting, 143–145, 186, 189, 276, 277, 312
Bladder control, 194–206, 265, 267, 270, 316
Blanchard, M. B., 320
Block building, 60, 262, 263, 264, 267, 268
Blood pressure, 26–27, 311
Body measurements, 21–23
Boisterousness, 124
Bones, ossification of, 24–25
Book, W. F., 333
Bowel control, 194–206, 260, 262, 267, 268, 270, 316
Bⁿhler, C., 332

C

Cap-on-head test, 64–65
Carmichael, L., 330
Climbing, 79–84, 259, 265
Communication, 275–306; answers to questions, 284–285, 293–295; non-vocal, 275–278; of evacuation needs, 203–206; vocal, 279–289
Comprehension of language, 289–306
Comprehension vocabulary, 297–306; of ape, 302–306; of child, 297–301
Conditioning, 37, 192, 284–285
Conrad, H. S., 320
Convergence of eyes, 35
Cooperation, 162
Coordination, of eyes, 34; of muscles, 59–63, 64–67, 315
Coughing, 32, 284
Crawling of child, 68, 142, 259
Crying, 150, 183, 184, 205, 247, 249, 251, 283, 286
Curti, M., 330, 331

D

Decision, behavior suggestive of making a, 256–257
Delayed-reaction experiment, 231–236, 274
Dependence, 157–159, 313
Destructiveness, 124
Detour experiment, 251–256
Dexterity, manual, 59–64
Diet, 41–42
Disappointment, 184
Disposition, 186–187
Docility, 162
Door opening, 191, 266, 270, 316

INDEX